Plays as Experience

The Odyssey Texts in Types of Literature

Stories in Verse

Lyric Verse

The Short Story Reader

Romance and Realism *(the novel)*

Plays as Experience *(one-act plays)*

The Drama Reader *(full-length plays)*

Portraits in Words *(biography)*

The Challenge of Ideas *(the essay)*

Plays
as Experience

One-Act Plays for the
Secondary School

REVISED EDITION

Edited by **IRWIN J. ZACHAR**

Chairman, Department of English, West Side High School, Newark

 THE ODYSSEY PRESS · *New York*

*Gratefully and affectionately dedicated to
the hundreds of boys and girls,
including my son Barry,
who, for more than a quarter of a century,
have helped in the selection of the plays
in this volume*

To the Teachers Who Will Use This Book

PLAYS AS EXPERIENCE was first published in 1944 as the second book in the series now well-known as *The Odyssey Texts in Types of Literature*. As an introduction to the study of drama as a type, it conformed to the basic educational convictions which have made this series so successful: (1) the reading of any type of literature involves special techniques which must be mastered; (2) with acquisition of skill, the reading of this type becomes a pleasure; (3) the material is suitable only if it is chosen with an eye to pupils' interests, or if it deals sincerely with life problems that are of concern to them; (4) the instruction is not entirely successful unless it establishes enthusiasms and a taste which project themselves forward into a lifetime of good reading.

In this revised edition of *Plays as Experience*, the first pedagogical aim continues to be the teaching of the special techniques involved in the reading and interpretation of plays, to the end that the drama may become a vital force in the lives of boys and girls in junior and senior high schools. Accordingly, no play is regarded merely as an end in itself; each play is presented as a step in the gradual development of ability in playreading. Instruction in how to read the types is, in fact, the chief business of the editorial equipment in Part One: here the introductory expositions and editorial aids are designed primarily to teach the techniques and terminology needed for intelligent, appreciative reading of drama. Further attention, but with less emphasis, is given to types in Part Two.

But, as the title indicates, *Plays as Experience* is an attempt to combine with the intellectual experience of learning to read dramatic literature certain dynamic experiences stimulating the awareness of adolescents to wider and deeper understanding of life. In Part Two, therefore, the plays have been selected with an eye to sincere grappling with problems of vital concern to young people in a democracy.

Furthermore, because the selections in *Plays as Experience* combine high interest value with a feasible level of reading difficulty, they are appealing and meaningful not only to capable and superior boys and girls, but, in the case of most of the plays, also to non-academic students and to handicapped readers. In a period extending over a quarter of a century, thousands of boys and girls, in the classrooms of my colleagues as well as in my own, representing virtually the entire range of the highly heterogeneous secondary school population of our time, have helped in the selection of plays in this volume. The present revision is based, in addition, upon (1) the reactions of student and teachers during the nearly two decades in which the first edition of the book was used in schools throughout the country and (2) upon the findings of investigations into the reading and other interests of secondary school pupils. Included in this volume are the short plays found to be most popular with the thousands of boys and girls in New York State whose reading interests were studied by George W. Norvell in his unique and monumental *The Reading Interests of Young People*.[1]

In the selections, activities, and other editorial aids of *Plays as Experience,* there is, moreover, an integration of the English language arts of literature, reading and vocabulary development, dramatics, writing, speaking, and listening.

The goal, in short, is, by conquest of a new literary field to extend the pupil's reading skill and horizon; and, by removal of a reading hazard, to increase the number of pleasurable experiences with literature awaiting him.

This book consists entirely of one-act plays because it is the editor's considered judgment that one-act plays are the best introduction to the study of the drama. Their shortness and relative simplicity make them comprehensible to secondary school students and readily adaptable to classroom situations. It has

[1] Published by D. C. Heath and Company in 1950.

been my experience that the one-act play offers ample study material for a first unit in the drama. Many boys and girls in my classes who would have been unable to cope with plays of full-length have been lead to a genuine taste for play-reading through a study of the one-act play. The liking for longer plays followed as a logical next step.

"Taste," of course, must mean more than mere liking; it must mean also discrimination—the ability to distinguish degrees of excellence, an ability which is acquired through extensive reading and analysis of the literary form. And discrimination has no real dynamic value if it stops with knowing the good from the bad. It becomes good taste only when there is a preference for the good. By careful selection of plays of unquestioned merit and distinguished authorship, the editor has endeavored to promote the truly dramatic discrimination which may be called good taste in literature. If *Plays as Experience* does indeed promote this kind of taste, the book has not failed of its purpose.

The last word is one of thanks: to the boys and girls and their teachers who helped in the selection of the plays; and to John Gehlmann, who, as supervisory editor of *The Odyssey Texts in Types of Literature,* has contributed invaluable editorial aid and guidance.

I. J. Z.

Contents

To the Teachers Who Will Use This Book   vii

To the Students Who Will Use This Book   1

PART ONE

Experiences with and through Types of Plays   13

Comedy: The Happy Ending   15
  THREE's A CROWD.
         Sara Sloane McCarty and E. Clayton McCarty   16

Melodrama: Adventure, Mystery, and Thrills   36
  THE RING OF GENERAL MACÍAS. *Josefina Niggli*   38

Farce: Anything for a Laugh   62
  THE BOOR. *Anton Chekhov*   63

Tragedy: Frustration and Defeat   81
  THE FIFTEENTH CANDLE. *Rachel Field*   83

Folk Play: Folk and Folkways   103
  GOODBYE TO THE LAZY K. *Robert Finch*   104

Fantasy: The Realm of the Unreal   124
  THE DEVIL AND DANIEL WEBSTER. *Stephen Vincent Benét*   125

Television Drama: The Theater of the People   157
  SHE WALKS IN BEAUTY. *James Truex*   159

PART TWO

Further Experiences with and through Plays 171

THE SOUNDS OF TRIUMPH. *William Inge* 174
JACOB COMES HOME. *William Kozlenko* 190
THE VALIANT. *Holworthy Hall and Robert Middlemass* 204
SPARKIN'. *E. P. Conkle* 236
BACK OF THE YARDS. *Kenneth Sawyer Goodman* 256
PAWNS. *Percival Wilde* 283
TRIFLES. *Susan Glaspell* 301

Staging the Plays 323

Writing Your Own Play 342

Those Who Wrote the Plays in This Book 351

Plays as Experience

To the Students Who Will Use This Book

OVER A PERIOD of many years, hundreds of boys and girls have helped me select and test the plays included in this volume. They have found the selections enjoyable and profitable; you will, I hope, find in them the same profit and enjoyment.

Plays have become favorite reading matter for boys and girls, and there are a number of good reasons for the increasing popularity of this type of literature. Plays are alive: they are almost always fast moving, packed with action, thrills, romance, and fun. Young people, in their reading, look for books with a lot of conversation; and plays consist almost entirely of conversation. The one-act play, particularly, has these further merits: it is short enough to be read at one sitting; for the most part, it presents a relatively simple and clear-cut situation, problem, or character study; and it makes possible a fascinating schoolroom activity—it is easily performed before an audience.

Reading plays, then, can be an excellent source of pleasurable recreation. A play is what its name implies—play; and you will derive the greatest satisfaction out of the selections in this book by working with them in the spirit of play. We are never too young or too old to get a great deal of fun from playing at make-believe.

But this book offers you much more than mere entertainment; from its use you will derive also a number of benefits. You may expect to improve your skill in reading plays, to enlarge your vocabulary, to become a better reader in general. I hope, also, that you will be inspired to perform some of these plays and to try your own hand at playwriting, no matter how modest your attempt may be. Toward this end, the book provides hints on how to interpret, how to stage, and how to write plays. Study

1

of the drama, moreover, helps you in your understanding and appreciation not only of plays written for the theater, but also of those popular pastimes: television and radio dramas and motion pictures.

Most of all, the reading of these plays and the suggested discussions and activities offer a better understanding of life itself. Of all the literary forms, the drama touches life most directly. Watch people as they are confronted with a play or a motion picture that moves them deeply; see how their faces, indeed their entire bodies, show their emotions; and note their reactions as they leave the theater. Truly, seeing a play is in itself a way of living, of growing in mind, in spirit, and in emotions. Similarly, reading a play may be an equally valuable experience. The plays in this book offer a deep understanding of humanity that will make you a more tolerant and sympathetic person; and they instill a devotion to the great American ideal of democracy.

THE READING OF PLAYS

One of the most satisfactory definitions of a play is that it is a *story* to be *acted*.

A play is first of all a *story*. Because plays belong to the narrative—or story-telling—forms of literature, the essential elements of a play are those which we find in any narrative: action, characters, setting, theme. All that you have learned about these narrative elements will stand you in good stead in your reading of plays.

But a play is a particular kind of story; it is a story to be *acted*. Plays are not written primarily to be read from a book; they are written primarily to be presented on a stage before an audience. It is of course true that the reading of plays is a pleasurable and profitable activity, and that many people turn to them just as they do to novels or short stories. But since plays are designed for acting rather than reading, there are certain skills required in reading them which are not necessary in reading other forms of narrative. These skills you will need to acquire, and it is the purpose of this book to help you to acquire them.

The skills necessary for successful play-reading may be summed up in the one rule: "Use your imagination." A play consists almost entirely of dialogue. From this dialogue the reader must visualize the action, analyze the characters, picture the setting, and get the message, or theme, of the playwright. All this requires an imagination trained to be especially active and alert.

Let us now examine the four essential elements of narrative and see how play-reading requires an especially vivid imagination in each element.

Action. A play—a one-act play, in particular—necessarily reveals life in a flash. It catches the characters in a crucial and revealing moment in their lives. Although we may get an insight into an entire lifetime, we actually see the characters for a very short time. In a one-act play, therefore, there is no time for leisurely introductory dialogue which will explain the details of the situation before the action begins. The action must start in the middle of things, and the explanation must be presented bit by bit as the action develops. As a result of this abruptness, the opening incidents of some plays appear somewhat confusing for a moment. Perhaps your experience with movies and television and radio plays—which frequently begin with automobiles racing at breakneck speed, guns blazing, telephones ringing—has prepared you for the reading difficulty presented by these abrupt openings. If not, do not be discouraged when you occasionally have to glance back at lines which you may not have understood at first. A situation worthy of even a short play cannot be presented in an instant.

A second difficulty of play-reading, one for which you, as a play-reader, are not prepared by your movie and television or radio experience, is the one presented by the limitations of the printed page. In the movie or on the stage, the action takes place before your eyes, and in a radio play you are aided by carefully trained voices and skillful sound effects; but as a reader you have to create both the action and the sounds out of your imagination, aided only by the printed dialogue. Thus the reading of a play makes a greater demand upon the imagination than watching it or listening to it.

Furthermore, reading plays requires a more alert imagination than does the reading of other kinds of printed stories. In a novel or a short story the author often tells his reader every move, every gesture, every intonation of voice which his characters make. But in a play the dramatist relies upon a few brief stage directions (printed in italics or enclosed in brackets or parentheses); from these the reader must construct imaginatively the details of the action.

So, more than a stage or television play, more than a movie or radio drama, more than a novel or short story, a printed play demands an attentive, alert imagination if you are to follow the action of the story.

Characters. As I have just pointed out, visualizing the action is more difficult in reading a play than in watching it, and also more difficult than in reading other kinds of stories. Likewise, understanding the characters is clearly more difficult in reading a play than in watching it, or in reading other forms of narrative.

As you watch a play on the stage or the screen, the actors soon let you know not only by what they say, but also by their actions, facial expressions, and tones of voice what sort of people they are portraying: a mean stepmother, or a giddy young wife, or a love-sick boy. You recognize them as you would in real life—mainly by seeing how they act and hearing how they talk. Also as in real life, you may judge these people and their motives by the way others act toward them. But in reading a play, you must imagine for yourself how the characters speak, what they do, what sort of people they are; and the only guide you have is the bare dialogue.

Similarly, when you read a novel you usually find that the author has supplied pages of information about his characters: what goes on in their minds, how they act, why they act and react as they do. (Indeed, sometimes you may wish that the author would keep out of your way and permit you to find out some of the facts for yourself!) But in reading plays you may at first deplore the absence of such help. For in contrast to the novelist, the playwright gives you little help in interpreting the characters; you must interpret for yourself. A scene opens. One person appears, then another. They converse. Who are these people? What relationship do they bear to one another? After you have read well into the play, the answers to such questions become apparent, but for a few minutes you may be somewhat bewildered.

To help you avoid this temporary confusion of characters, the playwright supplies a list of characters just before the play itself. Just as it is important for you when attending the theater to consult the list of characters printed in the program, so in reading a play it is helpful to keep before you the list of characters printed in the book. This list is particularly helpful in a modern play, because the modern playwright lists and describes the characters in the order of their appearance on the stage. (In Shakespeare's day they were listed in the order of their social or political rank, the men first and the women last.)

It will require considerable imagination on your part to create from the words of a printed page of dialogue images of living people speaking and acting in a real situation; but the better you succeed in doing this, the more enjoyable will be your reading of a play.

Setting. When the curtain rises on a play in a real theater, the setting is at once visible to the eyes of the audience. And much of the success of a dramatic production depends upon the craftsmanship, artistry, and accuracy with which the stage settings have been designed and executed. Not only does a setting picture for us the place where the story is being enacted, but it also helps to establish the mood and the atmosphere.

The play-reader, however, does not have the advantage of this concrete presentation of the scene. In the printed version of the play the author may present the scene in the briefest possible description: "A blackberry thicket near Tom Lincoln's farm. A tree; a rock; a rail fence; a stump; the open country behind; a summer sky over all." [1] With these few details you must create the setting in your imagination. Of course, you can get considerable pleasure from a play even if you fail to visualize the scene. But you will be handicapped in full enjoyment much as a theatergoer would be if all plays were presented on a bare stage without scenery and appropriate furnishings.

Sometimes the brief exposition is complicated by the use of technical terms: downstage, upstage, R. (right), L. (left), C. (center), U.C. (upper center). These must be understood by the reader.

Occasionally a book contains a diagram of the scene, or some pictures, and a few writers, like George Bernard Shaw and James M. Barrie, write out full and revealing descriptions. In most cases, however, the play-reader has to develop the ability to create the setting imaginatively from meager materials.

Theme. The theme is the idea which the play is designed to illustrate. It can generally be expressed in one sentence. Not all plays have themes in this sense; a play may be written, instead, just to tell a fascinating or an amusing story or to entertain us with its interesting characters. In many instances, however, the theme is the main concern of the writer, and he then composes his play primarily to present his message.

The reader or the audience, in trying to determine what the theme of a play is, must consider that there may have been a number of ideas brought out in the course of the play, and must not mistake a relatively unimportant thought for the most important idea, the one which constitutes the theme. If you have carefully visualized the whole play in your reading—action, characters, and setting—you will very likely also see clearly the main theme, if there is one.

Learning how playwrights deal with the problems of action, characters, setting, and theme costs you some trouble, to be sure; and it is, of course, possible to read a play without knowing much about these things. But knowledge of the dramatist's way of handling them increases your skill in reading plays, and thus

[1] E. P. Conkle, *Prologue to Glory.*

adds to your pleasure in this kind of reading. Your own increased enjoyment of plays will show that the effort it cost you to gain the knowledge is richly rewarded.

READING PLAYS ALOUD

Thus far our discussion has been devoted mainly to the silent reading of plays. Plays should first be read silently for understanding, but no doubt you will also wish to "act them out." That is a perfectly sensible desire, for it has been truly stated that not even lyric poetry has a better claim upon the human voice than has the drama. "To read a play only silently," says Dr. Reed Smith, "is to rob it of its birthright . . . a play is scarcely a play until it is given vocal life and movement." [2] Fortunately for you, and for your teachers, too, you young people scarcely need to be coaxed to read plays aloud; you demand to do so. It is great fun for all.

One way of acting plays out is, of course, to perform them on the stage. The principles of stage production are discussed in a later chapter.

The simplest and most informal way, however, is to read plays aloud before your own class—without memorizing lines and without costumes, scenery, or properties. Just clear a space at the front of the classroom, and use a few chairs and your teacher's desk for your furniture. If you have an artist in your group, ask him to sketch on the blackboard a ground plan of the stage setting and furniture, so that you may better visualize what your few chairs and desk are to represent. A miniature stage setting with tiny bulbs for footlights and spotlights, made by a member of the class who is gifted in the use of his hands, will also serve to stimulate the imagination.

This is not to say that all plays in this volume need to be read aloud. For the sake of variety, it is at times preferable to supplement the plays read in *Plays as Experience* with the oral reading and discussion of other plays similar in type or theme to those in this book.

[2] *The Teaching of Literature in the High School.* Copyright, 1935, by the American Book Company.

When you have learned to read with the full power of your imagination—to visualize the action, the characters, and the setting; to understand the theme; to interpret the lines orally—you will be able to enjoy plays long after you no longer have your teacher and this book with you. Whether you are rich or poor, whether you live in a large city or a tiny village, by using your reading skill you may bring the theater to yourself whenever you desire.

FOR DISCUSSION

1. What definition of a play is given at the beginning of this chapter? What is your opinion of that definition?
2. What four essential elements of narrative are generally found in plays as well as in other story-telling forms of literature?
3. Plays, and especially one-act plays, frequently start abruptly and in the middle of things. Why is this so? As a reader of plays, what should you understand and do in order not to be disturbed by the abrupt beginning of a play?
4. The skills necessary for successful play-reading may be summed up in the one rule: "Use your imagination." Explain why reading plays requires an alert imagination.
5. What differences are there (a) between reading a play and watching one? (b) between reading a play and reading other kinds of stories?
6. The cast of characters is listed at the beginning of a play. In what order are characters generally listed in modern plays? In what order were they listed in Shakespeare's day? Which way of listing characters is more helpful to a reader or playgoer—the modern or the Shakespearean? Why?
7. What is meant by the theme of a play? Need all plays have themes? Explain.
8. Why should plays also be read aloud?
9. What advice would you give to a friend who is eager to improve in his ability to read plays aloud?

KNOWING THE TYPE OF PLAY

A most important part of the background of the capable play-reader is a knowledge of the different kinds of plays. There are several major types; and each type differs from the others in various ways, especially in tempo, mood, and emphasis. Each type presents different problems for the writer and the actor; the different types should therefore be approached differently by the reader or the playgoer.

If you are not familiar with the types of plays and their characteristics, you are in danger of forming expectations that will never be realized. But if these characteristics are familiar to you, and if you know in advance what kind of play to expect, you can make the adjustments necessary to understand and enjoy each dramatic experience. You will be prepared in mind and mood to co-operate intelligently with the author. If the play is a tragedy, you will be prepared for an atmosphere of gloom and the frustration or defeat of the main character. If it is a farce or melodrama, you will not be surprised at a rapid tempo, with something funny or exciting happening all the time.

To get into the right mood without delay, then, you need to know what type of play you are about to read. At the movies, you usually can tell by the names in the cast whether the picture will be a western, a spy plot, or a musical comedy. In reading a play, you may have the luck to learn from the title page, or from a textbook on drama, or from your teacher, what kind of play it is. But you don't have to depend on such luck. With a little practice you will learn to discover in the first few pages definite clues which will enable you to classify the play promptly for yourself. Thus you will get into the right mood early, and your enjoyment of the reading will be increased accordingly.

In the earliest days of the drama all plays were classified under two heads: tragedies and comedies. A tragedy was a play in which the protagonist—the leading character—failed to achieve his main purpose; a comedy was a play in which he succeeded. More recently other classifications have been found useful, such as farces, melodramas, folk plays, fantasies, and television and radio plays. Today, also, many a play, rather serious in theme and tone, is labeled "a drama" or merely "a play," because it does not seem to fit into any of these other classifications.

Two warnings are in order. Avoid lengthy arguments about the classification of any play. It may happen that one person will call a play a tragedy, while another will be equally certain that the same play is a melodrama. And they may both be right. If the play has the characteristics of a tragedy, it is a tragedy; if it has also the characteristics of a melodrama, it is also a melodrama. Many a play is at the same time a tragedy and a melodrama; some plays are both comedies and melodramas; some are both comedies and fantasies, and of course a folk play is almost sure to belong to one of the other types. In a word, the types are not mutually exclusive.

Resist also any temptation to multiply the number of types. Setting up a complex system of classification merely for the sake of classification is really rather silly. Classifying plays according to dramatic types is of value only in so far as it makes you better prepared to read and watch plays, and to enjoy them.

In Part One you will read seven plays, each representing a different type. With each play the chief characteristics of its type are pointed out, to prepare you for a more intelligent reading and to make you a more appreciative reader and playgoer.

But while you are learning about types of plays, you must not forget that there is much more to play reading than merely studying plays as types. Have you heard commencement orators speak of graduation as a time of getting out of school and into life, as if school and life were entirely separate and distinct domains? The truth is that school itself is a phase of life, a highly important phase—and, fortunately, to most people a very happy one. Another way of saying the same thing is to say that everything that happens to you is *experience,* in the broad sense. Thus, being introduced to a comedy or a melodrama as an unfamiliar literary type, and learning how to read it, is certainly an experience. But at the same time that you are developing reading skill by repeated experience *with* different types of plays, you are also encountering life *through* the experiences of the persons in the play; through their triumphs or defeats, through their folly and error or courage and wisdom, you are learning about life at no cost to yourself. This double exposure—to the reading experience itself and to the reflection of life in the plays you read—this is what I mean by the title *Plays as Experience*. I sincerely hope, furthermore, that a thoughtful reading of the plays in this book together with a sincere participation in the activities that accompany each play will contribute toward your understanding and organizing your own experiences more wisely.

FOR DISCUSSION

1. Why is it important to be familiar with the different types of plays and their characteristics?

2. It sometimes happens that one person will call a play a tragedy, while another will be equally certain that the same play is a melodrama. Is it possible that they may both be right? Explain.

3. When is a play simply labeled "a drama"?

4. How may you expect to be better prepared for life through reading and discussing the plays in this book?

5. What books, plays, or movies have made important contributions to your outlook on life? Explain how they have done so.

PART ONE

Experiences with and through

Types of Plays

Comedy: The Happy Ending

FROM THE EARLIEST DAYS of the drama the basic factor in all plays called comedies has been the success of the protagonist—that is, the leading character. A comedy has to have a happy ending.

Therefore, when a play you are about to watch or read is labeled a comedy, you should prepare for a pleasant time. To get the full enjoyment from a comedy, you must be amused rather than too emotionally upset by any complicated situations in which the characters may find themselves. The author is deliberately keeping you on tenterhooks. This suspense is to be enjoyed, not agonized over; no matter how bad it may look for the hero, you may rest assured that in the end he will win out.

Then, too, you can expect in most comedies much highly amusing dialogue. The play of wit between characters is often one of the most amusing features of a comedy. Don't miss this added fun!

Another important point to remember is that in comedies the leading characters are real, recognizable people, whose actions are believable. The circumstances in which they find themselves (sometimes called situations) and the incidents which arise must also be credible. If, in a humorous play, the important characters are people whose actions strike us as not being true to life, then the play is not a real comedy but an exaggerated form of comedy called a farce.

Three's a Crowd *

SARA SLOANE MC CARTY AND E. CLAYTON MC CARTY

In this popular teen-age comedy, your imagination will not be too greatly overtaxed, for the character types are familiar to you, and the situation well within your experience. "Two's company; three's a crowd" is nothing new. All the boys have been Eddies, upon occasion; all the girls have been, or have known, Madelines and Ellens. So when you read *Three's a Crowd,* just be yourselves and relax and have fun.

CHARACTERS

EDDIE JOHNSON, JUNIOR
MADELINE
ELLEN
ELMER
EDWARD JOHNSON, SENIOR

SCENE: *A park*
TIME: *Between eight and nine o'clock on a warm, glamorous, summer evening*

The setting is a park. It might be at the steps which lead into the sunken gardens, or it might be a restful corner in the shrubbery. At any rate, there are two benches, one left and one right. Their upper ends slant toward each other. If it is in the sunken gardens, the steps lead up the center above these two benches.

Illumination comes from the moon, or possibly from one of those abominable lights placed by unfeeling park officials especially to annoy young lovers.

After the Curtain rises, and you begin to think nothing will happen, three figures become visible in the gloom. The first is MADELINE, *who sails angrily down the steps, managing beautifully in spite of a slight limp.* EDDIE *follows helplessly. He, in turn, is trailed meekly by* ELLEN.

MADELINE *is the kind of girl every boy has known from a distance and could never date. The world revolves and the moon shines especially for her benefit. Boys, for her, are mere creatures to jump through hoops at the wave of her glittering finger tips.*

Why EDDIE *has dated* MADELINE *is hard to see. He is too unsophisticated and serious minded for her.*

ELLEN *is* MADELINE'S *younger sister and she feels it. Because* MADELINE *always has offered too gorgeous a contrast, she has never discovered that she is pretty. There is no room for younger sisters in* MADELINE'S *scheme of things.*

All three are dressed for a dance. MADELINE'S *shoulder is not adorned with flowers, but* ELLEN *wears a gorgeously simple corsage, which she pats from time to time.*

EDDIE. Aw, Madeline. I'm sorry.
   [MADELINE *sits on right bench without a word.* EDDIE *stands beside her abjectly. She glares at him and then at her feet. They hurt.* ELLEN *slides like a shadow to a seat apart on the left bench.*]
It isn't so far now.
   [MADELINE *gives him a poisonous look and takes off her slippers.*]
It's just down to the end of this street and then three blocks over and then four more blocks and then just a half a block.
   [*Another withering glance.*]
Gee, you aren't goin' to get mad, are you? How was I to know about the tickets? I asked for tickets to the Tenth Street Station, didn't I? And I paid for tickets to the Tenth Street Station, didn't I? And haven't I ridden on that car with that same conductor a million times, haven't I? And haven't I always gone clear to the Tenth Street Station, haven't I? Gosh. [*Sits beside*

her.] Do your feet hurt awful bad? Let me see. [*Reaches toward her foot.*] Maybe I—

MADELINE. [*Hysterically.*] Don't touch me.

EDDIE. [*Gulps.*] Gosh, Madeline, you aren't goin' to get mad, are you?

ELLEN. [*Meekly.*] She'll get over it, Eddie.

EDDIE. [*Frantically.*] Keep still, you! Gee, Madeline, don't be mad. Aw gee, Madeline, you got the cutest little feet.

MADELINE. Ugh. [*Makes a disgusted face. Tries to hide feet under skirt.*]

EDDIE. It's kind of—well, you sittin' here with your shoes off— it's kind of—intimate—just like we were—just like there was no-body in the world but us.

[ELLEN *sighs romantically.*]

MADELINE. Ugh!

EDDIE. Way last fall when I saw you sittin' in the front row in history I said—I said, "Gee, she's some girl. I could fall for her in a big way, what I mean." And here you are, sittin' right here beside me. And here I am, sittin' right here beside you, sort of —intimate. Both of us sort of intimate. Like there was nobody else in the world.

ELLEN. [*Shivering.*] This bench is cold.

EDDIE. [*Annoyed.*] Keep still, you. [*Turns to* MADELINE.] Gee, Madeline, I'm just an old stick. I'm not any good—not like my cousin Elmer. I wasn't even hoping you'd say you'd go to the dance with me tonight. I thought you'd go with Elmer. Elmer can get any girl he wants. I'm not like Elmer. I'm just not like anybody.

MADELINE. Oh, will you shut up?

EDDIE. Gee, Madeline, you're not gettin' mad, are you? How'd I know I was goin' to shoot the rear end out of the car last week? And how'd I know Dad was goin' to take it away from me for shootin' the rear end? He's not playing square, he isn't. He should've told me before I asked you that I couldn't have the car.

MADELINE. Oh, I've heard all that before.

ELLEN. Madeline, don't be so cross.

EDDIE. Keep still, you.

MADELINE. The least you could do was call up and let me know you couldn't have the car.

EDDIE. Aw gee, Madeline, Dad didn't tell me till after supper and I didn't want to disappoint you and I walked clear over to your house so I'd have enough money to take us on the interurban, and I didn't want you to miss the dance—

MADELINE. [*Full of suppressed fury.*] I wouldn't have missed the dance.

EDDIE. Gosh, Madeline.

MADELINE. You aren't the only boy that asked me to go to that dance. Elmer asked me, and—

EDDIE. [*Grinning fatuously.*] Gosh, Madeline, it makes a fellow feel good. You could've had anybody you wanted. You could've had Elmer even, and you picked me.

MADELINE. Ugh.

EDDIE. [*Pacing center.*] And here on the most important night in my life Dad had to go take the car away from me, and that ticket man had to be a moron and give me tickets to the Thirty-fifth Street Station when I paid for tickets to the Tenth Street Station. He's a moron, that's what I mean. I've bought tickets to the Tenth Street Station a million times and he's always given me tickets to the Tenth Street Station, and here on this night he has to go give me tickets to the Thirty-fifth Street Station when I paid for tickets to the Tenth Street Station. If that conductor had been a gentleman, he'd have believed me.

MADELINE. Oh, shut up! It's bad enough missing the dance without having to sit here and listen to you rave.

EDDIE. But we won't miss it. It isn't much farther. Just down to the end of this street and three blocks—

MADELINE. If you think I'm going to walk all that way, Eddie Johnson, you're crazy.

EDDIE. [*Halting before her.*] But we gotta. I spent all my allowance on the dance tickets and the tickets to the Tenth Street Station and we gotta get to the dance so I can borrow some money from one of the fellows so we can get home.

MADELINE. I'm not going to move a step.

EDDIE. I'd have had enough money if you hadn't brought *her*

along. [*A sweeping gesture toward* ELLEN.] How was I to know I'd have to buy three tickets to the Tenth Street Station instead of two?

MADELINE. Well, if a fellow can't be nice to my little sister—

EDDIE. [*To* ELLEN.] Now, see what you've done! Just when I get the swellest girl in the world to go to a dance with me, she has to go have a little sister and make me buy three tickets and spend all my money—

ELLEN. [*Starting to cry.*] But Eddie, I'll go home if you want me to. I'll walk home. Right now.

EDDIE. Aw gee, Ellen— Well, you can't do that. Your mother said for me to take care of both of you and, by golly, I'm goin' to do it.

ELLEN. I don't want to be a burden on anyone. I didn't want to come anyway.

MADELINE. Ellen, you shut up. Don't you start sniffling.

ELLEN. I don't have any fun when I have to come along with Madeline. I know when I'm not wanted. I don't have any fun out of tagging along and making three and being treated like a child. I wish I'd never heard of your old dance. I wish I'd never come along. I wish I was dead.

[ELLEN *cries.* EDDIE *turns to her in consternation. He did not mean to hurt her. The whole situation is simply getting beyond him.*]

EDDIE. Aw, Ellen, I didn't mean to make you cry. Aw— Madeline, do something.

MADELINE. [*Nastily.*] Do it yourself. It's none of my business.

EDDIE. [*Pushing his handkerchief out toward* ELLEN.] Here. Here.

ELLEN. Thags. [*Blows nose.*]

EDDIE. [*Helplessly.*] Guess I don't know much about women.

MADELINE. Well, when are you going to get me home?

EDDIE. But I told you we gotta get to the dance so I can borrow some money from one of the fellows. It isn't far. It's only down to the end of this street and three blocks—

MADELINE. If you say that again, I'll scream.

EDDIE. Aw Madeline, don't go gettin' mad. Come on.

MADELINE. I won't stir a step.

EDDIE. [*Bewildered.*] Aw—

MADELINE. Do you think I'd be seen like this?

EDDIE. Aw, Madeline, I couldn't help it about the flowers. How could I help it because they didn't come from the flower shop? Mom didn't have any money to give me and I had to have all my allowance to buy the dance tickets and those three tickets to the Tenth Street Station—

MADELINE. Ugh.

EDDIE. They were swell flowers. Honest, they were. Mom picked them out of her prize bed. They're the same like she wins prizes with at the flower show.

MADELINE. Ugh.

EDDIE. And Mom makes swell bouquets—

MADELINE. Wouldn't I look swell at a dance wearing flowers out of a garden? My feet are so tired I couldn't dance a step anyway. My little toe feels like it's positively broken.

EDDIE. Aw gee, I'm sorry. Let me see it.

MADELINE. Keep away from me!

EDDIE. Aren't you feeling well or something, Madeline?

MADELINE. How do you suppose I feel? Missing the biggest dance of the season because a flat tire dragged me out on a street car and made me walk and couldn't pay the fare! I never was so embarrassed in all my life, with all those people gawking at me. I felt like a criminal.

EDDIE. Well, that conductor didn't need to put us off. He ought to know I always ride to the Tenth Street Station.

MADELINE. [*Beginning to work herself up.*] And after making me walk forty blocks—

ELLEN. Oh, it was not!

MADELINE. [*Beginning to cry.*] After making me walk forty blocks, he says it's just down to the end of the street and over three blocks and then four blocks more and then just half a block.

EDDIE. Aw, Madeline—

MADELINE. And I look a sight and I'll miss the dance and my

new pumps are ruined and I guess my little toe's broken. [*She cries.*]

EDDIE. [*Looks through pockets.*] Aw, golly—

ELLEN. [*Hands the handkerchief to him.*] Here.

EDDIE. Here. [*Offers it to* MADELINE.] Here.

MADELINE. Go away. [*Throws handkerchief down.*]

ELLEN. You shouldn't treat Eddie's clean handkerchief like that. [*Retrieves it, folds it, and pats it.*]

EDDIE. Aw, come on now, Madeline. Be a good sport.

MADELINE. Don't talk to me.

EDDIE. [*In desperation.*] Come on. We gotta get to the dance so I can borrow enough money to take you home.

MADELINE. Well, go on. I'm not stopping you.

EDDIE. But I can't leave you here without any protection.

MADELINE. A lot of protection you are.

ELLEN. Why, Madeline—

[*Voice of* ELMER *off stage. It is a self-satisfied, well-fed, breezy voice.*]

ELMER. Yoo-hoo!

EDDIE. Oh, darn it, that's Elmer.

MADELINE. [*Sitting up, puts on slippers.*] Oh! [*Powders nose.*]

ELLEN. How did he ever find us?

ELMER. Yoo-hoo!

MADELINE. Yoo-hoo, Elmer!

EDDIE. Aw, heck!

[ELMER *enters center. It will not be hard for* ELMER *to acquire the expanding waistline of a prosperous business man. Solidity and assuredness, when dealing with ladies, are* ELMER's *strong points. He stands at the top of the steps for a moment, surveying the scene with what he hopes is a humorous expression.*]

ELMER. Well, well, well, if it isn't Eddie Johnson and his harem.

MADELINE. [*Flirting.*] Oh, Elmer.

ELMER. [*Coming down between* EDDIE *and* MADELINE.] Weren't walking home from any place, were you?

MADELINE. How did you find us?

ELMER. I saw you from the street when I was drivin' by in my car.

MADELINE. Your car! Oh, Elmer, if I'd only known—

EDDIE. [*Truculently.*] Where'd you get a car?

ELMER. [*Chest out.*] What's it to you, big boy? What's it to you?

MADELINE. Oh, Elmer, if you only knew what I've been through.

EDDIE. You goin' to give us a lift down to the club house?

ELMER. [*Cautiously.*] How much money you got?

EDDIE. Nothing.

MADELINE. Oh, Elmer, I'm so tired. I've walked miles and miles and miles.

ELMER. [*To* EDDIE.] You're a swell guy, makin' a girl walk. There oughta be a law against people like you.

EDDIE. How could I help it because I shot the rear end out of the car and Dad took it away—

MADELINE. Eddie told me he was going to have his father's car tonight, and then he came over just about time to start and said he couldn't have it—

ELMER. Yeah. He would.

EDDIE. Aw—

MADELINE. And then we got on the car, and Eddie didn't have enough money, and the conductor put us off, and all the people laughed at us—

ELMER. Yeah. You poor kid.

MADELINE. I felt like a criminal and I've ruined my slippers and my little toe's broken.

ELMER. [*To* EDDIE.] You oughtn't to ask a girl to go out with you. I never make a date unless I have a car and some swell flowers and a pocket full of dough.

MADELINE. Oh, Elmer!

ELMER. You ought to keep your eyes open, Eddie. Get around a little, and learn the ropes.

ELLEN. [*Loyally.*] Eddie's all right. He knows his way around just as well as you do. He couldn't help it if he had a little bad luck.

ELMER. Who let *you* out?

EDDIE. How about that lift?

ELMER. I'll think about it.

MADELINE. Come on. We'll be late.

EDDIE. Yeah. Come on.

ELMER. [*To* MADELINE.] Yeah. You and your sister come on.

EDDIE. What about me?

ELMER. Only got room for two.

ELLEN. Eddie can stand on the running board.

ELMER. That's against the law.

EDDIE. You're a good one to talk about law, driving without a license tonight. Your six months isn't up yet.

MADELINE. Oh, come on. Let's don't talk all night.

ELLEN. Does Eddie ride on the running board?

ELMER. Nope.

EDDIE. You're trying to shake me, that's what you're doing, and take Madeline to the dance yourself.

ELMER. Says who?

EDDIE. I don't care if you are my cousin. I'm goin' to protect my women from parlor snakes like you.

ELMER. You and who else?

[*They begin a slow dance around each other like a pair of roosters getting ready to fight.*]

EDDIE. You needn't think you can pick any girl you want just because you got a car.

ELMER. [*To* MADELINE.] Are you riding with me or walking with Eddie?

EDDIE. You just try taking her away from me. I'll break you off at the ankles.

ELMER. [*Backing to* MADELINE.] You and how many more?

EDDIE. [*Following him around bench.*] You're goin' to take us to that dance if I have to break up that flivver of yours and make you eat it.

MADELINE. Oh, Elmer, stop your scrapping and take me to the dance. [*Turning on* EDDIE.] You would start a roughhouse, Eddie Johnson! It's just like you!

EDDIE. Gosh, Madeline, you're not going with him, are you?

MADELINE. What does it look like I'm doing? Do you think I'm going to walk forty more blocks? Do you think I'd have gone with you in the first place if you hadn't said you'd get your father's car? I wouldn't be seen at a dog fight with you—you poor sap!

EDDIE. Aw— [*Stands stunned.*]

ELLEN. Why, Madeline! After Eddie's spent all his money on you!

MADELINE. [*To* ELLEN.] Go sit on a tack and hang your feet over.

ELMER. You coming, Ellen? I'm in a hurry.

ELLEN. Not much, you big stiff. We started out with Eddie, and I'll stick by him.

MADELINE. All right. Be stubborn if you want to.

ELMER. So long, Romeo. Maybe your father wouldn't let you have his car tonight, but he sure gave it to me, first time I asked him.

EDDIE. [*Incredulously.*] Huh?

ELMER. Your old man loosened up with the car when he saw me coming. He trusts *me* all right. So long. You oughta make the track team if you walk.

EDDIE. Aw—

[EDDIE *sits dejectedly on bench.* ELLEN *stamps her foot.*]

ELLEN. The big stiff! Who does he think he is? [*Sits beside* EDDIE.] Oh, don't mind them.

EDDIE. Huh?

ELLEN. Don't mind them. The big cheese! I'd like to jump down his throat and swing on his tonsils.

EDDIE. Aw.

ELLEN. Cheer up, Eddie. [*No answer.*] Eddie—are you going to sit there and mope all the rest of the evening?

EDDIE. Gee, what's the use? Other fellows' fathers don't take the car away from them on the biggest night of their life. A man's got to have a car to rush a girl, hasn't he? He's got to have money for flowers and emergencies, hasn't he?

ELLEN. Poor Eddie!

EDDIE. Take like gettin' stranded out here at the Thirty-fifth

Street Station with a couple of women. How'd he like gettin' stranded out here at the Thirty-fifth Street Station with a couple of women?

ELLEN. [*Murmuring.*] He wouldn't like it, Eddie.

EDDIE. I guess he'd find out then. I guess he'd see that a fellow needs money for flowers and emergencies.

ELLEN. Yes, Eddie.

EDDIE. Don't emergencies come up every day? Don't they? And don't they come when you're not expectin' them?

ELLEN. That's why they're emergencies, Eddie.

EDDIE. Why, an emergency could kill a fellow. Take like this was a desert and we got stranded. I couldn't walk to the dance and borrow any money off the fellows so we could get home then. If I didn't have the money right ready in my pocket ready for the emergency, we might be here for days and days and never get home. Dad would be sorry then.

ELLEN. Yes, Eddie.

EDDIE. Elmer was right, all right, about me not knowing anything about women. They just run over me like I was nothing. I ain't—I'm not nothing, either.

ELLEN. Oh, you're all right, Eddie.

EDDIE. I never was nothing—anything, and I never will be nothing—anything.

ELLEN. Yes, you will, Eddie.

EDDIE. But how can a fellow be anything if he doesn't get any co-operation from his parents? Here I go and lose a swell date to the dance just because I shot the rear end on the car and Dad wouldn't let me take it and he wouldn't give me next week's allowance and the ticket man had to be a moron and sell me tickets to the Thirty-fifth Street Station when I paid to the Tenth Street Station, and Elmer had to come along— [*Breaks off.*] Elmer! How'd he ever get the car?

ELLEN. Your father just doesn't appreciate you, Eddie.

EDDIE. Dad said he had to use the car to go to lodge tonight. Why'd he ever go and lend it to Elmer? Why'd he do that?

ELLEN. Elmer gives me a pain.

EDDIE. Yeah.

ELLEN. But Mother likes him, and Madeline likes him—

EDDIE. She does, huh?

ELLEN. [*Quickly.*] But I don't, and Father doesn't.

EDDIE. Your father's a smart man. Yeah, and you're smart, too, Ellen.

ELLEN. Oh, I'm not, Eddie.

EDDIE. There's a lot of people never see through Elmer. Gosh, the way he can pull wool over anybody's eyes—especially women. But he didn't fool us, did he?

ELLEN. No, Eddie.

EDDIE. I wouldn't put it past him if he just didn't go steal Dad's car.

ELLEN. Oh, Eddie!

EDDIE. Yes sir! I bet you that's what he did. The big stiff! If I had him here now, he wouldn't run away with Dad's car.

[*A pause while* EDDIE *thinks dark thoughts, and* ELLEN *steals little glances at him from beneath her long eyelashes.*]

ELLEN. Eddie, hadn't we better do something?

EDDIE. Aw—I suppose so. Who'd have thought when I started out this evening that it would end up this way? I guess I'm no good.

ELLEN. Yes you are, Eddie.

EDDIE. It's always been like this. Elmer used to live next door to me, and he used to come over and take my tricycle, and when I started to hammer his face in, Mom would come out and make me stop and tell me Elmer was my cousin and I ought to be nice to him.

ELLEN. When Madeline used to take my dolls, Mother always took her part. Oh gee, it's hard, isn't it, Eddie?

EDDIE. And Elmer swiped my new bicycle and rode—

ELLEN. And Madeline always got new dresses and—

EDDIE. And rode it down the hill and—

ELLEN. And Mother made them over for me—

EDDIE. And smashed it into a car.

ELLEN. Even my party dresses.

EDDIE. Now Elmer goes and gets our car when they won't let me have it.

ELLEN. And I have to trail along after Madeline.

EDDIE. They treat me like a child at home, when I can think for myself. I've got some rights. They ask me if I wash and if I got a clean handkerchief, and they won't let me have the car, or give me next week's allowance, and make me miss the dance. [*His voice breaks.*]

ELLEN. Here. [*Hands him his handkerchief.*]

EDDIE. Thags. [*Blows nose.*]

ELLEN. All my life they've made me drag around after Madeline like a spare tire. I've always been little sister. I'm always the extra one. I never have any dates of my own. [*She cries.*]

EDDIE. Here. [*Hands back his handkerchief.*]

ELLEN. Thags. [*Blows nose.*]

EDDIE. Gosh, life's tough. Gosh.

[ELLEN *hands him handkerchief and he blows.*]

ELLEN. I feel so miserable.

[EDDIE *hands her handkerchief and she blows.*]

EDDIE. I guess I'm no good.

ELLEN. Yes you are, Eddie.

EDDIE. I'm not. Nobody in the world likes me.

ELLEN. Yes they do, Eddie.

EDDIE. Well, no girl, anyway—

ELLEN. I do, Eddie.

EDDIE. Aw, you don't, Ellen. You're just sayin' it.

ELLEN. I've sort of looked up to you ever since I saw you last fall, Eddie.

EDDIE. [*Beginning to squirm.*] Aw—

ELLEN. You were standing in the front hall telling new students where to go and you looked sort of—like you knew lots.

EDDIE. [*Squirming some more.*] Aw—

ELLEN. And when you pitched and pitched in the game last week and the team just couldn't seem to get behind you and dropped everything, Dad said, "There's a young fellow who'll get somewhere. He doesn't blow up in emergencies. He uses his head." And I nearly busted with pride because I knew you.

EDDIE. [*Raises his head.*] Aw—honest? [*He looks at her.*]

ELLEN. Yes—honest. It must be nice to be sort of a hero and be on the team.

EDDIE. Gosh. [*Still staring at her.*]

ELLEN. [*Startled.*] What are you looking at, Eddie?

EDDIE. [*Confused.*] Aw—I—I don't know.. [*Thinks.*] You know, you're not bad lookin'. [*Squirms.*] Gee, you're—kinda pretty.

ELLEN. Gee, that's nice of you, Eddie. But I'm not, honest.

EDDIE. Yes you are. You got a cute nose.

ELLEN. [*Pleased.*] Oh.

EDDIE. [*Suddenly seeing flowers on her shoulder.*] Say, you've got my flowers on.

ELLEN. Madeline threw them away and I thought you wouldn't mind. They're so pretty.

EDDIE. Gee, they look keen. But they're not store flowers. They're just garden flowers.

ELLEN. [*Patting them.*] I think they're beautiful.

EDDIE. Sure swell, you stayin' here when you could've ridden with Elmer.

ELLEN. Oh, that wasn't anything, Eddie. When a girl starts out with a fellow, she sticks by him.

EDDIE. [*Darkly.*] Some girls don't.

ELLEN. I'm sorry, Eddie.

EDDIE. Oh, that's all right. I've had an awful good time talkin' to you, Ellen. I never talked to anybody like you before.

ELLEN. And I had a good time, too, Eddie. I guess it's about the nicest time I've ever had.

[*Their Eden is interrupted by the entrance of* EDWARD JOHNSON, SENIOR. *Judging by his lowering brows and menacing stride, there is trouble in the offing.*]

JOHNSON. Well, here you are. What did you do with that car?

EDDIE. [*Surprised.*] Car?

JOHNSON. You heard what I said! Here I've been chasing all over looking for you, and I missed the lodge meeting. Didn't I tell you I wanted that car to go to lodge meeting?

EDDIE. [*Trying to make his voice behave.*] I haven't got the car, Dad. We came on the street car.

ELLEN. And Eddie bought us tickets to the Tenth Street Station and they sold him tickets to the Thirty-fifth Street Station instead—

EDDIE. And they made us get off the car and we had to walk because you wouldn't give me next week's allowance for emergencies—

ELLEN. And Madeline got tired and wouldn't walk any farther—

EDDIE. And Elmer came along and took her to the dance—

ELLEN. And Elmer said—

EDDIE. He said you gave him the car—

ELLEN. The first time he asked for it—

JOHNSON. *I gave* him the car?

EDDIE. You trusted Elmer and you wouldn't trust your own son.

JOHNSON. But I didn't give it to him, the confounded—

ELLEN. [*Breathlessly.*] He just took it without asking?

JOHNSON. Here, you two. You come along with me. I'm going to teach that puppy a lesson.

EDDIE. What are you goin' to do? [*He scents joyous revenge ahead.*]

JOHNSON. I've had enough trouble with that boy. We'll just have the police pick him up and give him a good scare.

EDDIE. [*Too virtuously.*] But he's my cousin—

JOHNSON. I don't care if he is. Yell for my taxi to drive down to this end of the block, will you? I'll drop you where you're going and then I'll take care of young Mr. Elmer.

EDDIE. Okay, Dad.

[EDDIE *leaves with a triumphant swagger.* ELLEN *turns to* JOHNSON *and speaks hurriedly.*]

ELLEN. Mr. Johnson, would you mind dropping me somewhere near home? You see, Eddie was going to the dance with Madeline, and I'm just her little sister. You see, when Eddie gets to the dance he'll have Madeline again, and they won't want me tagging along. Eddie's been perfectly wonderful to me, Mr. Johnson. He's such a gentleman.

JOHNSON. [*Amused.*] Oh, he is, eh?

ELLEN. He was a perfect gentleman even though his heart was breaking. [EDDIE *returns.*] And if you can help me to get home some way—

JOHNSON. I think that can be arranged. [*To* EDDIE.] I'll take Ellen home and drop you at the dance, Eddie, and then we'll—

EDDIE. Aw, gee, I still got two tickets to the dance, haven't I?

ELLEN. Oh!

EDDIE. What're you goin' home for?

ELLEN. I'm just Madeline's sister—

EDDIE. No you're not. From now on Madeline is just *your* sister. Boy, won't she burn when we drive up in a taxi!

ELLEN. Oh, Eddie. [*They all start toward the taxi as the Curtain falls.*]

UNDERSTANDING AND APPRECIATING THE PLAY

1. Evaluate this play by the three yardsticks of comedy mentioned on page 15. What incidents or bits of conversation in this play made you laugh or chuckle? How may the final exit be acted to emphasize that a comedy must have a happy ending? In your opinion do the characters in this play act and talk like real people? Support your opinion by references to the play.

2. The action of a one-act play is seldom very complicated, since the play is not long enough to present an involved series of incidents. Indeed, the story of a one-act play may often be stated in a few sentences. In one short paragraph give the essential action of *Three's a Crowd*.

3. In the end, how are the four young people coupled off to go to the dance? Are you satisfied that each should have gone to the dance with the person he or she selected? Why?

4. Madeline must have been gorgeous indeed, but she had her faults. Which two of her traits did you find most objectionable?

5. Elmer is obviously the villain. What do you consider to be his most villainous deeds?

6. Ellen turns out to be the heroine. What desirable qualities does she possess?

7. When a character in a play changes in the progress of the action, he is said to be a *developing* character. A character who is not influenced by the action and remains entirely unchanged is called

a *static,* or stationary, character. In a one-act play, of course, there is not nearly so much opportunity for a writer to show character development as there is in a long play or in a novel. In fact, a character generally changes but little in the course of a one-act play. Classify each character in *Three's a Crowd* as *developing* or *static,* and justify your classification.

VOCABULARY BUILDING

1. Explain the following phrases in your own words (the words causing difficulty are italicized): *abominable* lights; stands *abjectly;* a *withering* glance; moving forward *truculently;* looking *incredulously;* grinning *fatuously; menacing* stride.

2. The English vocabulary now contains about 600,000 words. One of the reasons given to explain why our language has so many words is that we have borrowed freely from other languages, and sometimes in borrowing as, for example, a single Latin word, we have made a whole family of English words from it. The root *cred-,* meaning *belief,* from Latin *credere,* is such a borrowing. It appears in the English words *credit, credulous, incredible.* Define these words, using the word *belief* in each definition. What other members of this *cred-* family can you find among English words?

THINGS TO DO

1. Develop one of the following topics: A Real Friend, What a Predicament!, Qualities I Admire in a Boy (or Girl), An Embarrassing Moment (or Situation), My First Date, When My Parents Didn't Understand Me, Three's a Crowd.

2. For discussion: Which are preferable, co-educational schools and colleges (those attended by boys and girls) or segregated ones? What are the advantages and disadvantages of each kind of school or college?

3. For discussion, topics pertaining to dating, such as the following: At what age should dating begin? Why? How should a boy ask for a date? Do you approve of a girl's taking the initiative in such matters as asking for a date or phoning a boy? How should one be gracious about declining a request for a date? Do you respect the decision of many boys and girls to do little or no dating while they

are in high school? Should dating be "Dutch Treat"—that is, with the girl paying her own way? What if your parents object to your dating at your age or object to the person you date?

4. Write a sequel to *Three's a Crowd*, in which you relate in play form what happens when the young people and Mr. Johnson arrive at the dance.

5. Write a plot summary of a play with a happy ending on a subject related to school life, to romance, or to young people in general.

6. Write a description of the setting of your play.

7. Write two or three pages of dialogue for your play.

8. Write and dramatize a humorous dialogue. Make the scene of your humorous conversation any place that you think appropriate.

9. For a try-out stunt, you might memorize and recite a humorous or dramatic poem: for example, "Casey at the Bat" by Ernest Lawrence Thayer, "The Cremation of Sam McGee" by Robert W. Service, or "Pershing at the Front" by Arthur Guiterman.

PRODUCTION NOTES

This play is simple in staging and in acting, and requires for essential props nothing more than a handkerchief, a corsage and a compact.

To set your stage, you need to provide only two benches; be sure that they are so placed that Eddie and the girls will be facing a large part of the audience when seated. Placing the benches so that each forms a forty-five degree angle with the footlights serves the double purpose of having the actors face each other naturally and, at the same time, having them face the audience. By borrowing one or two high-jump or pole-vault stands from the physical education department, you have something on which to attach an imitation park lamp or two.

In sharpening the acting, stage movement, and "business," there are a few details that require special attention. The "fight" scene between the boys must be carefully rehearsed and timed. They must really circle about each other like a pair of roosters—and the wider the circle, the better. They may start at the center of the stage, follow each other all the way around the bench at stage right, and then be separated by Madeline's coming between them. The handkerchief passing business between Eddie and Ellen is certain to get many laughs; pay careful attention to it. In fact, the entire scene in which Eddie and Ellen reminisce and get to know each other is worth a little extra effort in the preparation. When they are reminiscing, the couple may look straight out toward the audience. The cutting of one's lines into the other's should be timed correctly. An effective use of gestures will do much to bring out the sincerity, the "cuteness," and the lack of sophistication of these two young people.

The actress portraying Madeline should not only be charming and dynamic, but also she should convey Madeline's self-assurance, selfishness, and vanity. And the actor in the Elmer role must interpret the breezy brashness and lack of integrity of that character.

MORE GOOD ONE-ACT COMEDIES

At the end of each unit of this book more good plays similar in type or subject matter are recommended. When a play is published by more than one company, then the publisher that controls the amateur acting rights is generally given.

In reading other plays than those included in this book, everyone will derive the greatest benefit if there are reports, discussions, and dramatizations of the plays read. Before any oral work is done, your teacher or discussion leader may wish to have you submit a short written report in which you first give your reaction to the play in a sentence or two and then briefly summarize the plot and the theme— if there is one. You may, in addition, wish to discuss briefly such matters as characterization, dialogue, and mood and atmosphere.

In telling your group about a play you have read, it would be interesting, also, to read aloud an incident that you liked particularly. By enlisting the aid of some of the other people in your group, you can dramatize an incident or an entire scene. It isn't necessary to memorize lines for a presentation of this nature; your group will be certain to appreciate your efforts.

The Affected Young Ladies. Molière. [French] In this seventeenth-century comedy by the Shakespeare of France, two affected young ladies are taught a lesson by their lovers.

The Man Who Died at Twelve O'Clock. Paul Green. [French] One of the most amusing of the one-act folk comedies—the story of how a pair of Negro lovers convince the girl's grandfather that he has seen the devil and that he is dead. The reason? He had been preventing their marriage, of course.

'Op-o'-Me-Thumb. Frederick Fenn and Richard Royce. [French] A charming comedy in which a young girl weaves a romantic dream about a shirt left by a young man in the laundry in which she is employed.

The Princess Marries the Page. Edna St. Vincent Millay. [Harper] Written by America's foremost poetess, this verse play has elements of humor and suspense.

The Romancers. Edmond Rostand. [French]   A Romeo and Juliet type of play, to which, because it is a comedy in spirit, there is a happy ending.

The Ghost Story and *The Trysting Place.* Booth Tarkington. [Appleton]   If you enjoyed *Three's a Crowd,* you will also like the two Tarkington comedies about young people.

FULL-LENGTH PLAYS

Ah, Wilderness!, Eugene O'Neill [French];   *Cyrano de Bergerac,* Edmond Rostand [French];   *I Remember Mama,* John Van Druten [Dramatists Play Service];   *Junior Miss,* Jerome Chodorov and Joseph Fields [Dramatists Play Service];   *Life with Father* and *Life with Mother,* Howard Lindsay and Russel Crouse [Dramatists Play Service];   *Oklahoma!,* Oscar Hammerstein III and Richard Rodgers [Random House];   *The Male Animal,* James Thurber and Elliot Nugent [French];   *Pygmalion* and *The Devil's Disciple,* George Bernard Shaw [Dodd-Mead];   *As You Like It* and *Twelfth Night,* William Shakespeare;   *The Admirable Crichton* and *Quality Street,* Sir James M. Barrie [Dodd-Mead].

Melodrama: Adventure, Mystery, and Thrills

MELODRAMA is probably the most frequently encountered type of drama. Most Western films, murder mysteries, "crook" plays, "thrillers," and adventure plays on television, screen, or radio are of this kind. The object of melodrama—whether it is written for the stage or television, the screen or radio—is to keep us thrilled, to arouse emotion by means of exciting events. The melodrama, like the farce, moves at a fast and furious pace; it awakens such strong feelings as horror, terror, hate, pity, and joy. "This movie is a real thriller-diller," writes a movie critic. He could be talking of nothing but a melodrama.

Writers of this kind of play generally go to the extremes of black and white in their characterization; more often than not, characters are either blamelessly virtuous or very villainous indeed. There is a constant conflict between the forces of good and of evil. The ending is usually a "happy" one—that is, one in which the deserving are amply rewarded and the bad are properly punished. Children, after seeing a melodrama or listening to one on the radio, speak of "the good guys" who successfully outwitted "the bad guys."

If the play is good melodrama, the reader will be swept along with the story at a pace which will leave him no time to challenge anything that is happening; nor will what happens seem too unrealistic. It is only when the play is over and the reader comes back to reality that he may realize he has experienced an adventure which was probably pretty farfetched. But when a melodrama is not skillfully written, it is hard for even the friendliest of readers and playgoers to accept with anything but laughter the highly improbable situations and the hairbreadth escapes. The author has failed to achieve his purpose.

The main problem for the reader or playgoer in approaching melodrama is one of yielding willingly to the suspense and excitement of the play. An intelligent reader will not demand that a melodrama be entirely true to life. A reader who maintains a skeptical attitude throughout the reading of a well–written melodrama is not co-operating with the author as he should, and through his lack of co-operation is missing much of the pleasure offered by the play.

There was a time when the melodrama was regarded as the stepchild of the theater. Far too many plays and movies of that type were written in the old-fashioned tradition, in which the mustachioed villain would tie the beautiful heroine to the railroad tracks to the very audible accompaniment of hisses and boos from the audience.

In recent years, melodramas have been better written and a new kind of melodrama has appeared. This new melodrama— as exemplified by such plays as Robert E. Sherwood's *The Petrified Forest,* and Sidney Kingsley's *Dead End*—is much more subtle than the old, and much more sensible; but it is every bit as exciting. It has rightly been called "melodrama with a meaning," for it deals intelligently with such important ideas and causes as patriotism, understanding human nature, overcoming our enemies, and improving our democracy. And we don't object at all to being led by this new type of melodrama to a truer understanding of ourselves and our problems. We like it.

The Ring of General Macías *

JOSEFINA NIGGLI

In *The Ring of General Macías* we find melodrama at its best and most exciting. The action of the play is set against the background of the Mexican Revolution of 1912. Concerning that turbulent era, the Mexican historian Joaquin Peralta has written, "The Federal troops were fighting for a way of living; the Revolutionists were fighting for life itself. The outcome of such a struggle could never be in doubt."

As the play opens, we are in the living room of the aristocratic Federal general Macías. The general is away at war. The room is in darkness except for the moonlight that comes through the French windows. A young woman enters stealthily, carrying a lighted candle. She is desperately searching for something.

CHARACTERS

MARICA, *the sister of General Macías* [1]
RAQUEL, *the wife of General Macías*
ANDRÉS DE LA O, *a captain in the Revolutionary Army*
CLETO, *a private in the Revolutionary Army*
BASILIO FLORES, *a captain in the Federal Army*

PLACE: Just outside Mexico City
TIME: A night in April, 1912

The living room of General Macías' home is luxuriously furnished in the gold and ornate style of Louis XVI. In the Right wall are French windows leading into the patio. Flanking these

[1] Pronounced Ma sï'as. In Latin America a *c* before an *i* is pronounced like an *s*.

38

windows are low bookcases. In the Back wall is, Right, a closet door; and, Center, a table holding a wine decanter and glasses. The Left wall has a door Upstage, and Downstage a writing desk with a straight chair in front of it. Near the desk is an armchair. Down Right is a small sofa with a table holding a lamp at the Upstage end of it. There are pictures on the walls. The room looks rather stuffy and unlived in.

When the curtains part, the stage is in darkness save for the moonlight that comes through the French windows. Then the house door opens and a young girl in negligee enters stealthily. She is carrying a lighted candle. She stands at the door a moment listening for possible pursuit, then moves quickly across to the bookcase Down Right. She puts the candle on top of the bookcase and begins searching behind the books. She finally finds what she wants: a small bottle. While she is searching, the house door opens silently and a woman, also in negligee, enters. (These negligees are in the latest Parisian style.) She moves silently across the room to the table by the sofa, and as the girl turns with the bottle, the woman switches on the light. The girl gives a half-scream and draws back, frightened. The light reveals her to be quite young—no more than twenty—a timid, dovelike creature. The woman has a queenly air, and whether she is actually beautiful or not, people think she is. She is about thirty-two.

MARICA.[2] [*Trying to hide the bottle behind her.*] Raquel! What are you doing here?

RAQUEL.[3] What did you have hidden behind the books, Marica?

MARICA. [*Attempting a forced laugh.*] I? Nothing. Why do you think I have anything?

RAQUEL. [*Taking a step toward her.*] Give it to me.

MARICA. [*Backing away from her.*] No. No, I won't.

RAQUEL. [*Stretching out her hand.*] I demand that you give it to me.

MARICA. You have no right to order me about. I'm a married

[2] Pronounced Ma rē'ka.
[3] Pronounced Ra kĕll'.

woman. I . . . I . . . [*She begins to sob, and flings herself down on the sofa.*]

RAQUEL. [*Much gentler.*] You shouldn't be up. The doctor told you to stay in bed. [*She bends over* MARICA *and gently takes the bottle out of the girl's hand.*] It was poison. I thought so.

MARICA. [*Frightened.*] You won't tell the priest, will you?

RAQUEL. Suicide is a sin, Marica. A sin against God.

MARICA. I know. I . . . [*She catches* RAQUEL's *hand.*] Oh, Raquel, why do we have to have wars? Why do men have to go to war and be killed?

RAQUEL. Men must fight for what they believe is right. It is an honorable thing to die for your country as a soldier.

MARICA. How can you say that with Domingo out there fighting, too? And fighting what? Men who aren't even men. Peasants. Ranch slaves. Men who shouldn't be allowed to fight.

RAQUEL. Peasants are men, Marica. Not animals.

MARICA. Men. It's always men. But how about the women? What becomes of us?

RAQUEL. We can pray.

MARICA. [*Bitterly.*] Yes, we can pray. And then comes the terrible news, and it's no use praying any more. All the reason for our praying is dead. Why should I go on living with Tomás dead?

RAQUEL. Living is a duty.

MARICA. How can you be so cold, so hard? You are a cold and hard woman, Raquel. My brother worships you. He has never even looked at another woman since the first day he saw you. Does he know how cold and hard you are?

RAQUEL. Domingo is my—honored husband.

MARICA. You've been married for ten years. And I've been married for three months. If Domingo is killed, it won't be the same for you. You've had ten years. [*She is crying wildly.*] I haven't anything . . . anything at all.

RAQUEL. You've had three months—three months of laughter. And now you have tears. How lucky you are. You have tears. Perhaps five months of tears. Not more. You're only twenty. And in five months Tomás will become just a lovely memory.

MARICA. I'll remember Tomás all my life.

RAQUEL. Of course. But he'll be distant and far away. But you're young . . . and the young need laughter. The young can't live on tears. And one day in Paris, or Rome, or even Mexico City, you'll meet another man. You'll marry again. There will be children in your house. How lucky you are.

MARICA. I'll never marry again.

RAQUEL. You're only twenty. You'll think differently when you're twenty-eight, or nine, or thirty.

MARICA. What will you do if Domingo is killed?

RAQUEL. I shall be very proud that he died in all his courage . . . in all the greatness of a hero.

MARICA. But you'd not weep, would you? Not you! I don't think there are any tears in you.

RAQUEL. No, I'd not weep. I'd sit here in this empty house and wait.

MARICA. Wait for what?

RAQUEL. For the jingle of his spurs as he walks across the tiled hall. For the sound of his laughter in the patio. For the echo of his voice as he shouts to the groom to put away his horse. For the feel of his hand . . .

MARICA. [*Screams.*] Stop it!

RAQUEL. I'm sorry.

MARICA. You do love him, don't you?

RAQUEL. I don't think even he knows how much.

MARICA. I thought that after ten years people slid away from love. But you and Domingo—why, you're all he thinks about. When he's away from you he talks about you all the time. I heard him say once that when you were out of his sight he was like a man without eyes or ears or hands.

RAQUEL. I know. I, too, know that feeling.

MARICA. Then how could you let him go to war? Perhaps to be killed? How could you?

RAQUEL. [*Sharply.*] Marica, you are of the family Macías. Your family is a family of great warriors. A Macías man was with Ferdinand when the Moors were driven out of Spain. A Macías man was with Cortés when the Aztecans surrendered. Your grandfather fought in the War of Independence. Your own father was executed not twenty miles from this house by the French. Shall his son be any less brave because he loves a woman?

MARICA. But Domingo loved you enough to forget that. If you had asked him, he wouldn't have gone to war. He would have stayed here with you.

RAQUEL. No, he would not have stayed. Your brother is a man of honor, not a whining, creeping coward.

MARICA. [*Beginning to cry again.*] I begged Tomás not to go. I begged him.

RAQUEL. Would you have loved him if he had stayed?

MARICA. I don't know. I don't know.

RAQUEL. There is your answer. You'd have despised him. Loved and despised him. Now come, Marica, it's time for you to go to bed.

MARICA. You won't tell the priest—about the poison, I mean?

RAQUEL. No. I won't tell him.

MARICA. Thank you, Raquel. How good you are. How kind and good.

RAQUEL. A moment ago I was hard and cruel. What a baby you are. Now, off to bed with you.

MARICA. Aren't you coming upstairs, too?

RAQUEL. No . . . I haven't been sleeping very well lately. I think I'll read for a little while.

MARICA. Good night, Raquel. And thank you.

RAQUEL. Good night, little one.

[MARICA *goes out through the house door Left, taking her candle with her. Raquel stares down at the bottle of poison in her hand, then puts it away in one of the small drawers of the desk. She next selects a book from the Downstage case, and sits on the sofa to read it, but feeling chilly, she rises and goes to the closet, Back Right, and takes out an afghan. Coming back to the sofa, she makes herself comfortable, with the afghan across her knees. Suddenly she hears a noise in the patio. She listens, then convinced it is nothing, returns to her reading. But she hears the noise again. She goes to the patio door and peers out.*]

RAQUEL. [*Calling softly.*] Who's there? Who's out there? Oh! [*She gasps and backs into the room. Two men—or rather a man and a young boy—dressed in the white pajama suits of the Mexican peasants, with their sombreros tipped low over their faces, come into the room.* RAQUEL *draws herself up regally. Her voice is cold and commanding.*] Who are you, and what do you want here?

ANDRÉS. We are hunting for the wife of General Macías.

RAQUEL. I am Raquel Rivera de Macías.

ANDRÉS. Cleto, stand guard in the patio. If you hear any suspicious noise, warn me at once.

CLETO. Yes, my captain. [*The boy returns to the patio.*]
[*The man, hooking his thumbs in his belt, strolls around the room, looking it over. When he reaches the table at the back he sees the wine. With a small bow to* RAQUEL *he pours himself a glass of wine and drains it. He wipes his mouth with the back of his hand.*]

RAQUEL. How very interesting.

ANDRÉS. [*Startled.*] What?

RAQUEL. To be able to drink wine with that hat on.

ANDRÉS. The hat? Oh, forgive me, señora. [*He flicks the brim with his fingers so that it drops off his head and dangles down his back from the neck cord.*] In a military camp one forgets one's polite manners. Would you care to join me in another glass?

RAQUEL. [*Sitting on the sofa.*] Why not? It's my wine.

ANDRÉS. And very excellent wine. [*He pours two glasses and gives her one while he is talking.*] I would say Amontillado of the vintage of '87.

RAQUEL. Did you learn that in a military camp?

ANDRÉS. I used to sell wines . . . among other things.

RAQUEL. [*Ostentatiously hiding a yawn.*] I am devastated.

ANDRÉS. [*Pulls over the armchair and makes himself comfortable in it.*] You don't mind, do you?

RAQUEL. Would it make any difference if I did?

ANDRÉS. No. The Federals are searching the streets for us and we have to stay somewhere. But women of your class seem to expect that senseless sort of question.

RAQUEL. Of course, I suppose I could scream.

ANDRÉS. Naturally.

RAQUEL. My sister-in-law is upstairs asleep. And there are several servants in the back of the house. Mostly men servants. Very big men.

ANDRÉS. Very interesting. [*He is drinking the wine in small sips with much enjoyment.*]

RAQUEL. What would you do if I screamed?

ANDRÉS. [*Considering the request as though it were another glass of wine.*] Nothing.

RAQUEL. I am afraid you are lying to me.

ANDRÉS. Women of your class seem to expect polite little lies.

RAQUEL. Stop calling me "woman of your class."

ANDRÉS. Forgive me.

RAQUEL. You are one of the fighting peasants, aren't you?

ANDRÉS. I am a captain in the Revolutionary Army.

RAQUEL. This house is completely loyal to the Federal government.

ANDRÉS. I know. That's why I'm here.

RAQUEL. And now that you are here, just what do you expect me to do?

ANDRÉS. I expect you to offer sanctuary to myself and to Cleto.

RAQUEL. Cleto? [*She looks toward the patio and adds sarcastically.*] Oh, your army.

CLETO. [*Appearing in the doorway.*] I'm sorry, my captain. I just heard a noise. [RAQUEL *stands.* ANDRÉS *moves quickly to her and puts his hands on her arms from the back.* CLETO *has turned and is peering into the patio. Then the boy relaxes.*] We are still safe, my captain. It was only a rabbit. [*He goes back into the patio.* RAQUEL *pulls away from* ANDRÉS *and goes to the desk.*]

RAQUEL. What a magnificent army you have. So clever. I'm sure you must win many victories.

ANDRÉS. We do. And we will win the greatest victory, remember that.

RAQUEL. This farce has gone on long enough. Will you please take your army and climb over the patio wall with it?

ANDRÉS. I told you that we came here so that you could give us sanctuary.

RAQUEL. My dear captain—captain without a name . . .

ANDRÉS. Andrés de la O, your servant. [*He makes a bow.*]

RAQUEL. [*Startled.*] Andrés de la O!

ANDRÉS. I am flattered. You have heard of me.

RAQUEL. Naturally. Everyone in the city has heard of you. You have a reputation for politeness—especially to women.

ANDRÉS. I see that the tales about me have lost nothing in the telling.

RAQUEL. I can't say. I'm not interested in gossip about your type of soldier.

ANDRÉS. Then let me give you something to heighten your interest. [*He suddenly takes her in his arms and kisses her. She stiffens for a moment, then remains perfectly still. He steps away from her.*]

RAQUEL. [*Rage forcing her to whisper.*] Get out of here—at once!

ANDRÉS. [*Staring at her in admiration.*] I can understand why Macías loves you. I couldn't before, but now I can understand it.

RAQUEL. Get out of my house.

ANDRÉS. [*Sits on the sofa and pulls a small leather pouch out of his shirt. He pours its contents into his hand.*] So cruel, señora, and I with a present for you? Here is a holy medal. My mother gave me this medal. She died when I was ten. She was a street beggar. She died of starvation. But I wasn't there. I was in jail. I had been sentenced to five years in prison for stealing five oranges. The judge thought it a great joke. One year for each orange. He laughed. He had a very loud laugh. [*Pause.*] I killed him two months ago. I hanged him to the telephone pole in front of his house. And I laughed. [*Pause.*] I also have a very loud laugh. [RAQUEL *abruptly turns her back on him.*] I told that story to a girl the other night and she thought it very funny. But of course she was a peasant girl—a girl who could neither read nor write. She hadn't been born in a great house in Tabasco. She didn't have an English governess. She didn't go to school to the nuns in Paris. She didn't marry one of the richest young men in the Republic. But she thought my story very funny. Of course she could understand it. Her brother had been whipped to death because he had run away from the plantation that owned him. [*He pauses and looks at her. She does not move.*] Are you still angry with me? Even though I have brought you a present? [*He holds out his hand.*] A very nice present—from your husband.

RAQUEL. [*Turns and stares at him in amazement.*] A present! From Domingo?

ANDRÉS. I don't know him that well. I call him the General Macías.

RAQUEL. [*Excitedly.*] Is he well? How does he look? [*With horrified comprehension.*] He's a prisoner . . . your prisoner!

ANDRÉS. Naturally. That's why I know so much about you. He talks about you constantly.

RAQUEL. You know nothing about him. You're lying to me.

[CLETO *comes to the window.*]

ANDRÉS. I assure you, señora . . .

CLETO. [*Interrupting.*] My captain . . .

ANDRÉS. What is it, Cleto? Another rabbit?

CLETO. No, my captain. There are soldiers at the end of the street. They are searching all the houses. They will be here soon.

ANDRÉS. Don't worry. We are quite safe here. Stay in the patio until I call you.

CLETO. Yes, my captain. [*He returns to the patio.*]

RAQUEL. You are not safe here. When those soldiers come I shall turn you over to them.

ANDRÉS. I think not.

RAQUEL. You can't escape from them. And they are not kind to you peasant prisoners. They have good reason not to be.

ANDRÉS. Look at this ring. [*He holds his hand out, with the ring on his palm.*]

RAQUEL. Why, it's—a wedding ring.

ANDRÉS. Read the inscription inside of it. [*As she hesitates, he adds sharply.*] Read it!

RAQUEL. [*Slowly takes the ring. While she is reading her voice fades to a whisper.*] "D. M.—R. R.—June 2, 1902." Where did you get this?

ANDRÉS. General Macías gave it to me.

RAQUEL. [*Firmly and clearly.*] Not this ring. He'd never give you this ring. [*With dawning horror.*] He's dead. You stole it from his dead finger. He's dead.

ANDRÉS. Not yet. But he will be dead if I don't return to camp safely by sunset tomorrow.

RAQUEL. I don't believe you. I don't believe you. You're lying to me.

ANDRÉS. This house is famous for its loyalty to the Federal government. You will hide me until those soldiers get out of this district. When it is safe enough Cleto and I will leave. But if you betray me to them, your husband will be shot tomorrow evening at sunset. Do you understand? [*He shakes her arm.* RAQUEL *looks dazedly at him.* CLETO *comes to the window.*]

CLETO. The soldiers are coming closer, my captain. They are at the next house.

ANDRÉS. [*To* RAQUEL.] Where shall we hide? [RAQUEL *is still dazed. He gives her another little shake.*] Think, woman! If you love your husband at all—think!

RAQUEL. I don't know. Marica upstairs—the servants in the rest of the house—I don't know.

ANDRÉS. The General has bragged to us about you. He says you are braver than most men. He says you are very clever. This is a time to be both brave and clever.

CLETO. [*Pointing to the closet.*] What door is that?

RAQUEL. It's a closet . . . a storage closet.

ANDRÉS. We'll hide in there.

RAQUEL. It's very small. It's not big enough for both of you.

ANDRÉS. Cleto, hide yourself in there.

CLETO. But, my captain . . .

ANDRÉS. That's an order! Hide yourself.

CLETO. Yes, Sir. [*He steps inside the closet.*]

ANDRÉS. And now, señora, where are you going to hide me?

RAQUEL. How did you persuade my husband to give you his ring?

ANDRÉS. That's a very long story, señora, for which we have no time just now. [*He puts the ring and medal back in the*

pouch and thrusts it inside his shirt.] Later I will be glad to give
you all the details. But at present it is only necessary for you to
remember that his life depends upon mine.

RAQUEL. Yes—yes, of course. [*She loses her dazed expression
and seems to grow more queenly as she takes command of the
situation.*] Give me your hat. [ANDRÉS *shrugs and passes it over
to her. She takes it to the closet and hands it to* CLETO.] There
is a smoking jacket hanging up in there. Hand it to me. [CLETO
hands her a man's velvet smoking jacket. She brings it to ANDRÉS.]
Put this on.

ANDRÉS. [*Puts it on and looks down at himself.*] Such a pity
my shoes are not comfortable slippers.

RAQUEL. Sit in that chair. [*She points to the armchair.*]

ANDRÉS. My dear lady . . .

RAQUEL. If I must save your life, allow me to do it in my own
way. Sit down. [ANDRÉS *sits. She picks up the afghan from the
couch and throws it over his feet and legs, carefully tucking it in
so that his body is covered to the waist.*] If anyone speaks to you,
don't answer. Don't turn your head. As far as you are concerned,
there is no one in this room—not even me. Just look straight
ahead of you and . . .

ANDRÉS. [*As she pauses.*] And what?

RAQUEL. I started to say "and pray," but since you're a member of the Revolutionary Army I don't suppose you believe in
God and prayer.

ANDRÉS. My mother left me a holy medal.

RAQUEL. Oh, yes, I remember. A very amusing story. [*There
is the sound of men's voices in the patio.*] The Federal soldiers
are here. If you can pray, ask God to keep Marica upstairs. She
is very young and very stupid. She'll betray you before I can
shut her mouth.

ANDRÉS. I'll . . .

RAQUEL. Silence! Stare straight ahead of you and pray. [*She
goes to the French window and speaks loudly to the soldiers.*]
Really! What is the meaning of this uproar?

FLORES. [*Off.*] Do not alarm yourself, señora. [*He comes into the room. He wears the uniform of a Federal officer.*] I am Captain Basilio Flores, at your service, señora.

RAQUEL. What do you mean, invading my house and making so much noise at this hour of the night?

FLORES. We are hunting for two spies. One of them is the notorious Andrés de la O. You may have heard of him, señora.

RAQUEL. [*Looking at* ANDRÉS.] Considering what he did to my cousin—yes, I've heard of him.

FLORES. Your cousin, señora?

RAQUEL. [*Comes to* ANDRÉS *and puts her hand on his shoulder. He stares woodenly in front of him.*] Felipe was his prisoner before the poor boy managed to escape.

FLORES. Is it possible? [*He crosses to* ANDRÉS.] Captain Basilio Flores, at your service. [*He salutes.*]

RAQUEL. Felipe doesn't hear you. He doesn't even know you are in the room.

FLORES. Eh, it is a sad thing.

RAQUEL. Must your men make so much noise?

FLORES. The hunt must be thorough, señora. And now if some of my men can go through here to the rest of the house . . .

RAQUEL. Why?

FLORES. But I told you, señora. We are hunting for two spies . . .

RAQUEL. [*Speaking quickly from controlled nervousness.*] And do you think I have them hidden some place, and I the wife of General Macías?

FLORES. General Macías! But I didn't know . . .

RAQUEL. Now that you do know, I suggest you remove your men and their noise at once.

FLORES. But, señora, I regret—I still have to search this house.

RAQUEL. I can assure you, captain, that I have been sitting here all evening, and no peasant spy has passed me and gone into the rest of the house.

FLORES. Several rooms open off the patio, señora. They needn't have come through here.

RAQUEL. So . . . you do think I conceal spies in this house.

Then search it by all means. Look under the sofa . . . under the table. In the drawers of the desk. And don't miss that closet, captain. Inside that closet is hidden a very fierce and wicked spy.

FLORES. Please, señora . . .

RAQUEL. [*Goes to the closet door.*] Or do you prefer me to open it for you?

FLORES. I am only doing my duty, señora. You are making it very difficult.

RAQUEL. [*Relaxing against the door.*] I'm sorry. My sister-in-law is upstairs. She has just received word that her husband has been killed. They were married three months ago. She's only twenty. I didn't want . . .

MARICA. [*Calling off.*] Raquel, what is all the noise down-stairs?

RAQUEL. [*Goes to the house door and calls.*] It is nothing. Go back to bed.

MARICA. But I can hear men's voices in the patio.

RAQUEL. It is only some Federal soldiers hunting for two peas-ant spies. [*She turns and speaks rapidly to* FLORES.] If she comes down here, she must not see my cousin. Felipe escaped, but her husband was killed. The doctor thinks the sight of my poor cousin might affect her mind. You understand?

FLORES. Certainly, señora. What a sad thing.

MARICA. [*Still off.*] Raquel, I'm afraid! [*She tries to push past* RAQUEL *into the room.* RAQUEL *and* FLORES *stand between her and* ANDRÉS.] Spies! In this house. Oh, Raquel!

RAQUEL. The doctor will be very angry if you don't return to bed at once.

MARICA. But those terrible men will kill us. What is the matter with you two? Why are you standing there like that? [*She tries to see past them, but they both move so that she can't see* ANDRÉS.]

FLORES. It is better that you go back to your room, señora.

MARICA. But why? Upstairs I am alone. Those terrible men will kill me. I know they will.

FLORES. Don't be afraid, señora. There are no spies in this house.

MARICA. Are you sure?

RAQUEL. Captain Flores means that no spy would dare to take refuge in the house of General Macías. Isn't that right, captain?

FLORES. [*Laughing.*] Of course. All the world knows of the brave General Macías.

RAQUEL. Now go back to bed, Marica. Please, for my sake.

MARICA. You are both acting very strangely. I think you have something hidden in this room you don't want me to see.

RAQUEL. [*Sharply.*] You are quite right. Captain Flores has captured one of the spies. He is sitting in the chair behind me. He is dead. Now will you please go upstairs!

MARICA. [*Gives a stifled sob.*] Oh! That such a terrible thing could happen in this house. [*She runs out of the room, still sobbing.*]

FLORES. [*Worried.*] Was it wise to tell her such a story, señora?

RAQUEL. [*Tense with repressed relief.*] Better that than the truth. Good night, captain, and thank you.

FLORES. Good night, señora. And don't worry. Those spies won't bother you. If they were anywhere in this district, my men would have found them.

RAQUEL. I'm sure of it.

[*The Captain salutes her, looks toward* ANDRÉS *and salutes him, then goes into the patio. He can be heard calling his men. Neither* ANDRÉS *nor* RAQUEL *moves until the voices outside die away. Then* RAQUEL *staggers and nearly falls, but* ANDRÉS *catches her in time.*]

ANDRÉS. [*Calling softly.*] They've gone, Cleto. [ANDRÉS *carries* RAQUEL *to the sofa as* CLETO *comes out of the closet.*] Bring a glass of wine. Quickly.

CLETO. [*As he gets the wine.*] What happened?

ANDRÉS. It's nothing. Just a faint. [*He holds the wine to her lips.*]

CLETO. She's a great lady, that one. When she wanted to open the closet door my knees were trembling, I can tell you.

ANDRÉS. My own bones were playing a pretty tune.

CLETO. Why do you think she married Macías?

ANDRÉS. Love is a peculiar thing, Cleto.

CLETO. I don't understand it.

RAQUEL. [*Moans and sits up.*] Are they—are they gone?

ANDRÉS. Yes, they're gone. [*He kisses her hand.*] I've never known a braver lady.

RAQUEL. [*Pulling her hand away.*] Will you go now, please?

ANDRÉS. We'll have to wait until the district is free of them—but if you'd like to write a letter to your husband while we're waiting . . .

RAQUEL. [*Surprised at his kindness.*] You'd take it to him? You'd really give it to him?

ANDRÉS. Of course.

RAQUEL. Thank you. [*She goes to the writing desk and sits down.*]

ANDRÉS. [*To* CLETO, *who has been staring steadily at* RAQUEL *all the while.*] You stay here with the señora. I'm going to find out how much of the district has been cleared.

CLETO. [*Still staring at* RAQUEL.] Yes, my captain.

[ANDRÉS *leaves by the French windows.* CLETO *keeps on staring at* RAQUEL *as she starts to write. After a moment she she turns to him.*]

RAQUEL. [*Irritated.*] Why do you keep staring at me?

CLETO. Why did you marry a man like that one, señora?

RAQUEL. You're very impertinent.

CLETO. [*Shyly.*] I'm sorry, señora.

RAQUEL. [*After a brief pause.*] What do you mean: "a man like that one"?

CLETO. Well, you're very brave, señora.

RAQUEL. [*Lightly.*] And don't you think the general is very brave?

CLETO. No, señora. Not very.

RAQUEL. [*Staring at him with bewilderment.*] What are you trying to tell me?

CLETO. Nothing, señora. It is none of my affair.

RAQUEL. Come here. [*He comes slowly up to her.*] Tell me what is in your mind.

CLETO. I don't know, señora. I don't understand it. The captain says love is a peculiar thing, but I don't understand it.

RAQUEL. Cleto, did the general willingly give that ring to your captain?

CLETO. Yes, señora.

RAQUEL. Why?

CLETO. The general wanted to save his own life. He said he loved you and he wanted to save his life.

RAQUEL. How would giving that ring to your captain save the general's life?

CLETO. The general's supposed to be shot tomorrow afternoon. But he's talked about you a lot, and when my captain knew we had to come into the city, he thought perhaps we might take refuge here if the Federals got on our trail. So he went to the general and said that if he fixed it so we'd be safe here, my captain would save him from the firing squad.

RAQUEL. Was your trip here to the city very important—to your cause, I mean?

CLETO. Indeed yes, señora. The captain got a lot of fine information. It means we'll win the next big battle. My captain is a very clever man, señora.

RAQUEL. Did the general know about this information when he gave his ring to your captain?

CLETO. I don't see how he could help knowing it, señora. He heard us talking about it enough.

RAQUEL. Who knows about that bargain to save the general's life beside you and your captain?

CLETO. No one, señora. The captain isn't one to talk, and I didn't have time to.

RAQUEL. [*While the boy has been talking, the life seems to have drained completely out of her.*] How old are you, Cleto?

CLETO. I don't know, señora. I think I'm twenty, but I don't know.

RAQUEL. [*Speaking more to herself than to him.*] Tomás was twenty.

CLETO. Who is Tomás?

RAQUEL. He was married to my sister-in-law. Cleto, you think my husband is a coward, don't you?

CLETO. [*With embarrassment.*] Yes, señora.

RAQUEL. You don't think any woman is worth it, do you? Worth the price of a great battle, I mean?

CLETO. No, señora. But as the captain says, love is a very peculiar thing.

RAQUEL. If your captain loved a woman as much as the general loves me, would he have given an enemy his ring?

CLETO. Ah, but the captain is a great man, señora.

RAQUEL. And so is my husband a great man. He is of the family Macías. All of that family have been great men. All of them—brave and honorable men. They have always held their honor to be greater than their lives. That is a tradition of their family.

CLETO. Perhaps none of them loved a woman like you, señora.

RAQUEL. How strange you are. I saved you from the Federals because I want to save my husband's life. You call me brave and yet you call him a coward. There is no difference in what we have done.

CLETO. But you are a woman, señora.

RAQUEL. Has a woman less honor than a man, then?

CLETO. No, señora. Please, I don't know how to say it. The general is a soldier. He has a duty to his own cause. You are a woman. You have a duty to your husband. It is right that you should try to save him. It is not right that he should try to save himself.

RAQUEL. [*Dully.*] Yes, of course. It is right that I should save him. [*Becoming practical again.*] Your captain has been gone some time, Cleto. You'd better find out if he is still safe.

CLETO. Yes, señora. [*As he reaches the French windows she stops him.*]

RAQUEL. Wait, Cleto. Have you a mother—or a wife, perhaps?

CLETO. Oh, no, señora. I haven't anyone but the captain.

RAQUEL. But the captain is a soldier. What would you do if he should be killed?

CLETO. It is very simple, señora. I should be killed, too.

RAQUEL. You speak about death so calmly. Aren't you afraid of it, Cleto?

CLETO. No, señora. It's like the captain says . . . dying for what you believe in—that's the finest death of all.

RAQUEL. And you believe in the Revolutionary cause?

CLETO. Yes, señora. I am a poor peasant, that's true. But still I have a right to live like a man, with my own ground, and my own family, and my own future. [*He stops speaking abruptly.*] I'm sorry, señora. You are a fine lady. You don't understand these things. I must go and find my captain. [*He goes out.*]

RAQUEL. [*Rests her face against her hand.*] He's so young. But Tomás was no older. And he's not afraid. He said so. Oh, Domingo—Domingo!

[*She straightens abruptly, takes the bottle of poison from the desk drawer and stares at it. Then she crosses to the decanter and laces the wine with the poison. She hurries back to the desk and is busy writing when* ANDRÉS *and* CLETO *return.*]

ANDRÉS. You'll have to hurry that letter. The district is clear now.

RAQUEL. I'll be through in just a moment. You might as well finish the wine while you're waiting.

ANDRÉS. Thank you. A most excellent idea. [*He pours himself a glass of wine. As he lifts it to his lips she speaks.*]

RAQUEL. Why don't you give some to—Cleto?

ANDRÉS. This is too fine a wine to waste on that boy.

RAQUEL. He'll probably never have another chance to taste such wine.

ANDRÉS. Very well. Pour yourself a glass, Cleto.

CLETO. Thank you. [*He pours it.*] Your health, my captain.

RAQUEL. [*Quickly.*] Drink it outside, Cleto. I want to speak to your captain. [*The boy looks at* ANDRÉS, *who jerks his head toward the patio.* CLETO *nods and goes out.*] I want you to give my husband a message for me. I can't write it. You'll have to remember it. But first, give me a glass of wine, too.

ANDRÉS. [*Pouring the wine.*] It might be easier for him if you wrote it.

RAQUEL. I think not. [*She takes the glass.*] I want you to tell him that I never knew how much I loved him until tonight.

ANDRÉS. Is that all?

RAQUEL. Yes. Tell me, captain, do you think it possible to love a person too much?

ANDRÉS. Yes, señora. I do.

RAQUEL. So do I. Let us drink a toast, captain—to honor. To bright and shining honor.

ANDRÉS. [*Raises his glass.*] To honor.

[*He drains his glass. She lifts hers almost to her lips and then puts it down. From the patio comes a faint cry.*]

CLETO. [*Calling faintly in a cry that fades into silence.*] Captain. Captain.

[ANDRÉS *sways, his hand trying to brush across his face as though trying to brush sense into his head. When he hears* CLETO *he tries to stagger toward the window but stumbles and can't quite make it. Hanging on to the table by the sofa, he looks accusingly at her. She shrinks back against her chair.*]

ANDRÉS. [*His voice weak from the poison.*] Why?

RAQUEL. Because I love him. Can you understand that?

ANDRÉS. We'll win. The Revolution will win. You can't stop that.

RAQUEL. Yes, you'll win. I know that now.

ANDRÉS. That girl—she thought my story was funny—about the hanging. But you didn't . . .

RAQUEL. I'm glad you hanged him. I'm glad.

[ANDRÉS *looks at her and tries to smile. He manages to pull the pouch from his shirt and extend it to her. But it drops from his hand.*]

RAQUEL. [*Runs to French window and calls.*] Cleto. Cleto! [*She buries her face in her hands for a moment, then comes back to* ANDRÉS. *She kneels beside him and picks up the leather pouch. She opens it and, taking the ring, puts it on her finger. Then she sees the medal. She rises and, pulling out the chain from her own throat, she slides the medal on to the chain. Then she walks to the sofa and sinks down on it.*]

MARICA. [*Calling off.*] Raquel! Raquel! [RAQUEL *snaps off the lamp, leaving the room in darkness.* MARICA *opens the house* door. *She is carrying a candle which she shades with her hand. The light is too dim to reveal the dead* ANDRÉS.] What are you doing down here in the dark? Why don't you come to bed?

RAQUEL. [*Making an effort to speak.*] I'll come in just a moment.

MARICA. But what are you doing, Raquel?

RAQUEL. Nothing. Just listening . . . listening to an empty house.

[*Quick Curtain*]

UNDERSTANDING AND APPRECIATING THE PLAY

1. For its thrills a melodrama depends upon the suspense in its romantic, sensational plot. Therefore, to appreciate a good melodrama, you need to know something about plot design.

Plot Design

The plot design has been divided by students of the drama into four parts: the *exposition*, the *rising action*, the *climax*, and the *falling action*.

The *exposition*, or *introduction*, acquaints us with the people of the play, tells us about their present and past relationships, and informs us as to what and where the place is in which the story is to unfold.

The *rising action* is a series of incidents which reveal the two opposing forces in the struggle, develop the conflict, and finally work up to the moment of greatest suspense.

The *climax* is the highest point of suspense and interest toward which the rising action constantly drives and at which the opposing forces come to grips in the major and decisive struggle that will end in the victory of one side or the other.

The *falling action* is the series of events which follow the climax. Many plays, particularly those of only one act, have little falling action. Some may even end with the completion of the climactic incident.

How is the exposition given in *The Ring of General Macías?* How is the suspense built up? Is there a definite climax? If so, at what point is the climax reached?

2. Discuss *The Ring of General Macías* as an example of melodrama. Measure it against such criteria as the following: (a) far-fetched or unlikely situations and incidents; (b) keeping audience or reader thrilled and in suspense; arousing emotions by means of exciting events; (c) action moving at a fast pace.

3. Do you think this play has a theme? If so, express that theme in a sentence. If you decide that it has no theme, give your reasons. (See p. 6 for the meaning of theme.)

4. Describe and characterize each of these characters: (a) Raquel, (b) Andrés, (c) Cleto, (d) Marica. Make your descriptions and characterizations such as to be helpful to a director and actors who are about to stage the play.

5. Why does Marica want to poison herself? She asks, "Why should I go on living?" What do you think of Raquel's reply, "Living is a duty."?

6. Andrés tells Raquel about injustices and cruelties which the common people had suffered. Which of these incidents are particularly moving?

7. Is there any foreshadowing of what Raquel would do at the end of the play?

8. Why was Andrés confident that Raquel would not turn him and Cleto over to the Federal soldiers? And in view of what she did at the end of the play, why didn't Raquel betray Andrés and Cleto to Captain Flores?

9. When she is about to re-enter the living room, why doesn't Marica see Andrés as he sits in the chair?

10. Since she knew that her husband would be killed if Andrés and Cleto did not return safely, why did Raquel poison them? Do you find this incident credible?

11. At the end of the play, how does Raquel feel about the following: (a) her husband, (b) Andrés, (c) Cleto, (d) the Revolutionary cause?

VOCABULARY BUILDING

Explain the meanings of the italicized words as they are used in the following contexts: Raquel draws herself up *regally; ostentatiously* hiding a yawn; I am *devastated;* to offer *sanctuary* to myself and Cleto; the *notorious* Andrés de la O; *laces* the wine with poison.

THINGS TO DO

1. Develop one of the following topics: My First Fight; An Exciting Game; In Suspense; A Trip I Should Like to Take; Five Minutes of Adventure; My Greatest Surprise; A Narrow Escape.

2. If you feel like writing a thriller of your own, either in play or story form, go right ahead. By all means spin an adventure or mystery yarn, if you are so inclined. Much of life is of a melodramatic nature.

3. Nineteenth-century audiences certainly took their melodramas seriously. The villains were villainous indeed; the heroes incredibly heroic and virtuous; the heroines, oh, so helpless and beautiful! *Curse You, Jack Dalton!* by Wilbur Braun and *Fireman, Save My Child!* by Ned Albert are interesting one-act examples of this type of treatment. [Both plays are published by Samuel French.] You'll find it great fun to write and dramatize a melodrama in the Gay-Nineties tradition, giving a humorous turn, however, to the struggle between the treacherous, mustachioed scoundrel and the noble, handsome hero.

4. Write a review of one of the plays in this volume. Do not restrict yourself to a mere discussion of plot, but consider, in addition, other phases of dramatic structure, such as dialogue, characterization, the theme, and the struggle.

PRODUCTION NOTES

The opening scene between Raquel and Marica contains some of the most dramatic dialogue in the literature of the one-act play. In those roles be certain to cast actresses who can do justice to the dialogue and action.

In characterization, actors should bear in mind the following traits. Of Raquel, her beauty, aristocratic bearing, courage, cleverness, and resourcefulness. Since Raquel is on stage virtually throughout the play, it takes a capable actress to carry the role. Of Andrés, his self-assurance, masculinity, romantic appeal, and fantastic devotion to the common people and the cause for which they are fighting. Of Marica, that she is a timid, dove-like, attractive young woman, driven to distraction by the death of her husband only three months after their marriage. Of the youthful peasant Cleto, his child-like, but not childish, devotion to Andrés and the Revolutionary army.

Since the tendency of inexperienced actors is to rush through pantomime and stage business, the opening and closing moments of the play require particularly painstaking planning and rehearsal. At the opening of the curtain, Marica should pace herself effectively in entering the darkened living room; standing poised for a moment, lighted candle in hand, actively listening for possible pursuit; then mysteriously searching behind the books in the bookcase; and finally finding what she wants in the contents of a small bottle. Raquel's entrance and action just as Marica is about to take poison should be carefully timed and executed. The play ends with important pantomime and business by Raquel. The quick curtain must not be so rapid as to interrupt Raquel's last line and the concomitant physical interpretation of her desolation.

All involved in the production of the play should combine their talents in emphasizing the suspenseful melodrama, beguiling romanticism, and the skilfully-, sometimes beautifully-written dialogue. Variety in the intensity of lighting and in the use of lighting areas can be quite helpful.

MORE GOOD ONE-ACT MELODRAMAS

The Crowsnest. William F. Manley. [Dramatists Play Service] One of the most popular dramas ever to come out of the famous Harvard 47 Workshop. A stirring sea play of gunrunning, mutiny, and treachery.

Drums of Oude. Austin Strong. [French]   Noted for its effective use of atmosphere and dramatic suspense. The setting is India during an uprising of the natives.

The Game of Chess. Kenneth Sawyer Goodman. [Stage Guild] One of the best liked of the short thrillers. It takes place in old Russia, in the palace of a ruler.

Hand of Siva. Kenneth Sawyer Goodman and Ben Hecht. [Appleton-Century]   A French secret service agent exposes a German spy in the First World War.

In the Net. Percival Wilde. [Baker]   Simple and funny satire on the "crook" play.

Knives from Syria. Lynn Riggs. [French]   A picturesque and romantic little drama, set in a Midwestern farm and involving an exotic Syrian peddler.

Two Crooks and a Lady. Eugene Pillot. [French]   Thrilling burglar play. A crippled elderly woman saves her pearls by outwitting two thieves.

FULL-LENGTH PLAYS

The Bat, Mary Roberts Rinehart and Avery Hopwood [French]; *The Cat and the Canary,* John Willard [French]; *Cock Robin,* Philip Barry and Elmer Rice [French]; *Dead End,* Sidney Kingsley [Dramatists Play Service]; *Golden Boy,* Clifford Odets [Dramatists Play Service]; *Margin for Error,* Clare Boothe [Dramatists Play Service]; *Missouri Legend,* E. B. Ginty [Dramatists Play Service]; *The Petrified Forest,* Robert E. Sherwood [Dramatists Play Service]; *Seven Keys to Baldpate,* George M. Cohan [French]; *Treasure Island,* Jules Eckert Goodman [French].

Farce: Anything for a Laugh

THE WORD FARCE originally meant "to stuff." When we note how liberally the farce is stuffed with hilarious horse-play, boisterous "wisecracks" and gags, very funny and highly improbable situations and people—anything and anybody, in fact, calculated to make us laugh uproariously—we realize that this kind of light play is aptly named.

Farces are not so plausible as pure comedies. Instead of the real people and credible situations we find in ordinary comedies, in farces we find certain comic types of characters which are usually overdrawn to make them even funnier. These cartoon characters are placed in familiar comic situations: the absent-minded professor in the midst of practical-minded people; the deaf gossip helping to spread false rumors; the lover smitten too suddenly and too violently; the timid little man placed in a predicament that would try the stoutest of heart and of body.

Farce moves at a faster rate of speed, or tempo, than does pure comedy. Something is almost always going on to make us laugh. The characters dash about; they chase each other in every conceivable kind of conveyance, from roller skates to airplanes; they play tricks on one another; they shout loudly; they gesticulate wildly. Incident follows incident with great rapidity, as though the author and the actors didn't want us to reflect long enough to see the improbabilities in the play.

But unless the whole thing is utterly silly and far-fetched, we don't object. For one thing, a well-written farce reminds us that we are men, not gods; and that if we are too proud or foolish or stubborn, we must pay the price of being laughed at. Then, too, without the light-hearted gayety of farce, life would be duller. We want to laugh heartily. It's good for us.

The Boor*

ANTON CHEKHOV

TRANSLATED BY HILMAR BAUKHAGE

The Boor is an uproarious farce. Presented upon the stage by capable actors, it is farcical entertainment at its best, good for a constant succession of laughs from the audience. But an unimaginative reading of this farce from the book will not make you laugh. You will miss the fun completely unless you visualize the farcical elements upon which the humor depends: the ludicrous actions, the exaggerated emotions, the overcharged voices. When the widow weeps, she must weep buckets. When the visitor shouts, the pictures must be jarred from the walls. When the servant is frightened, he must visibly tremble in his boots and all but faint dead away. This is the spirit of farce; you must yield to it to find the humor in this play.

CHARACTERS

HELENA IVANOVNA POPOV, *a young widow, mistress of a country estate*

GRIGORI STEPANOVITCH SMIRNOV, *proprietor of a country estate*

LUKA, *servant of* MRS. POPOV

A gardener   A coachman   Several workmen

SCENE: *The estate of* MRS. POPOV

TIME: *Summer, 1890*

SETTING: *A well-furnished reception room in* MRS. POPOV's *home.* MRS. POPOV *is discovered in deep mourning, sitting upon a sofa, gazing steadfastly at a photograph.* LUKA *is also present.*

LUKA. It isn't right, ma'am. You're wearing yourself out! The maid and the cook have gone looking for berries; everything that breathes is enjoying life; even the cat knows how to be happy—slips about the courtyard and catches birds—but you hide yourself here in the house as though you were in a cloister. Yes, truly, by actual reckoning you haven't left this house for a whole year.

MRS. POPOV. And I shall never leave it—why should I? My life is over. He lies in his grave, and I have buried myself within these four walls. We are both dead.

LUKA. There you are again! It's too awful to listen to, so it is! Nikolai Michailovitch is dead; it was the will of the Lord, and the Lord has given him eternal peace. You have grieved over it and that ought to be enough. Now it's time to stop. One can't weep and wear mourning forever! My wife died a few years ago. I grieved for her, I wept a whole month—and then it was over. Must one be forever singing lamentations? That would be more than your husband was worth! [*He sighs.*] You have forgotten all your neighbors. You don't go out and you receive no one. We live—you'll pardon me—like the spiders, and the good light of day we never see. All the livery is eaten by the mice—as though there weren't any more nice people in the world! But the whole neighborhood is full of gentlefolk. The regiment is stationed in Riblov—officers—simply beautiful! One can't see enough of them! Every Friday a ball, and military music every day. Oh, my dear, dear ma'am, young and pretty as you are, if you'd only let your spirits live—! Beauty can't last forever. When ten short years are over, you'll be glad enough to go out a bit and meet the officers— and then it'll be too late.

MRS. POPOV. [*Resolutely.*] Please don't speak of these things again. You know very well that since the death of Nikolai Michailovitch my life is absolutely nothing to me. You think I live, but it only seems so. Do you understand? Oh, that his departed soul may see how I love him! I know, it's no secret to you; he was often unjust toward me, cruel, and—he wasn't faithful, but I shall be faithful to the grave and prove to him how *I* can love. There, in the Beyond, he'll find me the same as I was until his death.

LUKA. What is the use of all these words, when you'd so much rather go walking in the garden or order Tobby or Welikan harnessed to the trap, and visit the neighbors?

MRS. POPOV. [*Weeping.*] Oh!

LUKA. Madam, dear Madam, what is it? In Heaven's name!

MRS. POPOV. He loved Tobby so! He always drove him to the Kortschagins or the Vlassovs. What a wonderful horseman he was! How fine he looked when he pulled at the reins with all his might! Tobby, Tobby—give him an extra measure of oats today!

LUKA. Yes, ma'am.

[*A bell rings loudly.*]

MRS. POPOV. [*Shudders.*] What's that? I am at home to no one.

LUKA. Yes, ma'am. [*He goes out, center.*]

MRS. POPOV. [*Gazing at the photograph.*] You shall see, Nikolai, how I can love and forgive! My love will die only with me— when my poor heart stops beating. [*She smiles through her tears.*] And aren't you ashamed? I have been a good, true wife, I have imprisoned myself and I shall remain true until death, and you—you—you're not ashamed of yourself, my dear monster! You quarreled with me, left me alone for weeks—

[LUKA *enters in great excitement.*]

LUKA. Oh, ma'am, someone is asking for you, insists on seeing you—

MRS. POPOV. You told him that since my husband's death I receive no one?

LUKA. I said so, but he won't listen; he says it is a pressing matter.

MRS. POPOV. I receive no one!

LUKA. I told him that, but he's a wild man; he swore and pushed himself into the room; he's in the dining room now.

MRS. POPOV. [*Excitedly.*] Good. Show him in. The impudent—!

[LUKA *goes out, center.*]

MRS. POPOV. What a bore people are! What can they want with me? Why do they disturb my peace? [*She sighs.*] Yes, it is clear I must enter a convent. [*Meditatively.*] Yes, a convent.

[SMIRNOV *enters, followed by* LUKA.]

SMIRNOV. [*To* LUKA.] Fool, you make too much noise! You're an ass! [*Discovering* MRS. POPOV—*politely.*] Madam, I have the honor to introduce myself: Lieutenant in the Artillery, retired, country gentleman, Grigori Stepanovitch Smirnov! I'm compelled to bother you about an exceedingly important matter.

MRS. POPOV. [*Without offering her hand.*] What is it you wish?

SMIRNOV. Your deceased husband, with whom I had the honor to be acquainted, left me two notes amounting to about twelve hundred rubles.[1] Inasmuch as I have to pay the interest tomorrow on a loan from the Agrarian Bank, I should like to request, madam, that you pay me the money today.

MRS. POPOV. Twelve hundred—and for what was my husband indebted to you?

SMIRNOV. He bought oats from me.

MRS. POPOV. [*With a sigh, to* LUKA.] Don't forget to give Tobby an extra measure of oats.

[LUKA *goes out.*]

MRS. POPOV. [*To* SMIRNOV.] If Nikolai Michailovitch is indebted to you, I shall of course pay you, but I am sorry, I haven't the money today. Tomorrow my manager will return from the city and I shall notify him to pay you what is due you, but until then I cannot satisfy your request. Furthermore, today it is just seven months since the death of my husband and I am not in a mood to discuss money matters.

SMIRNOV. And I am in the mood to fly up the chimney with my feet in the air if I can't lay hands on that interest tomorrow. They'll seize my estate!

MRS. POPOV. Day after tomorrow you will receive the money.

SMIRNOV. I don't need the money day after tomorrow, I need it today.

MRS. POPOV. I'm sorry I can't pay you today.

SMIRNOV. And I can't wait until day after tomorrow.

MRS. POPOV. But what can I do if I haven't it?

SMIRNOV. So you can't pay?

[1] The ruble is the Russian dollar.

Mrs. Popov. I cannot.

Smirnov. Hm! Is that your last word?

Mrs. Popov. My last.

Smirnov. Absolutely?

Mrs. Popov. Absolutely.

Smirnov. Thank you. [*He shrugs his shoulders.*] And they expect me to stand for all that. The tollgatherer just now met me in the road and asked me why I was always worrying? Why in Heaven's name shouldn't I worry? I need money; I feel the knife at my throat. Yesterday morning I left my house in the early dawn and called on all my debtors. If even one of them had paid his debt! I worked the skin off my fingers! The devil knows in what sort of inn I slept: in a room with a barrel of brandy! And now at last I come here, seventy versts [2] from home, hope for a little money and all you give me is moods! Why shouldn't I worry?

Mrs. Popov. I thought I made it plain to you that my manager will return from town, and then you will get your money?

Smirnov. I did not come to see the manager, I came to see you. What the devil—pardon the language—do I care for your manager?

Mrs. Popov. Really, sir, I am not used to such language or such manners. I shan't listen to you any further. [*She goes out, left.*]

Smirnov. What can one say to that? Moods! Seven months since her husband died! Do I have to pay the interest or not? I repeat the question, have I to pay the interest or not? The husband is dead and all that; the manager is—the devil with him!—traveling somewhere. Now, tell me, what am I to do? Shall I run away from my creditors in a balloon? Or knock my head against a stone wall? If I call on Grusdev he chooses to be "not at home"; Iroschevitch has simply hidden himself; I have quarreled with Kurzin and came near throwing him out of the window; Masutov is ill; and this woman has—moods! Not one of them will pay up! And all because I've spoiled them, because I'm an old whiner, dish-rag! I'm too tenderhearted with them.

[2] A verst is a Russian measure of distance—about three-quarters of a mile.

But wait! I allow nobody to play tricks with me; the devil with
'em all! I'll stay here and not budge until she pays! Brr! How
angry I am; how terribly angry I am! Every tendon is trembling
with anger and I can hardly breathe! I'm even growing ill! [*He
calls out.*] Servant!

   [LUKA *enters.*]

   LUKA. What is it you wish?

   SMIRNOV. Bring me kvas ³ or water! [LUKA *goes out.*] Well,
what can we do? She hasn't it on hand? What sort of logic is
that? A fellow stands with the knife at his throat, he needs
money, he is on the point of hanging himself, and she won't pay
because she isn't in the mood to discuss money matters. Woman's
logic! That's why I never liked to talk to women and why I dislike doing it now. I would rather sit on a powder barrel than
talk with a woman. Brr!—I'm getting cold as ice, this affair has
made me so angry. I need only to see such a romantic creature
from a distance to get so angry that I have cramps in the calves!
It's enough to make one yell for help!

   [*Enter* LUKA.]

   LUKA. [*Hands him water.*] Madam is ill and is not receiving.

   SMIRNOV. March! [LUKA *goes out.*] Ill and isn't receiving!
All right, it isn't necessary. I won't receive, either! I'll sit here
and stay until you bring that money. If you're ill a week, I'll sit
here a week. If you're ill a year, I'll sit here a year. As Heaven
is my witness, I'll get the money. You don't disturb me with your
mourning—or with your dimples. We know these dimples! [*He
calls out the window.*] Simon, unharness! We aren't going to
leave right away. I am going to stay here. Tell them in the stable
to give the horses some oats. The left horse has twisted the
bridle again. [*Imitating him.*] Stop! I'll show you how. Stop!
[*Leaves window.*] It's awful. Unbearable heat, no money, didn't
sleep last night and now—mourning-dresses with moods. My
head aches; perhaps I ought to have a drink. Ye-s, I must have
a drink. [*Calling.*] Servant!

   LUKA. What do you wish?

   SMIRNOV. Something to drink! [LUKA *goes out.* SMIRNOV

³ A beer—thin and sour—but a great favorite with Russians.

sits down and looks at his clothes.] Ugh, a fine figure! No use denying that. Dust, dirty boots, unwashed, uncombed, straw on my vest—the lady probably took me for a highwayman. [*He yawns.*] It was a little impolite to come into a reception room with such clothes. Oh, well, no harm done. I'm not here as a guest. I'm a creditor. And there is no special costume for creditors.

LUKA. [*Entering with glass.*] You take great liberty, sir.

SMIRNOV. [*Angrily.*] What?

LUKA. I—I—I just—

SMIRNOV. Whom are you talking to? Keep quiet.

LUKA. [*Angrily.*] Nice mess! This fellow won't leave! [*He goes out.*]

SMIRNOV. Lord, how angry I am! Angry enough to throw mud at the whole world! I even feel ill! Servant!

[MRS. POPOV *comes in with downcast eyes.*]

MRS. POPOV. Sir, in my solitude I have become unaccustomed to the human voice and I cannot stand the sound of loud talking. I beg you, please to cease disturbing my rest.

SMIRNOV. Pay me my money and I'll leave.

MRS. POPOV. I told you once, plainly, in your native tongue, that I haven't the money at hand; wait until day after tomorrow.

SMIRNOV. And I also had the honor of informing you in your native tongue that I need the money, not day after tomorrow, but today. If you don't pay me today I shall have to hang myself tomorrow.

MRS. POPOV. But what can I do if I haven't the money?

SMIRNOV. So you are not going to pay immediately? You're not?

MRS. POPOV. I cannot.

SMIRNOV. Then I'll sit here until I get the money. [*He sits down.*] You will pay day after tomorrow? Excellent! Here I stay until day after tomorrow. [*Jumps up.*] I ask you, do I have to pay that interest tomorrow or not? Or do you think I'm joking?

MRS. POPOV. Sir, I beg of you, don't scream! This is not a stable.

SMIRNOV. I'm not talking about stables, I'm asking you whether I have to pay that interest tomorrow or not?

MRS. POPOV. You have no idea how to treat a lady.

SMIRNOV. Oh, yes, I have.

MRS. POPOV. No, you have not. You are an ill-bred, vulgar person! Respectable people don't speak so to ladies.

SMIRNOV. How remarkable! How do you want one to speak to you? In French, perhaps! *Madame, je vous prie!* Pardon me for having disturbed you. What beautiful weather we are having today! And how this mourning becomes you! [*He makes a low bow with mock ceremony.*]

MRS. POPOV. Not at all funny! I think it vulgar!

SMIRNOV. [*Imitating her.*] Not at all funny—vulgar! I don't understand how to behave in the company of ladies. Madam, in the course of my life I have seen more women than you have sparrows. Three times have I fought duels for women; twelve I jilted and nine jilted me. There was a time when I played the fool, used honeyed language, bowed and scraped. I loved, suffered, sighed to the moon, melted in love's torments. I loved passionately, I loved to madness, loved in every key, chattered like a magpie on emancipation, sacrificed half my fortune in tender passion, until now the devil knows I've had enough of it. Your obedient servant will let you lead him around by the nose no more. Enough! Black eyes, passionate eyes, coral lips, dimples in cheeks, moonlight whispers, soft, modest sighs,—for all that, madam, I wouldn't pay a kopeck! [4] I am not speaking of present company, but of women in general; from the tiniest to the greatest, they are conceited, hypocritical, chattering, odious, deceitful from top to toe; vain, petty, cruel with a maddening logic and [*He strikes his forehead.*] in this respect, please excuse my frankness, but one sparrow is worth ten of the aforementioned petticoat-philosophers. When one sees one of the romantic creatures before him, he imagines he is looking at some holy being, so wonderful that its one breath could dissolve him in a sea of a thousand charms and delights; but if one looks into the soul—it's nothing but a common crocodile. [*He seizes the arm-*

[4] The Russian penny.

chair and breaks it in two.] But the worst of all is that this crocodile imagines it is a masterpiece of creation, and that it has a monopoly on all the tender passions. May the devil hang me upside down if there is anything to love about a woman! When she is in love, all she knows is how to complain and shed tears. If the man suffers and makes sacrifices she swings her train about and tries to lead him by the nose. You have the misfortune to be a woman, and naturally you know woman's nature; tell me on your honor, have you ever in your life seen a woman who was really true and faithful? Never! Only the old and the deformed are true and faithful. It's easier to find a cat with horns or a white woodcock, than a faithful woman.

MRS. POPOV. But allow me to ask, who is true and faithful in love? The man, perhaps?

SMIRNOV. Yes, indeed! The man!

MRS. POPOV. The man! [*She laughs sarcastically.*] The man true and faithful in love! Well, that is something *new!* [*Bitterly.*] How can you make such a statement? Men true and faithful! So long as we have gone thus far, I may as well say that of all the men I have known, my husband was the best; I loved him passionately with all my soul, as only a young, sensible woman may love; I gave him my youth, my happiness, my fortune, my life. I worshiped him like a heathen. And what happened? This best of men betrayed me in every possible way. After his death I found his desk filled with love letters. While he was alive, he left me alone for months—it is horrible even to think about it —he made love to other women in my very presence; he wasted my money and made fun of my feelings,—and in spite of everything, I trusted him and was true to him. And more than that: he is dead and I am still true to him. I have buried myself within these four walls and I shall wear this mourning to my grave.

SMIRNOV. [*Laughing disrespectfully.*] Mourning! What on earth do you take me for? As if I didn't know why you wore this black domino and why you buried yourself within these four walls. Such a secret! So romantic! Some knight will pass the castle, gaze up at the windows and think to himself: "Here dwells the mysterious Tamara, who, for love of her husband, has buried herself within four walls." Oh, I understand the art!

Mrs. Popov. [*Springing up.*] What? What do you mean by saying such things to me?

Smirnov. You have buried yourself alive, but meanwhile you have not forgotten to powder your nose!

Mrs. Popov. How dare you speak so?

Smirnov. Don't scream at me, please; I'm not the manager. Allow me to call things by their right names. I am not a woman, and I am accustomed to speak out what I think. So please don't scream.

Mrs. Popov. I'm not screaming. It is you who are screaming. Please leave me, I beg of you.

Smirnov. Pay me my money and I'll leave.

Mrs. Popov. I won't give you the money.

Smirnov. You won't? You won't give me my money?

Mrs. Popov. I don't care what you do. You won't get a ko-peck! Leave me!

Smirnov. As I haven't the pleasure of being either your hus-band or your fiancé, please don't make a scene. [*He sits down.*] I can't stand it.

Mrs. Popov. [*Breathing hard.*] You are going to sit down?

Smirnov. I already have.

Mrs. Popov. Kindly leave the house!

Smirnov. Give me the money.

Mrs. Popov. I don't care to speak with impudent men. Leave! [*Pause.*] You aren't going?

Smirnov. No.

Mrs. Popov. No?

Smirnov. No!

Mrs. Popov. Very well! [*She rings the bell.*]

     [*Enter* Luka.]

Mrs. Popov. Luka, show the gentleman out.

Luka. [*Going to* Smirnov.] Sir, why don't you leave when you are ordered? What do you want?

Smirnov. [*Jumping up.*] Whom do you think you are talking to? I'll grind you to powder.

LUKA. [*Puts his hand to his heart.*] Good Lord! [*He drops into a chair.*] Oh, I'm ill; I can't breathe!

MRS. POPOV. Where is Dascha? [*Calling.*] Dascha! Pelageja! Dascha! [*She rings.*]

LUKA. They're all gone! I'm ill! Water!

MRS. POPOV. [*To* SMIRNOV.] Leave! Get out!

SMIRNOV. Kindly be a little more polite!

MRS. POPOV. [*Striking her fists and stamping her feet.*] You are vulgar! You're a boor! A monster!

SMIRNOV. What did you say?

MRS. POPOV. I said you were a boor, a monster!

SMIRNOV. [*Steps toward her quickly.*] Permit me to ask what right you have to insult me?

MRS. POPOV. What of it? Do you think I am afraid of you?

SMIRNOV. And you think that because you are a romantic creature you can insult me without being punished? I challenge you!

LUKA. Merciful heaven! Water!

SMIRNOV. We'll have a duel.

MRS. POPOV. Do you think because you have big fists and a steer's neck I am afraid of you?

SMIRNOV. I allow no one to insult me, and I make no exception because you are a woman, one of the "weaker sex"!

MRS. POPOV. [*Trying to cry him down.*] Boor, boor, boor!

SMIRNOV. It is high time to do away with the old superstition that it is only the man who is forced to give satisfaction. If there is equity at all let there be equity in all things. There's a limit!

MRS. POPOV. You wish to fight a duel? Very well.

SMIRNOV. Immediately.

MRS. POPOV. Immediately. My husband had pistols. I'll bring them. [*She hurries away, then turns.*] Oh, what a pleasure it will be to put a bullet in your impudent head. The devil take you! [*She goes out.*]

SMIRNOV. I'll shoot her down! I'm no fledgling, no sentimental young puppy. For me, there is no weaker sex!

LUKA. Oh, sir! [*Falls to his knees.*] Have mercy on me, an old

man, and go away. You have frightened me to death already, and
now you want to fight a duel.

SMIRNOV. [*Paying no attention.*] A duel. That's equity, emancipation. That way the sexes are made equal. I'll shoot her
down as a matter of principle. What can a person say to such a
woman? [*Imitating her.*] "The devil take you. I'll put a bullet in
your impudent head." What can one say to that? She was angry,
her eyes blazed, she accepted the challenge. On my honor, it's
the first time in my life that I ever saw such a woman.

LUKA. Oh, sir. Go away. Go away!

SMIRNOV. That *is* a woman. I can understand her. A real
woman. No shilly-shallying, but fire, powder, and noise! It would
be a pity to shoot a woman like that.

LUKA. [*Weeping.*] Oh, sir, go away.

[*Enter* MRS. POPOV.]

MRS. POPOV. Here are the pistols. But before we have our duel
please show me how to shoot. I have never had a pistol in my
hand before!

LUKA. God be merciful and have pity upon us! I'll go and get
the gardener and the coachman. Why has this horror come to
us? [*He goes out.*]

SMIRNOV. [*Looking at the pistols.*] You see, there are different
kinds. There are special dueling pistols with cap and ball. But
these are revolvers, Smith & Wesson, with ejectors; fine pistols!
A pair like that cost at least ninety rubles. This is the way to
hold a revolver. [*Aside.*] Those eyes, those eyes! A real woman!

MRS. POPOV. Like this?

SMIRNOV. Yes, that way. Then you pull the hammer back—
so—then you aim—put your head back a little. Just stretch your
arm out, please. So—then press your finger on the thing like that,
and that is all. The chief thing is this: don't get excited, don't
hurry your aim, and take care that your hand doesn't tremble.

MRS. POPOV. It isn't well to shoot inside; let's go into the
garden.

SMIRNOV. Yes. I'll tell you now, I am going to shoot into the
air.

MRS. POPOV. That is too much! Why?

SMIRNOV. Because—because. That's my business.

Mrs. Povov. You are afraid. Yes. A-h-h-h. No, no, my dear sir, no flinching! Please follow me. I won't rest until I've made a hole in that head I hate so much. Are you afraid?

Smirnov. Yes, I'm afraid.

Mrs. Popov. You are lying. Why won't you fight?

Smirnov. Because—because—I—like you.

Mrs. Popov. [*With an angry laugh.*] You like me! He dares to say he likes me! [*She points to the door.*] Go.

Smirnov. [*Laying the revolver silently on the table, takes his hat and starts. At the door he stops a moment gazing at her silently, then he approaches her, hesitating.*] Listen! Are you still angry? I was mad as the devil, but please understand me—how can I express myself? The thing is like this—such things are— [*He raises his voice.*] Now, is it my fault that you owe me money? [*Grasps the back of the chair, which breaks.*] The devil knows what breakable furniture you have! I like you! Do you understand? I—I'm almost in love!

Mrs. Popov. Leave! I hate you.

Smirnov. Lord! What a woman! I never in my life met one like her. I'm lost, ruined! I've been caught like a mouse in a trap.

Mrs. Popov. Go, or I'll shoot.

Smirnov. Shoot! You have no idea what happiness it would be to die in sight of those beautiful eyes, to die from the revolver in this little velvet hand! I'm mad! Consider it and decide immediately, for if I go now, we shall never see each other again. Decide—speak—I am a noble, a respectable man, have an income of ten thousand, can shoot a coin thrown into the air. I own some fine horses. Will you be my wife?

Mrs. Popov. [*Swings the revolver angrily.*] I'll shoot!

Smirnov. My mind is not clear—I can't understand. Servant —water! I have fallen in love like any young man. [*He takes her hand and she cries with pain.*] I love you! [*He kneels.*] I love you as I have never loved before. Twelve women I jilted, nine jilted me, but not one of them all have I loved as I love you. I am conquered, lost! I lie at your feet like a fool and beg for your hand. Shame and disgrace! For five years I haven't been in love; I thanked the Lord for it, and now I am caught, like a carriage tongue in another carriage. I beg for your hand! Yes or no? Will you?—Good! [*He gets up and goes quickly to the door.*]

Mrs. Popov. Wait a moment!

Smirnov. [*Stopping.*] Well?

Mrs. Popov. Nothing. You may go. But—wait a moment. No, go on, go on. I hate you. Or—no: don't go. Oh, if you knew how angry I was, how angry! [*She throws the revolver on to the chair.*] My finger is swollen from this thing. [*She angrily tears her handkerchief.*] What are you standing there for? Get out!

Smirnov. Farewell!

Mrs. Popov. Yes, go. [*Cries out.*] Why are you going? Wait —no, go! Oh, how angry I am! Don't come too near, don't come too near—er—come—no nearer.

Smirnov. [*Approaching her.*] How angry I am with myself! Fall in love like a schoolboy, throw myself on my knees. I've got a chill! [*Strongly.*] I love you. This is fine—all I needed was to fall in love. Tomorrow I have to pay my interest, the hay harvest has begun, and then you appear! [*He takes her in his arms.*] I can never forgive myself.

Mrs. Popov. Go away! Take your hands off me! I hate you —you—this is— [*A long kiss.*]

[*Enter Luka with an axe, the gardener with a rake, the coachman with a pitchfork, and workmen with poles.*]

Luka. [*Staring at the pair.*] Merciful Heavens! [*A long pause.*]

Mrs. Popov. [*Dropping her eyes.*] Tell them in the stable that Tobby isn't to have any oats.

[*Curtain*]

UNDERSTANDING AND APPRECIATING THE PLAY

1. Discuss *The Boor* as an example of the farce type of play, using the following elements as a guide: (a) implausible incidents and situations; (b) overdrawn, exaggerated comic characters who do not

act and talk as people do in real life; (c) the ridiculing of the foolishness or stubbornness or false pride of the principal characters; (d) fast rate of action, or tempo; (e) light-hearted gayety.

2. Find lines in the *The Boor* which prove that Mrs. Popov's grief is not genuine.

3. "Tell them in the stable that Tobby isn't to have any oats," Mrs. Popov tells her servants at the end of the play. What is the significance of that command?

4. Smirnov and Mrs. Popov climax their violent quarrel by falling madly in love with each other. What traits of character and personality do they have in common?

5. Smirnov doesn't weaken suddenly and all at once; there are previous signs of his succumbing to the charms of the lady whom he has challenged to duel unto death. What signs of weakening on his part did you notice?

6. In plays, particularly those of only one act, writers often find it impossible to develop their characters fully into well-rounded individuals. Instead, they find it convenient to use oversimplified "type characters"—the "typical" butler, the "typical" villain, the "typical" cowboy, the "typical" sheriff. When he makes use of type characters, the dramatist is usually content to portray one or two characteristics considered typical, and to make little or no effort to develop those special distinguishing qualities which set the individual apart from the type. Try to classify each of the characters of *The Boor* as *type* or *individualized*. In each case, justify your answer by reference to specific passages in the play.

7. What suggestions can you make for stage setting, costuming, and action at the very beginning of the play that will create the desired mood of hilarity at once? See whether you can read Mrs. Popov's first speech aloud so that it makes your listeners laugh.

8. Select a character, and point out places in the play where the person acting this character has opportunities to secure laughs. Perform the actions or read the lines and see whether you can make them funny.

VOCABULARY BUILDING

1. Explain the meanings of the following phrases: they are *vain* and *petty;* that's *equity;* forever singing *lamentations;* you're a *boor*.

2. The Latin word *aequus,* which appears in English as a root, *equ-,* or as a prefix, *equi-,* means *equal.* With this as a clue, work

out the meanings of the following words: *equation, equator, equidistant, equilateral, equilibrium, equity, equivalent, equivocate.* Can you think of other words built up from this Latin word element?

THINGS TO DO

1. Develop one of the following topics into a composition, dramatization, or short short story: My First Party (or Dance); What a Farce!; When I Thought I Was in Love; Love at First Sight?; Entertaining Sister's (or Brother's) Company; Just for the Fun of It; My Opinion of a Flirt; A Comparison of a Comedy with a Farce.

2. Make a list of five humorous television plays, movies, or stage plays you have seen recently and classify each as a comedy or a farce. Justify your classification.

3. Make a list of television and movie personalities who are regarded as comedians. Which of these perform principally in farce roles? Which, in comedy roles? Explain.

4. Conduct a Variety Program, in the course of which the talented members of your group—the singers, dancers, instrumental players, comedians, mimics, and actors—get a chance to perform. The degree of talent does not matter; it is the spirit that counts.

5. Make a bulletin-board collection of the best television and radio gags and jokes heard by members of the class. You may set up a committee to select the best jokes for that purpose.

PRODUCTION NOTES

The first requirement in producing *The Boor* is to make sure that you have the right attitude toward the play. It is not a study in character, nor is it a realistic representation of life. It is a farce. It is intended to evoke hilarious laughter by its ludicrous extremes of gesture, attitude, emotion, and speech. All the emotions suggested in the speeches should be carried to absurd extremes. When this is done, both actors and audience will enter into the proper mood of farcical unreality, and the show becomes pure fun.

On the other hand, the actors must not make the mistake of breaking down and laughing at each other, or of indicating to the audience that they realize that they are overacting. They should take the situation and the overacting seriously, no matter how farcical the situation is or how uproarious the audience may become.

There must be a loud-ringing bell, a photograph of the dear dead Popov, an axe for Luka, an inadequate handkerchief for the tearful widow—but it's the stage manager's business to make an inventory of properties; let him finish the list!

MORE GOOD ONE-ACT FARCES

Atalanta in Wimbledon. Lord Dunsany. [French] Do you remember the Atalanta of Greek mythology? Here is a farce about a modern English Atalanta who specializes in ping-pong games instead of foot races.

The Man in the Bowler Hat. A. A. Milne. [French] This unusual farce employs melodramatic devices to satirize the overdone "crook" melodrama.

Pyramus and Thisbe. William Shakespeare. [Holt] The delightful farce scenes from *A Midsummer Night's Dream.*

Quiet, Please! Howard Buerman [Dramatists Play Service] Hilarious short play about two brothers who, although they shared a room, did not speak to each other.

The Still Alarm. George S. Kaufman. [French] A rather pointless but quite funny farce about two young men who refuse to get excited over a fire in their hotel.

The Warrior's Husband. Julian Thompson. [Appleton-Century] A riotous farce about the Amazons, the fierce women warriors of Greek mythology.

The Pot Boiler, by Alice Gerstenberg [Brentano's] and *Rehearsal,* by Christopher Morley [Doubleday, Doran] are amusing dramatic accounts of play rehearsals. They provide interesting reading, and they may be performed on a bare stage, without settings.

FULL-LENGTH PLAYS

Dear Ruth, Norman Krasna [Dramatists Play Service]; *You Can't Take It with You* and *The Man Who Came to Dinner,* Moss Hart and George S. Kaufman [Dramatists Play Service]; *My Sisten Eileen,* Joseph Fields and Jerome Chodorov [Dramatists Play Service]; *Of*

Thee I Sing, George S. Kaufman and Morrie Ryskind [French];   *The Solid Gold Cadillac,* Howard Teichman [Dramatists Play Service]; *Tall Story,* Howard Lindsay and Russel Crouse [Dramatists Play Service];   *What a Life,* Clifford Goldsmith [Dramatists Play Service]; *The Taming of the Shrew* and *A Comedy of Errors,* William Shakespeare;   *H.M.S. Pinafore, The Mikado,* and *The Pirates of Penzance,* William S. Gilbert and Sir Arthur Sullivan [Random House].

Tragedy: Frustration and Defeat

A TRAGEDY is a serious play which results in the defeat of the hero. In a tragedy the leading character—the so-called tragic hero—does not conquer, but is conquered.

The nature of the tragic hero has varied with the times. In ancient Greece and even in Shakespeare's day, he was a great personality, one of noble blood, whose struggle with insurmountable obstacles ended in his death. In our more democratic twentieth century, people from any walk of life, however humble, may be the protagonists in a tragedy.

Each age has varied from other periods also, in the nature of the forces which are arrayed against the protagonist. In ancient Greece it was generally fate, or chance, that crushed the tragic hero. In Elizabethan England—the age of Shakespeare—it was most likely to be the hero's own weakness or shortcomings. In our century it is frequently the unfavorable forces in his environment.

What pleasure or value can we find in the reading of tragedies? To this question there is no single answer which applies to all plays of this type. From one tragedy we may gain a broader sympathy with those who are frustrated and defeated, through acquaintance with great souls who have suffered deeply and passionately. From another we may see that our troubles are so much smaller than those of the tragic hero that we leave the play better prepared to face our own problems again with courage and serenity. From still another we may learn the true sources of much unhappiness and, fortified with this knowledge, by-pass these evils in our own lives. Certain it is that real life is not all joy and happiness; thus the reading of tragedies can at the very least help us to see life whole and warn us of the defeats and frustrations that confront us.

Then there is the cleansing quality of "enjoying a good cry," cither inwardly or outwardly, when we are deeply moved by the plight of the characters in a tragedy. Over two thousand years ago, the Greek philosopher Aristotle referred to this kind of experience as *catharsis*, a purifying of our hearts and souls "by filling them with pity and awe."

The Fifteenth Candle *

RACHEL FIELD

The Fifteenth Candle opens on one of the most important days in Rosa's young, poverty-stricken life—when she is to have her first birthday cake. She has just completed with marked success a year in high school and is eagerly making plans for the next step in her educational program. The day should be one of joyous celebration, but the promise of the day may turn to bitter frustration and tragic defeat. As you read, try to picture Rosa's father and her older sister and to understand the motives of these two, between whom there is an intense conflict as to what Rosa is to do and what is to become of her. Furthermore, visualize the dingy basement room in which this unfortunate family lives and works and eats, and contrast it with the home that a girl of Rosa's artistic love of beauty would choose. The very setting forecasts the tragedy to be enacted in it.

The action of this play takes place years ago, when the compulsory education laws of most states did not require young people to attend school beyond the age of fourteen. But the questions and problems brought to mind by this play are still very important today.

CHARACTERS

VEDETTA, *an old Italian shoemaker*
STELLA, *his daughter, a seamstress*
ROSA, *another daughter, aged fourteen*

MR. SCHNEIDER, *an unprincipled man, who acts as labor agent for a factory*
MISS ROBERTS, *an art teacher in the high school*

SCENE: *A small dark room in the basement of a city block. It serves as kitchen, dining- and living-room. A stove occupies most of one wall, and a table, covered with a red cloth and piled with dishes, the center of the room. Several chairs are drawn up to the table. A window [back center] faces a line of dingy washing, or some equally uninspiring view. Near this a rocking-chair is drawn close beside a small table which holds a large cardboard box, overflowing with sewing-materials and garments in various stages of completion. A door [back left] is partly open, revealing a tiny bedroom beyond; while still another door leads into the front room, or shop, facing the street.*

When the Curtain rises STELLA *is seated in the chair by the window, her body bent forward to make the most of the fading light, as she sews rows of beads carefully on a dress. The beads catch the light, but her face is in shadow, bent over the work. She is singing snatches of a popular song, and her pronunciation of the words, though careful, still bears a trace of foreign accent. Presently a man's voice calls out irritably in very broken English from the adjoining room.*

MAN'S VOICE. Stella, Stella, what for you maka so mooch noise?

STELLA. [*Calling back.*] Just singin', Poppa, like Rosa teach me!

MAN'S VOICE. Singa'? huh! Soun' more lika ole-clothes man! You wanta drive away ma trade, hey?

STELLA. [*Cheerfully.*] All right, Poppa, I'll stop; I gotta go out now anyways.

[STELLA *rises, gathering up her things and putting them away carefully in the box. While she is doing this, the owner of the voice appears in the doorway; an old man, grizzled and bent, in a shirt and an old waistcoat, with a large dark apron tied over baggy trousers. He holds in one hand a shoe he is mending, and in the other the long thread and needle with which he is stitching it. This is* MR. VE-DETTI, *shoemaker, father of* STELLA.]

VEDETTI. [*Eyeing her preparations suspiciously.*] What for you go out dis time day? You theenk maybe clock strike seex, not five?

STELLA. Why, Poppa, you don't forget so soon what day eet is?

VEDETTI. [*With a shrug.*] Work alla same everra day.

STELLA. [*Hastily.*] Sure, I know that, Poppa. Ain't I got the sewin' most done to take back to the shop tonight? [*She goes over to a small mirror hanging on the wall, putting on a shabby coat and hat. Her face, as we see it under the light, is an odd mixture of youth and age. It is pale, the eyes near-sighted from much piecework, and the shoulders rounded from sitting over sewing. Wistful in repose, it lights up quickly as she talks and moves.*] You don't forget already about Rosa—that it is her birthday?

VEDETTI. Well, dat don' make it da holiday. No, Meester Reilly he come getta da rent just da same! Next month he say we pay two dollar more.

STELLA. [*Sobering.*] Maybe I get more work next month; but don't you tell Rosa yet, Poppa, on her birthday. I gotta get the party and the presents ready 'fore Rosa gets back from school.

VEDETTI. She should be back now—why she so late?

STELLA. [*Smiling.*] On Fridays she always stay late that her teacher may show her how to draw better the pictures—

VEDETTI. [*Crossly.*] Pictures?

STELLA. [*Eagerly.*] Such grand pictures she can make, Poppa! She take a pencil and paper and pretty soon it is not a piece of paper any more, but it is a horse, a dog, or maybe a little house with trees around it, and children playing like you see them run and jump out in the park—anything she see, and [*With proud awe.*] even the things she have never seen, she can make them so you see them, too. Sometimes it most scare me the things she can make with her pencil.

VEDETTI. What good dat do me?

STELLA. Some day she will make the grand pictures, in books maybe. But I must go now, and remember, Poppa, how it's her birthday and she's fourteen—Rosa's fourteen year old.

VEDETTI. [*With a slow smile of meaning.*] No—I don' forget dat Rosa be fourteen year ole. [*He nods his head slyly to himself.*]

STELLA. [*Pausing, speaking reminiscently.*] Seem like yesterday, she was too little to walk, an' I have to carry her everawhere I go, an' now she go to the high school, an' read the great beeg books, an' write so fast, an' draw the pictures. All day I am so glad because I think how many things Rosa know some time.

VEDETTI. [*Shaking his head.*] Rosa know plenty ting now.

STELLA. [*Eagerly.*] No, no, Poppa, she tell me only yesterday, how next year she learn new ones.

VEDETTI. [*Grunting unsympathetically.*] Humph!

[*As* STELLA *moves toward the door, she points proudly to a package and a bright-colored knitted sweater, carefully folded on the table.*]

STELLA. [*Beaming.*] I get the present already—see. [*She holds up the small package.*] A paint-box, with all the colors, and the brushes so fine. Now she won't have to paint only at school; she can do it at home with her own paints.

VEDETTI. What you waste the good money for?

STELLA. [*Quickly.*] So's Rosa can make the pictures here. [*On the defensive quickly.*] An' it was my money, Poppa, that I sew extra evenings for. Don't I give you every week the same from what they pay me? What good is it that I work hard sewing the beads on the dresses if I cannot give Rosa presents on her birthday?

VEDETTI. [*Shrugging again.*] Da rent it is raised, an' you spenda money for dese foolishnesses and dat— [*He peers at the gay sweater.*]

STELLA. [*Proudly.*] But this I make for her myself. See. [*She holds up a bright knitted sweater.*] Same as all the other girls wear to school. [*Pointing to a plate containing a round cake covered with paper.*] And I bake a cake—with sugar on top. [*Moving again toward the door.*] I go now to get the candles.

VEDETTI. Don' needa candles—

STELLA. Oh, but yes, they bring the good luck. Fifteen candles there must be—one for each year, and one more besides. Rosa, she go to Sadie's birthday party, an' she tell me so. For every year a candle, an' one for the year that is coming—"one to grow on," that's how they say.

VEDETTI. She grow anyways; candles maka no difference!

STELLA. But Rosa must grow, an' learn all the things she want to know—so I get fifteen candles—one for each year.

[*She goes out through the shop door smiling to herself; she has hardly left before the shop bell sounds, tinkling in the front room.* VEDETTI *ambles to the door, looks into the next room, beginning to smile ingratiatingly, bowing and speaking to someone in the room beyond.*]

VEDETTI. [*Politely.*] Dat you, Mr. Schneider? Come-a right in, dis-a way.

[*A short, heavy man, prosperous-looking in a cheap sort of way, appears in the door. His clothes are a bit showy, his manner is bland and condescending, and he speaks with no accent other than a cheap street Americanism.* VEDETTI *addresses him as a superior of whom he is decidedly in awe.*]

SCHNEIDER. [*Familiarly.*] Hello there! Thought I wasn't going to show up, did you? Well, here I am, all right!

VEDETTI. I theenk maybe you change-a your mind about—

SCHNEIDER. [*Interrupting.*] No, they kept me up to the factory—got to work hard to keep business going these days, Vedetti, hey?

VEDETTI. [*Nodding.*] Yes. [*Motioning him to sit down.*] You sitta down, no one bodder us here, an' I hear if anybody come in da shop.

SCHNEIDER. [*Seating himself.*] No, Vedetti, I didn't forget you, and our little talk last week, and I've got things all fixed up fine—like I said I would, so's the little girl can start right in at the works the first of next week.

VEDETTI. [*Rubbing his hands with satisfaction.*] Dat's good —you speak to the bigger boss?

SCHNEIDER. [*Laughing.*] Ha, ha! "The bigger boss," that's a good one! Sure I spoke to him and he told me to go right ahead. 'Course we mostly start the girls in the packing room— they're only green hands at fourteen, but I figured on doing a little better for your Rosy.

VEDETTI. [*Eagerly.*] How mooch she make?

SCHNEIDER. Well, let's see—you said she was good at painting, so's I thought there'd be a place in the finishing room, touchin' up the paper flowers last thing 'fore they go out.—It takes a good eye, and you need to be quick with your hands.

VEDETTI. [*Eagerly.*] Rosa verra quick.

SCHNEIDER. Yes, we like 'em young there—can't keep 'em at it very long. No, three or four years and they get so's all the colors look alike, and then we send 'em down to one of the other rooms—packin' or cuttin' out the flowers. But your Rosy'll be good at it for a while, and we'll start her right in at ten dollars.

VEDETTI. Ten dollar—a week?

SCHNEIDER. [*With a short laugh.*] Sure! What d' you think I meant—a day? It's a good chance for the kid, and it's lucky you told me 'bout her bein' so near fourteen.

[*Here there is a sound of footsteps off stage, and ROSA bursts into the room. We hear her voice calling before she enters, and she does not see the visitor when she first comes in, she is so excited. She is small for her age, sprightly and pretty, dressed cheaply but becomingly. Her hair is down her back, and she seems, if anything, younger than her years. Her face is round, and her eyes are dreamy. It is the sort of face that may easily become beautiful or coarse—it all depends on the next few years.*]

ROSA. [*Calling.*] Stella—Poppa—where are you?

VEDETTI. [*To SCHNEIDER.*] Dat's Rosa now.

SCHNEIDER. She know yet?

VEDETTI. [*Shaking his head warningly.*] No tella her.

ROSA. [*Entering.*] Poppa, where's Stella?

VEDETTI. She go out—come-a back soon, she say.

SCHNEIDER. Hello, Rosy, ain't you goin' to speak to me no more?

ROSA. [*Simply.*] Hello, Mr. Schneider, I didn't see you.

SCHNEIDER. [*Playfully.*] You don't see me because you ain't lookin' for me, hey?

ROSA. [*Laughing back.*] No, Mr. Schneider, I mean, yes!

SCHNEIDER. [*With a meaning glance at* VEDETTI.] Well, I tell you what, Rosy, you're going to see a lot more of me from now on! That so, Vedetti?

VEDETTI. [*Nodding.*] Yes. [*To the girl.*] Now, listen here, Rosa—

ROSA. [*Breaking in.*] Oh, Poppa, I can't—I gotta go back for Miss Roberts, the one who teaches me drawing; she's coming here to see you and Stella. She said so, soon as class was over, but I run back quick to tell you first.

VEDETTI. [*Not pleased.*] She come-a here—now—what for? [*Searchingly.*] You not been bad girl?

ROSA. [*Quickly.*] No, no! Poppa, it's about—[*She hesitates and her eyes shine with suppressed excitement.*] about a surprise and me—only I told her I wouldn't tell you first, and I told her how it was my birthday and everything.

SCHNEIDER. Your birthday—sure—your papa told me how you're fourteen.

ROSA. Yes. [*Turning again to* VEDETTI.] I gotta go back and show her the way. You tell Stella just the minute she comes in so she'll be all ready—and, Poppa—[*Half hesitant, half eager.*] won't you put on your coat, Poppa, please, like it's Sunday, 'cause Teacher's coming?

VEDETTI. Why should I put it on for her?

ROSA. [*Turning at the door, and smiling at him.*] Please, Poppa! [*To* SCHNEIDER.] Good-bye, Mr. Schneider. [*Exit.*]

VEDETTI. [*Looking after her.*] Rosa verra smart girl—

SCHNEIDER. [*Approvingly.*] Yep! She'll do fine in the work—a smart girl like that!

VEDETTI. [*Grinning.*] Dat's right.

SCHNEIDER. Yes, Vedetti, soon she'll be bringing you in a

pay envelope 'stead of teachers and pictures. [*He points to one of the drawings pinned on the wall.*] Here, you've got to sign this paper, just to show she's fourteen all right and you're willing for her to work. [*He has taken a paper from his pocket which he holds out.*] It's just a form, you know, and I'll take her round to the boss myself on Monday, and see she starts in all right. 'Course, maybe she won't make her ten the first week—they're kind of slow at first—and we can't pay 'em for what they don't do; figure on their paintin' 'bout two hundred and fifty flowers a day when we've learned 'em how, but she'll do better'n that once she's broken in to it. [*Taking out his fountain pen.*] You sign your name here.

VEDETTI. [*Reaching out to take it.*] Alla right. [*Hearing sound of footsteps in shop.*] Dat's Stella. [*A little nervously.*] I not tell Stella yet—she no like, maybe.

SCHNEIDER. Oh-h, that's it, is it? Well, I guess you ain't goin' to let her feelin's stand between Rosa earning good money for you every week. No, sir, you take my advice, and start her right in 'fore she gets any more nonsense 'bout books an' paintin' in her head!

VEDETTI. [*Motioning him toward shop.*] Sure. [*Urging him into the shop.*] Dis-a way. [*Exeunt.*]

[*They have hardly gone into the shop before* STELLA *enters from it, her arms full of bundles. She stands in the doorway staring after them and her face is tense. The audience should begin to feel that she scents trouble, but that she tries to go on as usual.* STELLA *takes off her things and begins putting away the bundles, most of which contain food. She lights the gas, and finally takes some small candles from a bag, removes the cover from the cake after she has placed it in the middle of the table, and begins sticking the candles on it. She places each one carefully, counting as she does so under her breath, and in spite of herself she forgets her fear at* SCHNEIDER's *presence in the shop, and hums a little happily to herself.*]

STELLA. [*Going to the door, and calling.*] Poppa, Poppa, come here a minute!

VEDETTI. [*Shuffling to the door.*] Well, what you want?

STELLA. [*Peering beyond him into the shop.*] There is no-body?

VEDETTI. [*Hastily.*] No, but Rosa, she come-a back while you are gone. She say she bring her teacher here soon. [*Shrugging his shoulders.*] What I want with her teacher, when my business is menda da shoe?

STELLA. [*Her face lighting up suddenly.*] Her teacher—come here?

VEDETTI. [*Nodding.*] They be here soon, I theenk.

STELLA. [*Facing him apprehensively.*] Poppa—Mr. Schneider, he was here just now after I go to get the things?

VEDETTI. [*Evasively.*] Well, maybe he come to see me, yes—

STELLA. If he come—he come because he thinks he can get something from you, Poppa; I know he's that kind—he wouldn't never come here less he wanted something off'n you.

VEDETTI. [*Crossly.*] I tella you he come to see me.

STELLA. [*Searching his face intently.*] He come here to ask you something 'bout Rosa, didn't he?

VEDETTI. [*Narrowly.*] Well?

STELLA. [*Facing him squarely.*] You tell me, Poppa; I know there's something up. [*Almost fiercely.*] You don't look like that only when you got something you're scared to tell me.

VEDETTI. [*Irately, throwing out his hands.*] Santa Maria, can't you leave me alone five minute?

STELLA. [*Going nearer to him.*] You gotta tell me if it's about Rosa, and I know it is. You gotta tell me; ain't I got the right to know?

VEDETTI. Rosa's ma girl—

STELLA. [*With determination.*] And she's mine, too, Poppa, same's yours. Didn't I take care of her since our mother died, an' she a baby an' so little an' sick? Sixteen year ole I was an' Rosa three when you leave Italy and bring us here, an' didn't I take care of her all day when you mend the shoes, and didn't I cook and wash and sew the clothes the best way I could till she get big enough to go to school? And didn't I get the sewing from the dress factory then that I do at home? I got as good a right to Rosa as you got, Poppa!

VEDETTI. Well, it time Rosa go to work, too, an' Schneider he get good place for her in the factory. He say she will paint the paper flowers—

STELLA. [*Pleading.*] Rosa can't go there; don't you see, Poppa, how she's gotta have the chance to learn more? I ain't had it, an' you ain't, but Rosa's going to. An' if she go through the high school she don't need to work in a factory—she can work in fine offices, or maybe teach school—think, Poppa, if Rosa be teacher!

VEDETTI. [*Shaking his head stubbornly.*] Two year 'fore she be through high school.

STELLA. [*Earnestly and persuasively.*] But she make more money then—

VEDETTI. [*Skeptically.*] How you know dat? And I needa the ten dollar now everra week.

STELLA. Poppa, listen; you have seen the Ludovitch girls in the next block, and the rest of them that go by every day to the factory. You saw what they were like three year ago when they start the work—just little girls like Rosa is now—and you see them come back from work every night, and how they stand hours on the street corners talking, and how they make red the cheeks, and white the nose, and wave the hair, so. They think of nothing but to go to the picture show each night, or to the beach to dance. You don't want for Rosa to get like them—an' she will—

VEDETTI. Rosa fourteen—time she go to work. [*In self-defense.*] Da rent it is raised all time.

STELLA. [*Eagerly.*] I'll help you pay the rent, Poppa—maybe not that much every week but I'll take more work. I can sew nights, and Rosa will help, too. Mrs. Swartz say she pay her a quarter every afternoon she takes care of the baby. She'll do that 'stead of staying late for more lessons at school, only don't you say nothin' to her 'bout the factory!

VEDETTI. [*Stubbornly.*] She go to work Monday. Place alla ready; if she don' go now Mr. Schneider won' help her get another one, an' I lose ma trade with him.

STELLA. You get other trade; an' anyway, don't you care more that Rosa have her chance? Two year now and she will be big and know plenty to make more money than Schneider give her. I don't want her like those Ludovitch girls, Poppa, with their painted faces and their empty heads. I don't want Rosa to be like me neither, and live in a little dark room, an' sew an' sew all day the things for other people to wear, and cook and eat and sleep like this—[*She gives a quick gesture that takes in the room.*] or have the great big machines making their noises round her so she can no longer make the pictures out of her head because her head it is too tired to have anything in it but the noise of those machines.

VEDETTI. [*Crossly.*] Stella, listen here—it don' do no good that you talka like dis—Rosa got to leave high school. Earn ten dollar everra week so we pay da rent, and I get bigger shop and maybe some day buy tenement justa like Meester Reilly.

STELLA. [*Fiercely.*] But what good that be to Rosa—then—when she cannot make the pictures any more? Better that you give her to graduate from high school—and she help you then, she—

VEDETTI. [*Breaking in angrily.*] I tella you dat I signa dat paper an' she go to work.

[*Here there comes a sound of footsteps and voices in the shop, and* ROSA'S *laugh.* STELLA *turns on her father quickly.*]

STELLA. They're coming—don't you say nothin' to her—not on her birthday. [*Fixing him with her eyes, so that he shifts uneasily under their intensity.*] You hear me, Poppa; don't you say a word to her 'bout this!

VEDETTI. [*Grudgingly.*] Well, maybe I don' tonight.

[ROSA *and* MISS ROBERTS *enter from the door leading to the shop. The latter is a woman in the thirties, simply dressed, but in good taste. She is direct and sympathetic in her manner toward them, particularly when she speaks to* ROSA *and to* STELLA.]

ROSA. [*Beaming.*] Teacher, this is Stella, my sister, like I told you takes care of me. And here's Poppa, Miss Roberts. [*Her face falls as she notices that he is still in his shirt sleeves. Then she pulls him a little aside and speaks softly to him.*] I'll go get your coat, Poppa, now. [ROSA *slips out.*]

MISS ROBERTS. [*Pleasantly, pretending not to hear this aside.*] I'm so glad you're both in, for I've been wanting to come and tell you how much everyone over at the high school thinks of your Rosa.

STELLA. [*Her face lighting up at this.*] Rosa, she likes all her teachers, but she talk most 'bout you, cause you teacha her to make the pictures.

[ROSA *returns with the coat, urging* VEDETTI *into it, though he does so under protest, his shoulders expressing what he does not say in the way of disgust and unwillingness to comply.* MISS ROBERTS, *though evidently taking in and being amused by this bit of play, goes on as if nothing out of the ordinary were happening during the call.*]

MISS ROBERTS. And there's something I've come especially to see you about; isn't there, Rosa?

ROSA. [*After successfully accomplishing the coat business.*] I thought I'd just have to tell them, Miss Roberts, but I didn't!

STELLA. [*Eager to be hospitable.*] You'll sit down and I'll make you the cup of coffee—yes?—or maybe Poppa will get out the bottle of wine his friend in the country make from his own grapes?

MISS ROBERTS. Oh! thank you, but I mustn't stay long enough for that. I'll just sit down here and show you what we've brought. [*She opens her bag and takes out a small box.* ROSA *hovers over her excitedly.*]

ROSA. Look, Stella! Look, Poppa! It's all silver and I won it for a prize!

VEDETTI. [*Showing interest for the first time.*] Money? You maka da money?

ROSA. No, it's a medal for drawing!

STELLA. [*Breathless, almost forgetting the shadow of the factory hanging over them.*] Rosa she win it all by herself? For the pictures she make?

MISS ROBERTS. Yes, and next year she's going to win the gold medal, we hope. She's worked hard, and we all think she has real talent in these fingers of hers. [*She takes the girl's hand affectionately in hers.*]

STELLA. [*Her arms about* ROSA.] Didn't I tell you so, Poppa, just now?

VEDETTI. [*Shortly.*] Humph! medal!

MISS ROBERTS. [*Nothing daunted by his attitude.*] I wanted to bring it myself and tell you how pleased we all are. And we want to give Rosa a special chance next year to work after hours in the advanced class, the one that will fit her for commercial designing.

ROSA. [*Putting in a word eagerly.*] I'll learn to make pictures for the wall papers and cloth and dresses, and how to draw for the magazines maybe.

MISS ROBERTS. And if she does as well in that class as she's been doing this year, one of the big firms that keep in touch with us will have a good place waiting for her in its art department. In a few years she'll be making a good salary, and if she goes on studying nights at the art school there's no reason why she shouldn't do really big things some day. She has the ability; it's just a question of these next two years, and what she learns to do in them.

STELLA. [*Her face filled with apprehension.*] Two years—she can do so much in them?

MISS ROBERTS. They're the most important ones. I'm sure you understand how everything depends on them. I can see you do, and that you'll do anything to help your sister.

STELLA. I would do anything—anything—for her; but it's this way, I— [*Here* ROSA, *who has been lighting a second gas jet at the other side of the room, comes forward, cutting* STELLA *short.*]

ROSA. [*Happily.*] Isn't it fine, sister, all Miss Roberts says I'll learn to do? And look at the medal! [*Holding it proudly under the light.*] All silver, Poppa; and, see, it's got my name on this side!

VEDETTI. [*Taking it in his hand and weighing it critically.*] Can't tell if it be realla silver, if you don' bite it—so— [*He starts to do this when* ROSA *takes it again.*]

MISS ROBERTS. And think of all its stands for! Aren't you proud to have your Rosa get the second prize, Mr. Vedetti? She's one of the youngest in the class, too.

STELLA. [*Proudly, hugging* ROSA, *though she is very near to tears.*] Rosa have always the pictures in her head, that the big girls they don't see!

ROSA. [*Chatting happily.*] And I'll get work in a store and study, and have my pictures in books some day, just like a real artist, won't I, Miss Roberts?

MISS ROBERTS. [*With a quick look at* STELLA.] I hope so, Rosa. [*To* STELLA.] But I mustn't stay any longer; it's growing dark; I only came to bring the medal and tell you about it. Rosa said it was her birthday, and I wanted you to know how—[*She hesitates.*] how things stand, and that we want to help her have a good start. We can't bear to see talent wasted in factories and behind counters, and it happens so often at fourteen, when just two years more would make a difference in all the rest of their lives.

STELLA. [*Despairingly.*] Why don't the law say sixteen then instead of fourteen? [*Suddenly, her face lighting, she turns to the teacher hopefully.*] Miss Roberts, maybe, maybe it does say so now? [*Her voice is tremulous with hope.*]

MISS ROBERTS. [*Shaking her head.*] No, it doesn't say so, Stella —not yet.

STELLA. [*Pleading.*] Oh, Miss Roberts, can't you tell those people that make the laws how it is?

MISS ROBERTS. [*Slowly.*] Some day perhaps things will be different—

STELLA. [*Throwing out her hands with a little hopeless gesture.*] But then it is too late—Rosa will be grown up.

ROSA. [*Catching at some of her words.*] Too late for what, sister?

MISS ROBERTS. [*To* STELLA.] I know you'll remember what I said. I can see how much you care, and I'll come again. I must go now. Good night. [*She takes* STELLA's *hand.*] Good night, Mr. Vedetti.

[*He grunts something in return.*]

Rosa. [*Eagerly.*] I'll go with you to the corner and show you where to take the car.

[*With another word of good night* Miss Roberts *goes out preceded by* Rosa. Stella *takes a step toward her father, and makes a last stand.*]

Stella. Poppa, you see it's like how I told you it was. Ain't you goin' to let her stay on?

Vedetti. [*Throwing up his hands.*] Santa Maria in Paradiso! No! No! No! Is it not enough that I hear that woman talk all time same as you? If you aska me dat again, I tell Rosa tonight, on her birthday!

Stella. Don't you do that! You promised not to, Poppa, but—but—

[*She tries to go on but she cannot, and* Vedetti *shuffles out to the shop, pulling his coat off as he goes, and muttering to himself half under his breath.* Stella *tries to go on fixing the cake on the table, and arranging the little gifts, but she grows absent-minded, staring before her, hopelessly. Then* Rosa *comes in again, glowing from the visit. She runs to* Stella *happily.*]

Rosa. Oh, sister, isn't it grand to have a medal on my birthday? It's just fine to be fourteen! [*Seeing the cake and crying out with joy.*] Oh, it's a cake, just like Sadie's, with pink candles on top! [Stella *begins lighting them one by one, and* Rosa *counts them gleefully as she does so.*] One—two—three [*and so on to fourteen with eager pleasure.*] And another to bring good luck! Fifteen candles—there's one to grow on!

Vedetti. [*Entering and hearing her words.*] What you say—grow on?

Rosa. Yes. Oh, Stella, I can grow a lot next year on that candle!

Stella. [*Breaking down.*] No—no, I don't like that candle—I'm afraid for what you grow into—maybe—

[*Curtain*]

UNDERSTANDING AND APPRECIATING THE PLAY

1. The conflict in a tragedy may be mental, moral, or physical. It may entail the matching of wits, the struggle between good and evil, or open physical combat. An individual may struggle against human opponents, against unfavorable surroundings, or against his own worse or better self. It is conflict, of whatever nature, that provides the important dramatic elements of interest and suspense. Frequently our chief interest in a play is the desire to see which of the two opposing forces will win. In this play there is a conflict between two characters. Who are they? Who wins? Do you think the play would have been more effective if it had ended differently? Give your reasons. Tell of some motion picture or some television or radio drama in which the ending did not seem logical to you.

2. Which of the benefits which may be obtained from reading tragedies (p. 81) did you receive from reading this play?

3. What were Rosa's plans for her education? How did her sister, her father, and her teacher react to her plans?

4. Who do you think is the principal character of the play? Why do you think so?

5. Vedetti is scarcely what one would call an ideal father. (He is, of course, no more representative of foreign-born parents than he is of those who are native-born.) What do you consider his two outstanding faults? What can you say in his defense?

VOCABULARY BUILDING

1. Explain the meanings of the following phrases: his manner *bland* and *condescending;* beginning to smile *ingratiatingly;* regarding them *skeptically;* a face *wistful* in repose; replying *evasively;* unwillingness to *comply;* facing him *apprehensively;* an old man, *grizzled* and bent.

2. The prefix *com-* or *con-* usually means *with* or *together. Comply* means literally *to bend with,* which in turn suggests its usual meaning, *to agree.* In like manner work out the meanings of the following: *connect, conjunction, confederation, compare, contact.* Have a roll call around the class, each person being expected to answer with an English word containing this prefix—one not given by another member of the class.

THINGS TO DO

1. Relate to the class the most tragic example of frustration or defeat you have suffered or observed. Tell why you thought the story particularly tragic.

2. What defeats and frustrations are connected directly with school life? Write a story or a short play illustrating one of these.

3. Among the forces in the world that bring frustration and defeat into human lives are war, intolerance, greed, intemperance, crime. What others can you add to the list? Write a story illustrating the tragedy caused by one of these forces. Or you may prefer to write an essay or give a floor talk proving that the force you have selected creates tragedy.

4. Write a scenario (see p. 345) of a play dealing with a person who has run afoul of the law. Make your play emphasize a theme —perhaps that a criminal is the product of his environment and of his heredity, or that a criminal is mentally ill, or that crime does not pay. You may base your play on a newspaper story. Read your scenario to the class, and after it has been discussed and approved by your teacher and your classmates, you may write your play.

5. Develop one of the following topics into a theme: What Good Is High School?; Plans for My Future: My Plans and My Parents' Plans; A Teacher Who Has Helped Me; Why I Want (or Do Not Want) to Complete My High School Education; Should I Leave School for a Job?; What I Have Liked Best about My School; My Plans and Problems Concerning College.

6. For discussion:

Suggestion: Various groups or rows should volunteer for or be assigned the responsibility of preparing for and discussing these topics.

A. *The problem of drop-outs.* Why do so many boys and girls leave, or drop out, of school before they graduate? What can be done to reduce the number of drop-outs?

B. *Compulsory education:* "Why don't the law say sixteen instead of fourteen?" Stella asks despairingly and ungrammatically. In many states the compulsory education law does require boys and girls to attend school until they are sixteen or even older. Why do state lawmakers pass compulsory education laws? What are the advantages of compulsory education? What are the disadvantages? Do young people have to be protected from themselves—and possibly in rare instances from their parents—by compulsory education laws? If you believe in compulsory education, are you satisfied with the compulsory age in your state? Do you believe that the age up to which young people are compelled to attend school should be increased or lowered? If so, to what age, and why?

C. *The importance of a high school education.* How important is a high school education? What are the advantages? Are there any disadvantages? If so, what are they?

D. *The importance of a college education.* Apply the first three questions of the preceding topic to this one. Then also discuss such sub-topics as these: Who should go to college? Who should not? What college or colleges would you like to attend? Why? What are the reasons that prevent many qualified students from going to college? What should be done to help greater numbers of qualified students to attend college?

E. *Difficulties that affect students' achievement in high school.* What are some of the difficulties that prevent boys and girls from doing their best in school work? How can these difficulties be recognized by all concerned—students, parents, and teachers? What can be done to help young people overcome these difficulties?

F. *Do Americans glorify white-collar jobs?* Americans in general and young people in particular have been criticized for glorifying white-collar jobs and for looking down upon other types of work. Do you think that this criticism is justified? What are your ideas on the subject?

PRODUCTION NOTES

The title of this play points out its significance. For Rosa's fourteen years there are fourteen candles, plus one to grow on. But her high hopes of future growth should contrast cruelly with the drab routine to which her father's agreement with Schneider condemns her. Even the stage setting should emphasize the drabness of Rosa's probable future. It is a living-place where no money is spent for pleasantness or beauty. The dingy washing outside the window (perhaps also a glimpse of a fire escape) is important, though not indispensable; so is the dim, wholly inadequate light from the gas jets (or kerosene lamps).

The teacher should betray a conviction at last that she is on the losing side. And Stella's admission of defeat should be almost heartbreaking. The thwarting of Rosa's ambitions must seem tragic. Overacting the parts, however, will not do; restraint will secure the effect much better.

Stella sings in the first part of the play. But if a girl is available who would do the Stella part splendidly except for the singing, by all means use her. You can furnish the song by victrola or radio, and Stella can hum to it. Indeed, the use of music to provide a sad, wistful background throughout the play would enhance its emotional effect. Suggestion: the famous tenor aria from *The Pearl Fishers*.

Properties are few. In making out the list, be sure to remember the tinkling shop bell, Stella's knitting, and a shoe for Mr. Vedetti to work on.

MORE GOOD ONE-ACT TRAGEDIES

The Birthday of the Infanta. Stuart Walker. [Little, Brown] Excellent adaptation of Oscar Wilde's sad tale of the ugly little hunchback who was hired to entertain the beautiful princess.

The Dreamy Kid. Eugene O'Neill. [French] The Dreamy Kid, a young Negro gangster, is being hunted by the police on a murder charge, yet he is moved by superstitious fear to go to the bedside of his dying grandmother. The play is exciting and approaches perfection in technique, but it scarcely presents an accurate picture of Negro life.

Good Vintage. Dan Totheroh. [French] A wedding in a California ranch house ends in a tragic shooting.

The Intruder. Maurice Maeterlinck. [Baker] A beautiful and symbolic play of the coming of death.

Riders to the Sea. J. M. Synge. [French] One of the most distinguished of the one-act tragedies. Like Paul Green's *Last of the Lowries*, which it may have inspired, it is the story of a sorrowful but fatalistic mother losing her last son.

Submerged. H. S. Cottman and L. V. Shaw. [Row, Peterson] Tense realistic tragedy of men who are trapped at the bottom of the ocean in a submarine.

White Dresses. Paul Green. [French] Composed in Professor Koch's playwriting class at the University of North Carolina, *White Dresses* is the first of the many excellent plays of Negro life written by Paul Green. It tells the deeply moving story of an attractive mulatto girl, Mary McLean, who is in love with a white youth, the son of the plantation owner. "A tragedy in black and white," Paul Green calls it. He wrote the part of Mary for a talented Negro girl, who later starred on Broadway.

FULL-LENGTH PLAYS

Beyond the Horizon, Eugene O'Neill [Random House];   *Death of a Salesman,* Arthur Miller [Dramatists Play Service];   *The Diary of Anne Frank,* Frances Goodrich and Albert Hackett [Dramatists Play Service];   *A Doll's House,* Henrik Ibsen [Random House];   *Ethan Frome,* Owen Davis and Donald Davis [Dramatists Play Service]; *Saint Joan,* George Bernard Shaw [French];   *Winterset, Elizabeth the Queen,* and *Mary of Scotland,* Maxwell Anderson [Dramatists Play Service];   *Julius Caesar, Macbeth, Romeo and Juliet, Hamlet, Othello,* and *King Lear,* William Shakespeare;   *Antigone* and *Oedipus Rex,* Sophocles.

Folk Play: Folk and Folkways

ORIGINALLY the term *folk play* referred to plays that came from the folk themselves, much as did the old ballads and the Paul Bunyan stories. Often they were never written, but merely developed through countless repetitions. Today, however, the name "folk play" is also applied to any play depicting the life of the common folk—their joys and sorrows, their customs and beliefs, their speech and manners, their songs and dances, their legends and superstitions.

The folk play tells a story—one all the more fascinating because of the plain folk with whom it deals; but in addition to the story, it gives us an insight into the lives of the people in the particular region which the dramatist has chosen for his setting. And the best of the folk dramatists manage to do more than merely describe some narrow locality; in the process of doing so, they reveal some of the emotions and character traits which are common to human nature everywhere. They try to interpret life for all mankind.

A folk play may also belong to one of the other families of the drama. Josefina Niggli's play of the Mexican Revolution, *The Ring of General Macías*, is a suspenseful melodrama. Anton Chekhov's play about Russian life in the nineteenth-century, *The Boor*, is a hilarious farce. And the American folk play by Robert Finch, *Goodbye to the Lazy K*, which you are about to read, is either a comedy or a farce—depending upon your point of view.

Goodbye to the Lazy K *

ROBERT FINCH

A humorous folk play of cowboy life in the American Northwest, *Goodbye to the Lazy K* deals in a whimsical manner with the
problem of how and how quickly one can arrive at a very important decision. Our cowboy hero, Slim Williams, has to decide whether to remain on the Lazy K ranch and marry Bonnie, the ranch owner's pretty
daughter, or to postpone marriage and leave for town to seek that
"great big opportunity for the right man" by buying a butcher shop.
But Bonnie's father, Mr. Lash, wants no "more o' this shilly-shallyin'."
Slim has to make up his mind "right-quick"!

CHARACTERS

SLIM
BONNIE
MR. LASH
FRISCO
TEX
STUB

THE TIME: *Late last summer. Evening, and the first faint chill of
autumn in the air.*
THE PLACE: *The Lazy K.*[1]
THE SETTING: *The back porch of the ranch house. The house extends from somewhere off at left to its corner at right center.
Beyond the corner and in the distance off at right can be
seen a far-off mountain range, the low sagebrush foothills
and the blue sky of early evening.
Somewhat right of center is the back door of the house; be-*

* From *100 Non-Royalty One-Act Plays*, edited by William Kozlenko,
copyright 1940, Chilton Company, Philadelphia and New York. Professional
production on stage, radio or television requires permission.
[1] The Lazy K ranch gets its name from the fact that its branding-iron
mark is the letter K lying on its side, like this ⋈ .

*yond it the kitchen. A small, low porch has been attached
to the door—merely a few planks hammered crudely together, and protected by a small plank roof. Left of the porch
is a window, curtained with bright red and white checked
curtains and opening on the kitchen. A table may be seen
through the window, with a small, unlighted kerosene lamp
on it. Although it is early evening, and not yet dark, another
lamp within the room is lighted.*

AT RISE: *The screen door to the kitchen is closed, but the door
itself is open, and the warm lamplight streams out on the
porch.*

*The stage is empty for a moment; then someone is heard
approaching from left; and* SLIM *appears, walking toward
the back porch. He is a slender, boyish cowboy, wearing
flannel, checked shirt, "levis," high-heeled boots, battered
sombrero. He carries a big roll of bedding wrapped in a
canvas tarpaulin; he brings the roll over to the porch and
drops it. Then he knocks gently on the screen door, calls
softly:*

SLIM. Bonnie!

[*Someone moves about in the kitchen, then* BONNIE *appears
in the door. She is a pretty, healthy-looking girl of 19,
dressed in a gingham house dress.*]

SLIM. I brung the beddin' over from the bunkhouse. Your
father'll prob'ly need the blankets these cold nights.

[BONNIE *comes close to him, looks tenderly at him, then
hides her head against his chest.*]

BONNIE. Aw, Slim . . . *don't go. Please.*

SLIM. [*Pleased by this attention, he speaks comfortingly.*]
There, Bonnie. [*Awkwardly, he caresses her hair.*] You oughta be
plumb ashamed o' me for not makin' my mark in the world. Gotta
go to town so's I'll amount to somethin'.

BONNIE. O' *course* you'll amount to somethin'. A whole lot.
But . . . [*Troubled, she says no more.*]

SLIM. [*Glancing up at the sky.*] Better get this here beddin'
inside. Don't want it to get rained on. If it rains. [*He steps inside*

with the bedroll. A moment, then he calls.] Got any hot water, Bonnie?

BONNIE. There's a whole kettleful on the stove.

SLIM. I'll wash myself real thorough-like so's to make a good impression on them city folks. [*He comes out on the porch, pours water into the tin wash basin that stands on the wash-bench at the side of the porch, then washes noisily while talking away confidently.*] Oh, say! . . . [*Remembering something, he reaches into a shirt pocket and brings out a newspaper clipping.*] Here's the advertisement. I cut it out o' the paper. [*He hands it to* BONNIE.] See what it says? "A great big opportunity for the right man." [*As he washes his face,* BONNIE *tucks the clipping back in his shirt pocket. While he dries his face briskly on the towel that hangs from a nail on the porch, he speaks with pride.*] I even got a name for my store. Gonna call it the "Paradise."

BONNIE. [*Touched, she speaks lovingly.*] Aw . . . Slim . . .

SLIM. The Paradise Butcher Shop.

BONNIE. Ain't you sorta—*scared*—goin' into business by yourself?

SLIM. Nary a bit. I can't help but make good. All my friends are gonna bring me the stray cows and calves they find—the mavericks nobody owns . . . gosh, I'll *coin* money.

BONNIE. I like you fine this way. Even without any money.

SLIM. Yeah. Thanks, Bonnie. But I gotta be a success, so's you'll be proud o' me.

BONNIE. Don't you *wanta* marry me now?

SLIM. [*He gives her a comforting hug.*] O' course! That's all settled. But you see . . . [*A far-away look comes into his eyes.*] . . . Well, Bonnie, it's fall time. Everybody's goin' away somewheres to do big things. Even the ducks are sailin' away over the ranch. Goin' south to make somethin' out o' theirselves. Why, gosh, Bonnie—there ain't no limit to what I can do once I get started. Might even get to be alderman . . . I guess you'd be proud to be Mrs. Alderman Slim Williams.

BONNIE. Or even just Mrs. Slim Williams.

SLIM. But you'll have more respect for me when I'm rich. [*He puts an arm about her, tenderly.*] When I come back to marry you in six weeks or so, with my pockets full o' money, you'll be mighty proud. [*He quickly takes his arm away as he sees* MR. LASH *approaching from right, carrying a pail of milk in each hand.* MR. LASH *is a man of middle age, ruddy, healthy, somewhat heavy-set. He is kindly, but in a very gruff way.* LASH *is followed by* FRISCO, *a thin-faced, cheerful and amiable cowboy of 25.* FRISCO *also carries a pail of milk in each hand.*] I put my bedroll in the kitchen, Mr. Lash. You can use my blankets if you want.

[MR. LASH *is trying to open the screen door with his elbow, and he can't quite do it. After several tries he speaks loudly and gruffly.*]

LASH. Open the door! [*Slim jumps to open the screen door.* FRISCO *enters first;* MR. LASH *stays behind to speak irritably to the world at large.*] Punched cattle for the Lazy K for two years. An' don't know enough to open the door! [*Grumbling,* MR. LASH *goes on inside.*]

SLIM. Your father don't seem very friendly-like t'night. [*There is a pause.*] He must be upset over me a-leavin' him.

BONNIE. I guess so. He said you're goin' on a wild-goose chase.

SLIM. He *did?* [*He is greatly mystified.*] I wonder what he meant?

BONNIE. He says if we're a-gonna get married we oughtta get it over with. Like takin' a cold bath. The thing to do is jump in.

FRISCO. [*He comes out, without the milk pails.*] You really goin' into town, Slim?

SLIM. Yep. Catchin' that nine-o'clock train to Jackson.

FRISCO. [*He pulls a big dollar watch from his pocket and examines it.*] You better shake a leg. It's after eight now.

SLIM. Yeah. I better go over to the bunkhouse an' put my store clothes on so's I'll be ready.

FRISCO. I'll high-tail down to the corral an' tell the boys. They'll want to say g'bye to you. [*As he starts out at right, he slaps his thigh, laughs boisterously as he exits.*] Goin' in the butcher business! Dangdest thing I ever heard of!

SLIM. Well . . . G'bye for a minute, Honey. I'm a-gonna put my city clothes on. [SLIM *starts out at left.*]

LASH. [*He appears in the doorway.*] You better make it fast if you want to flag that train. It's two miles to the railroad tracks.

SLIM. Yeah! It won't take me but a minute, Bonnie. I'll be right back. [*He hurries off at left.*]

LASH. [*He comes out on the porch, lights his pipe, and in a roughly tender way, he pats* BONNIE *on the shoulder.*] You think a lot o' that boy, Bonnie?

BONNIE. [*Emphatically.*] A whole lot.

LASH. And he likes you?

BONNIE. Says he does, all right.

LASH. Then what in the world is he a-goin' away for?

BONNIE. I wish he wasn't. He says he'll be back in six weeks. To marry me and take me off to town.

LASH. Boy must be outa his mind. Them city folks'll skin 'im alive.

BONNIE. [*With a sudden start.*] Oh! I forgot the cake! I been bakin' it for a present for Slim. [BONNIE *hurries into the kitchen.*]

LASH. [*He smokes and talks while* BONNIE *stirs about in the kitchen.*] When your Maw an' I got married I had even less'n Slim's got. Now I own me a fine big cattle ranch. It belonged to your Maw's father.

[BONNIE *appears in the doorway, carrying a square box, tied with a red ribbon.*]

BONNIE. It's angel food. With lots o' frosting. Just the kind Slim likes.

LASH. All I got to say is—he don't know when he's well off.

BONNIE. [*As she sees* SLIM *approaching from left.*] Sh-h-h.

LASH. [*Starting into the house.*] I guess you two can say g'bye better if I go in the house.

[LASH *goes in.*]

SLIM. [*He comes to a halt in front of* BONNIE. *He now wears a striped silk shirt with pink sleeve-holders; high-water pants, high buttoned shoes, a tight-fitting jacket with short sleeves, which clutches him in the wrong places. His hat it too small, his shirt collar is too tight, his necktie droops out of his jacket. Altogether he looks thoroughly miserable. He carries a paper suitcase in one hand, in the other a silver mounted bridle, a fishingrod and a guitar. He speaks proudly.]* How do I look?

BONNIE. *[Sincerely; she'd like him whatever he wore.]* You look just fine, Slim.

SLIM. *[Relieved.]* That's good. I sent away for these clothes, and I was afraid they wouldn't fit.

BONNIE. I—I got something for you. Cake. *[BONNIE holds out the box, which she has been concealing behind her back.]*

SLIM. *[He is touched.]* Aw . . . you shouldn't 'a' done it, Bonnie . . . slavin' over the hot stove, just for me. Say! *[He thinks of something, fishes in his pocket, brings out a ring.]* I got something for *you*, too . . . *[He holds out the ring.]*

BONNIE. *[Breathlessly.]* Oh-h-h-h . . .

SLIM. For our engagement. It's a real gold nugget ring. *[BONNIE holds out her hand; he slips the ring on her finger, kisses her, awkwardly.]* It's shaped sort o' like a heart . . . see?

BONNIE. *[Softly.]* Yeah. It . . . it's beautiful, Slim.

SLIM. I'm sure glad you like it. You can show it to your father if you want. Just to prove I'm in earnest . . . about you, I mean.

BONNIE. *[Calling.]* Dad!

LASH. *[He appears immediately in the doorway, as though he might have been listening.]* What?

BONNIE. Look! Slim gave it to me.

LASH. *[He examines the ring; he seems impressed by it.]* Hm . . . did you mine that nugget yourself, Slim?

SLIM. Well . . . sort o'. I found it in a chicken gizzard. Chicken musta thought it was corn.

LASH. It's mighty purty. *[He warms up a little toward SLIM.]* You know, Son—I'm mighty sorry to see you go.

SLIM. I hate to leave, Mr. Lash. I like it here pretty good.

LASH. I know how it is between you and Bonnie.

SLIM. *[Somewhat embarrassed.]* Oh . . .

LASH. Whyn't you two have a weddin'?

SLIM. Pretty quick we will. I wanta make a success o' myself first, an' have a home o' my own. Wouldn't be fair to you if we got married now an' you had us under your feet all the time. Better have my own place.

LASH. You could move out to the bunkhouse an' set up house-keepin' there.

SLIM. Aw, I wouldn't like that. All them other fellas around. Wouldn't seem right.

LASH. They could sleep out in the hayloft. Just as good there anyhow. Maybe better. If I turn the cows out.

SLIM. Thanks . . . thanks a whole lot, Mr. Lash. But I gotta go. I'm *bound* t' make good.

FRISCO. [*He appears at right, stands staring at* SLIM, *dumbfounded.*] Look at them fancy duds!

[TEX *and* STUB *appear.* TEX *is a slow-moving, quiet cowboy with a drawl. He is about 27 years of age.* STUB *is cheerful and smiling, perhaps 25.*]

TEX. Purty, ain't they?

STUB. He's handsome as a travelin' man. Look at them there sleeveholders!

[SLIM *has removed his jacket, carries it over his arm.*]

FRISCO. Purty as a school-marm's garters.

SLIM. I brung along some o' my stuff . . . things I won't need in town. I want you fellers to have 'em. This here bridle's for you, Frisco. Silver-mounted.

FRISCO. Thanks, pardner. It's mighty handsome.

TEX. Ain't you gonna need that bridle when you ride to the railroad tracks to flag the train to Jackson? Can't ride a horse without no bridle.

SLIM. I'm gonna walk. I'm through with horses, and I might as well get used to it. Besides, I want to break in these here new shoes. Here, Stub, you take this here fish-pole.

STUB. Sure you can spare it?

SLIM. Oh, I can spare it fine. Tex, this guitar's for you. I can't be a-wastin' my time around the butcher shop playin' the guitar.

BONNIE. Play something on it, Tex. So's Slim won't feel bad about leavin'.

LASH. Sure! Cheer 'im up! Give 'im a big send-off!

Tex. [*He strums the guitar and sings in a clear, melancholy tenor.*]

> He was just a lone-ly cowboy,[2]
> With a heart so brave and true,
> And he learned to love a maiden,
> With eyes of heav'n's own blue.

Bonnie. [*Speaking as* Tex *comes to the end of the stanza.*] Have some cake, boys.

Frisco. Don't mind if I do. [*He takes a piece of cake.*]

Tex. [*Helping himself.*] Seems like a farewell party'd oughta be had on the *front* porch.

Lash. We'd just hafta walk around to the back to say g'bye to him—since the road goes from here.

Tex. [*Strumming the guitar he sings softly.*]

> They learned to love each other,
> And had named their wedding day
> When a quarrel came between them,
> And Jack he rode away.

Frisco. Nothin' like singin' to cheer people up when they're goin' away, is there, Slim?

Slim. [*He shakes his head, somewhat morosely.*] Sure isn't. Thet's a mighty cheerful song.

Tex. The next fifteen verses don't amount to much. But after that it goes . . .

> But when he reached the prai-rie,
> He found a new-made mound,
> And his friends sadly told him,
> They'd laid his lov'd one down.

[*He stops.*] Can't remember no more.

Stub. That's enough. Feel better, Slim?

Slim. I feel fine . . . [*Much affected by the sadness of it all, he wipes his eyes, blows his nose sadly.*] . . . I guess. [*He sighs morosely.*] Well . . . [*He picks up his suitcase, kisses* Bonnie *sadly.*] G'bye, Bonnie . . .

[2] The song is "Cowboy Jack," and it may be found in various collections of Western songs or folk songs.

BONNIE. G'bye, Slim.

SLIM. So long, fellas.

STUB. So long.

FRISCO. Good luck.

TEX. Adios.

SLIM. [*He gets nearly out at left, then turns and waves.*] G'bye.

ALL. [*They wave somberly.*] G'bye.

SLIM. It was nice of you to cheer me up about goin' . . . [*He shuffles out; BONNIE sadly watches him go.*]

TEX. Ain't he lucky? Goin' away to town?

STUB. Mighty lucky. He can go to the movies every doggone night if he wants to. When they're open.

FRISCO. He's a danged fool, if you ask me. Leavin' a girl like Bonnie.

BONNIE. [*Waving off at left to SLIM.*] G'bye, Slim!

SLIM. [*Off, calling.*] G'bye!

STUB. [*He notices the box.*] Hey! He forget his cake. We better stop him!

TEX. [*He quickly grabs the box.*] Wait. [*He takes a piece of cake; the others follow suit. TEX carefully puts the cake back in the box, speaks with his mouth full.*] Now call him.

FRISCO. [*Calling.*] Hey! Slim! Come back and get your cake!

TEX. Gosh, thet's good cake.

LASH. Boys, I already said my g'bye to Slim. Don't like to say it twice in a row. Guess I'll go to bed. G'night.

BONNIE. G'night, Dad. [*The others also bid him goodnight.*]
[SLIM *appears at left, slightly out of breath, carrying his hat.*]

FRISCO. You forgot your cake.

SLIM. Yeah. Lucky you noticed it. Well . . . [*He takes the box, kisses BONNIE tenderly once more. He is plainly melancholy and reluctant to go.*] Take care o' yourself, Bonnie . . .

BONNIE. Sure, Slim . . . [*She puts her handkerchief to her eyes.*] I'll light the lamp an' leave it in the window—so's you can look back an' see it while you're walkin'. [*She goes in the kitchen door.*]

TEX. Slim, you look sort o' peaked.

SLIM. I—I can't understand it. I felt fine a while ago. Now I feel . . . well, sort o' sad-like. [*Suddenly his face lights up.*] Say! I *could* wait over till tomorra night . . .

TEX. Better not. Thet feller in Jackson'll be waitin' to sell you thet butcher shop. You don't want somebody else should grab thet big opportunity away from you.

SLIM. [*Doubtfully.*] Well, no—I guess not.

[BONNIE *can be seen through the kitchen window, lighting the little kerosene lamp and placing it on the table by the window.*]

TEX. I guess I better sing some more for you, Slim. [*Playing the guitar, he begins singing, sadly.*]

> When the cur-tains of night [3]
> Are pinned back by the stars
> And the beautiful moon sweeps the sky-y-y.

[BONNIE *comes out.* SLIM *kisses her again, sadly.*]

SLIM. So long, Bonnie.

BONNIE. Be good, Slim.

TEX. [*Playing and singing.*]

> I'll remember you, Love,
> In my prayers.

FRISCO. [*Touched by the song, he wipes his eyes.*] Gosh!

[*It is getting* SLIM, *too. He is almost in tears, holding* BONNIE's *hand, unable to tear himself away.*]

SLIM. [*Overcome by the sadness of it all, he stares at* BONNIE *and the others, ready to burst into tears.*] Golly! I—I . . . [*The lump in his throat overcomes him and he quickly hurries out at left.*]

STUB. Well—he's gone.

BONNIE. Oh, don't talk about it, Stub!

[BONNIE *puts her handkerchief to her eyes.* TEX *softly strums the guitar through the next three speeches.*]

STUB. [*Apropos of nothing.*] Them folks at Jackson got four

[3] The song is "The Curtains of Night."

butcher stores now. Need another one about as much as I need a broodin' pair o' rattlesnakes.

FRISCO. [*Looking off left.*] Hey! Slim's stopped walkin' . . . [TEX *continues to play, but they all look off at left.*] He's turnin' back!

BONNIE. He musta forgot somethin'.

TEX. [*He has stopped playing.*] He took the cake with him. [*Calling.*] What's the trouble?

[SLIM *appears at left, carrying his hat and coat, looking sad and troubled, limping a bit from his new shoes.*]

SLIM. I just wanted to talk to you folks about somethin' . . . thet is . . . them little calves thet you make veal out of . . .

TEX. Yeah?

SLIM. [*Haltingly.*] Well-l-l . . . it's this way . . . I . . . well . . . [*Blurting it out.*] *Somebody's* gotta *slaughter* them veals!

FRISCO. *You* slaughter 'em.

BONNIE. Oh, no! He couldn't. Slim's too tender-hearted.

FRISCO. Sure he could. He has to. He's the butcher.

SLIM. Gosh, no! I . . . I'm afraid I couldn't.

TEX. Well—you might grease the slaughter-house floor. Maybe they'd slip an' bust their necks!

SLIM. Look. How 'bout one o' you fellers goin' along with me an' helpin' out for a few days? You could slaughter the veals. How about you, Tex?

TEX. No thanks, Slim. I like it too good here.

STUB. Me too.

FRISCO. You better hire somebody in Jackson.

SLIM. I . . . I'd feel better if somebody was to come along. I . . . [*Clutching at a straw.*] Bonnie—I *might* be able to come back before six weeks . . .

BONNIE. Thet'd be fine, Slim.

SLIM. Yeah. Sure I could. Maybe *three* weeks. Or even two. [*He kisses her, starts out, sadly, very lonesome.*] Sure none o' you fellers wanta come with me?

TEX. Dead sure.

FRISCO. You're the head butcher now, Slim.

STUB. You're *it*.

SLIM. Yeah. I am, ain't I? Well . . . thanks for cheerin' me up. [*He starts to shuffle out at left.*]

TEX. [*Softly.*] He sure looks peaked. [*He strums the guitar very quietly.*]

SLIM. [*As he is almost out of sight, he suddenly turns, calls, loudly.*] Mr. Lash!

LASH. [*Offstage, very gruffly.*] What!

SLIM. I'm a-goin' now. G'bye again!

LASH. [*He appears in the doorway in nightshirt and slippers, looking mad; he sticks his head out the door.*] Good-bye!

[LASH *slams the screen door, stamps angrily inside.*]

SLIM. [*Again starting his miserable shuffle off at left. Suddenly he turns back again, calls.*] G'bye, Bonnie . . . Don't forget to write three times a day!

BONNIE. G'bye, Slim. I won't.

FRISCO. Slim, don't you worry none 'bout Bonnie. We'll take care of 'er for you.

STUB. Yeah. We'll see she don't get lonesome. Take 'er to all the dances and such.

SLIM. [*He is surprised and somewhat alarmed.*] Oh . . . *will* ya?

TEX. [*Comfortingly.*] *Sure.*

FRISCO. Glad to. Thet's one worry off your mind. Don't give it another thought.

STUB. We'll take turns.

SLIM. [*Very dubious about it all.*] Well . . . uh . . . look, fellers—maybe you better not keep 'er out too late. She looks sorta puny-like lately. Better bring 'er home pretty early. 'Fore dark, anyhow.

TEX. [*In a hoarse whisper to* STUB.] What makes 'im look so sad? I better play some more. I jest remembered another verse to thet there song. [*Softly strumming the guitar, he sings.*]

> They said as she was dying,[4]
> She breathed her sweetheart's name,

[*The others join in the next line, softly and lugubriously.*]

[4] From the song "Cowboy Jack."

> And asked them with her last breath
> To tell him when he came:

FRISCO. [*Pointedly.*] G'bye, Slim. You better hurry.
SLIM. Yeah.
[*He wipes his eyes, blows his nose, waves feebly at* BONNIE,
and starts out. The others sadly finish the song.]
TEX, STUB AND FRISCO.

> Your sweetheart waits for you, Jack,
> Your sweetheart waits for you-u-u . . .

[*They trail off into silence. There is a pause, then . . .*]
TEX. Thet boy done forgot 'is cake again!
FRISCO. Might's well eat it ourself now. He's gone. Boss'll go
on a awful tear if we call 'im back any more.
TEX. I'm sick an' tired o' sayin' g'bye to 'im anyhow.
STUB. [*With a sigh.*] Sad night, ain't it?[5]
TEX. [*Suddenly he starts to play and sing, loudly, gayly and
violently.*]

> I started on the trail October twenty-third,[6]
> I started on the trail with the 2U herd . . .
> Singin' ki-yi-yippi-yippi-yi-yippi-yay!
> Singin' ki-yi-yippi-yippi-yay!

[FRISCO, STUB *and* TEX, *eating cake, and feeling better because of the cheerful music, begin to sing.* BONNIE *still gazes
off left after* SLIM.]
FRISCO, TEX AND STUB. [*Loud and cheerful.*]

> It's cloudy in the west, a-lookin' like rain,
> And my danged old slicker's in the wagon again,
> Singin' ki-yi-yippi-yippi-yi-yippi-yay!
> Singin' ki-yi-yippi-yippi-yay!

[FRISCO *begins to stamp around in an awkward attempt at
dancing.*]
FRISCO, TEX AND STUB.

[5] In staging the play, this may be a good place for additional folk music
and folk dancing. See production notes.
[6] From "The Chisholm Trail."

My slicker's in the wagon and I'm gettin' mighty cold,
   And these long-eared sons-o'-guns are gettin' hard to hold.
Singin' ki-yi-yippi-yippi-yi-yippi-yay!
Singin' ki-yi-yippi-yippi-yay!

FRISCO. [*Offers his hand to* BONNIE, *inviting her to dance. Silently she shakes her head.*] Aw . . . come on!

    Oh, it's bacon and beans most every day,
    I'd as soon be a-eatin' prairie hay.
    Singin' ki-yi-yippi-yippi-yi-yippi-yay!
    Singin' ki-yi-yippi-yippi-yay!

[*Urged by* FRISCO, BONNIE *finally accepts and* FRISCO *dances with her gayly and boisterously, if awkwardly.*]

    I herded and I hollered and I done very well,
    Till the boss said, "Boys, just let 'em go . . ."

[*They suddenly stop in the middle of the line, as in the distance is heard a long-drawn-out, distant whistle of a locomotive. All stop dead-still, shocked.* TEX *speaks, lugubriously.*]

TEX. By golly, there's the train!

STUB. Slim's gone at last!

FRISCO. Maybe forever.

TEX. Ain't it *terrible?*

[SLIM *appears at left, carrying his coat, hat and necktie. He looks very bedraggled.*]

SLIM. Here I am! I'm back!

[BONNIE *hurries to him; he takes her in his arms. The others only look irritated.*]

FRISCO. *Again?*

SLIM. Yeah. Train's gone. Missed 'er a mile.

TEX. Oh.

SLIM. [*He is offended.*] You folks seemed to be havin' a awful good time—even with me gone.

BONNIE. We weren't, though. Not a bit.

SLIM. Well, I can leave *tomorra* night, anyhow.

TEX. Slim, I don't think I could stand another set o' farewells.

STUB. Me neither.

FRISCO. You better start out walkin', so's we can get it over with.

SLIM. [*Irritated.*] Say! You fellas stop tryin' to drive me offa this ranch! I got as much right here as you have! [*He suddenly thinks of something.*] Say! Bonnie, I better tell your father I missed the train. He'll be relieved to know I'm still here. [*He calls loudly.*] Mr. Lash!

[LASH *appears in the door.*]

LASH. Boy, I already *said* g'bye. *Twice.*

SLIM. Well—hello, then. [*Lamely.*] Train's gone.

LASH. [*Grimly.*] Son—you better make up your mind. Are you a-goin' or a-stayin'?

SLIM. I—well, Mr. Lash . . . if it's all the same to you—I—well . . . [*Suddenly he bursts out.*] I . . . *doggone* it! I think I'll *stay!*

FRISCO. You might's well go. You give us all this here stuff an' we're a-gonna keep it.

SLIM. No sir! I ain't gonna budge one step offa this here ranch!

BONNIE. [*Happily.*] Oh, Slim!

SLIM. [*To* LASH.] If—if I can have my job back . . . ?

LASH. Well, I don't want any more o' this shilly-shallyin'. If you're gonna stay, you an' Bonnie better get married right off. You can move out to the bunkhouse an' set up housekeepin'.

SLIM. Well—gosh. I don't know about thet, Mr. Lash.

LASH. You can buy you some steers with that butcher shop money—and I'll give you some range land to feed 'em on.

SLIM. I don't know. I *still* don't amount to much . . . Bonnie —*would* you—even if I prob'ly won't ever be a alderman now?

BONNIE. O' *course!* That's what I wanted all the time!

SLIM. Ya *did?* Well, why didn't you say so? [*He takes her in his arms.*]

STUB. Golly! Weddin's always make me sad! Play some more, Tex.

[TEX *bursts forth with the "2U Trail" once more, loudly and gayly.* SLIM *grabs* BONNIE *around the waist, dances with her, stamping around happily, holding her tight.*]

LASH. Frisco, you better hightail down an' get old man Houston at the Diamond O Ranch. He used to be a preacher. He can marry 'em. If he ain't lost 'is Bible. [TEX *plays louder.* STUB, BONNIE *and* SLIM *dance and stamp their feet.* LASH *shouts to make himself heard above the music.*] And tell 'im to hurry up so's we can all get some sleep!

[*The music is very loud and gay now.* SLIM *happily hugs* BONNIE *as . . .*]

[*The Curtain Falls*]

UNDERSTANDING AND APPRECIATING THE PLAY

1. What characteristics of a folk play does *Goodbye to the Lazy K* have?

2. Is the play a comedy or a farce? Explain.

3. Do you think Slim would have succeeded as a butcher? How realistic was he in his ambition to become a butcher?

4. Why were the other cowboys so eager to have Slim leave?

5. Frisco asks, "Nothin' like singin' to cheer people up when they're goin' away, is there, Slim?" Slim replies, "Sure isn't. That's a mighty cheerful song." What is ironic in both the question and the reply?

6. As soon as it appears that Slim has gone for good, why does Tex launch vigorously into the happy, spirited "2U Trail" song?

7. How good a play is it? Why did you like or dislike it?

VOCABULARY BUILDING

Explain the meanings of the following groups of words: a man of middle age, *ruddy;* an *amiable* cowboy; They wave *somberly; apropos* of nothing; speaks *lugubriously;* somewhat *morosely;* looks very *bedraggled.*

Incidentally, for a humorous play, doesn't this one have a lot of synonyms for *sadly* or *gloomily?*

THINGS TO DO

1. "There is a commonplace in the theater that an author deals most successfully with the land and people he knows best," wrote Samuel Selden when he was Director of the Carolina Playmakers. Write a scenario or plot summary of a play about a place and about people you know best. You may want to develop your scenario or plot summary into a dramatization.

2. Theme topics: My Family, My Best Friend, My Favorite Sport (or Pastime), After High School—What? My Ambition, A Job I Have Had.

3. Write a theme or give a floor talk on someone you have known or read about who made a wise or courageous decision.

4. Write a theme on an important decision (or on important decisions) which you have had to make.

5. Report to your class on an interesting bit of local history or on a fascinating legend of your locality which might form the basis for a play or story.

6. Write a character study of a neighborhood personality—perhaps the town gossip, the town drunk, the corner druggist, the teller of tall tales, etc. You may wish to develop your character study in the form of a dialogue.

7. Make a miniature stage setting of a folk play which you have read or which you may plan to write.

8. The poems of Eugene Field, James Whitcomb Riley, and T. A. Daly offer fine opportunities for practice in speaking dialects. Find one that you like and prepare to read it before the class.

PRODUCTION NOTES

Don't worry unduly about the porch. You may do without one, in fact, by merely having a door leading into the kitchen; or you may follow the description of the stage setting and construct a small, low porch—possibly with only one step to take you into the kitchen. If there is a skilled carpenter in your technical crew, you may wish to obtain multi-level variety by having him and his assistants construct a fairly large and high porch. But it is a moot point whether you should undertake such major construction for a short play.

You're fortunate if you have a slender actor with a flair for comic portrayal to play the part of Slim Williams. If your best comic actor does not happen to be streamlined, use him and give him a name other than Slim.

Since the script allows insufficient time for Slim to change costumes, Mr. Lash and Bonnie have to pace themselves slowly in the little scene between them, with one of them possibly also singing a snatch or two of a song as if to himself. Furthermore, someone must be assigned to help Slim offstage to effect the quick change of costume and to gather up all the "gift" props which he brings on stage at his next entrance.

As long as he can sing passably well, Tex need not be a guitarist. Someone else may accompany him on a harmonica or guitar.

In the order in which they appear in the script, the three songs in the play are, "Cowboy Jack," "The Curtains of Night," and "The Chisholm Trail." One source in which all three may be found is the pamphlet *Western Heart Throbs,* published by Bob Miller, Inc., 1619 Broadway, New York City. The songs appear in various collections of cowboy and folk songs, however. You may, of course, want to replace these songs with those you prefer or find more readily available.

When Mr. Lash appears in his nightshirt and slippers, you will get additional laughs if the nightshirt is dyed a bright fireman's red and if he wears a matching red nightcap. In his curtain-closing lines, Mr. Lash has to shout above the din of singing and dancing, building up to "And tell 'im to hurry up so's we can all get some sleep!"

The play may be enriched with additional folk or "show" music and with folk dancing. A good spot for this entertainment is after Stub's line "Sad night, ain't it?" which follows Tex's "I'm sick an' tired o' sayin' g'bye to 'im anyhow." Cowboys and cowgirls from the Diamond O Ranch may then be heard approaching, possibly singing. A bit of additional dialogue and business, like the following, may then be inserted:

Tex: 'Taint so sad any more, boys. It's the bunch from the Diamond O Ranch!

　　[Enter Diamond O's; they exchange hearty greetings with the Lazy K's.]

Diamond O Cowboy or Cowgirl: What are you boys and Bonnie so sad about?

Tex: Slim's gone and we're kinda glum about it.

Diamond O: Gwan, you wolves! Y'oughta be glad Slim's gone! Gives you a chance with Bonnie now.

Second Diamond O: What say we hit it up a bit?

　　[Chorus of "Sure thing!" "You bet!" "Let's get going!"]

The entertainers then launch into the songs and dances. This part ends with the script's being picked up by Tex's singing "The Chisholm Trail" or another gay song, in the course of which he is joined by Frisco and Stub or others. During the song, there is the dance business between Frisco, or another cowboy, and Bonnie. The play is then completed according to the script.

MORE GOOD ONE-ACT FOLK PLAYS

The American Scene. Edited by Barrett H. Clark and Kenyon Nicholson. [Appleton-Century] An unusually appealing collection of one-act plays dealing with various phases of American life.

Carolina Folk Plays. Edited by Frederick H. Koch. [Holt] Written over a period of two decades by students in playwriting classes at the University of North Carolina, these volumes of short plays reveal the remarkable development of folk drama that took place under the inspiring leadership of the late Professor Frederick H. Koch.

Crick Bottom Plays. E. P. Conkle. [French] Five Midwestern sketches, which include the justly popular *Sparkin'*, *Minnie Field*, and *'Lection.*

The Happy Journey. Thornton Wilder. [French] In this charming and amusing play about a typical American family going on an auto trip, Thornton Wilder has captured a good deal of the spirit and utilized many of the devices of his successful full-length play *Our Town.*

Jephthah's Daughter. Elma Ehrlich Levinger. [French] Splendid dramatization of the tragic Bible story of Jephthah and his daughter.

A Marriage Proposal. Anton Chekhov. [French] Authentic folk play of old Russia, written in the merry farcical spirit that characterizes *The Boor.*

Mexican Folk Plays. Josefina Niggli. [Holt] An excellent collection for reading and staging.

Money. Michael Gold. [French] This is at once an exciting drama and a serious study of immigrant life in the New York slums.

Out of the South. Paul Green. [Harper] A collection of the plays (one-act and full length) of Paul Green, which he himself considers most representative of his work. Some of the finest plays in our dramatic literature are in the volume.

Plays of the American West. Robert Finch. [Chilton] Fifteen plays of the American Northwest by the author of *Goodbye to the Lazy K.*

Seven Short Plays. Lady Gregory. [Putnam] The best of Lady Gregory's Irish folk plays, including the very popular *Spreading the News.*

This Bull Ate Nutmeg. Josefina Niggli. [French] A delightful Mexican folk comedy by the author of *The Ring of General Macías.* The staging may be enriched by the addition of Latin-American songs and dances.

FULL-LENGTH PLAYS

A Bell for Adano, Paul Osborn [Dramatists Play Service]; *The Cradle Song,* G. Martinez-Sierra [French]; *The Crucible,* Arthur Miller [Dramatists Play Service]; *The Cherry Orchard,* Anton Chekhov [Brentano's]; *Green Grow the Lilacs,* Lynn Riggs [French]; *High Tor,* Maxwell Anderson [Dramatists Play Service]; *The Playboy of the Western World,* J. M. Synge [French]; *A Raisin in the Sun,* Lorraine Hansberry [French].

Fantasy: The Realm of the Unreal

A FANTASY is a play in which the action is far removed from reality, and lies definitely in the realm of make-believe. In such a play, things happen that have no scientific or realistic explanation. If the play contains supernatural characters or events, it is a fantasy. (It may, of course, be also tragedy or comedy, or any other type of play.)

One reason for writing fantasies is the simple desire to entertain. The dramatist may wish to appeal to the love of the fantastic that is so strong in all of us. The person who is most fond of dramatic entertainment of this nature is the one who wants "to get away from it all"—to find or to create a world more to his liking than his own world of sorrow, evil, and defeat. We call him the escapist. In times of war and great crisis the light, whimsical variety of fantasy has its greatest vogue.

The other principal reason for a dramatist's turning to fantasy is far different from the desire to escape. The playwright may wish to present an idea—to dramatize a theme—which he feels he can best emphasize by a non-realistic, supernatural treatment. In the full-length play *On Borrowed Time,* for example, Paul Osborn employs fantasy to inquire into the nature of death and the hereafter.

The Devil and Daniel Webster *

STEPHEN VINCENT BENÉT

To most of us, Daniel Webster is an orator, with one hand stuck in the bosom of his frock coat. But Stephen Vincent Benét discovered another Webster, one "whose legend lingers still in the rocks of New England—the great neighbor, the bountiful farmer, the matchless shot and fisherman, with his shotgun, 'Wilmot Proviso,' and his fishing rod, 'Old Killall.' "

Mr. Benét was fascinated by this conception of Daniel Webster as a Yankee superman, whose great ram Goliath could butt his way through a stone wall. "What would happen," he wondered, "if a man like that ever came to grips with the devil—and not an imported devil, either, but a genuine home-grown product, Mr. Scratch himself?" The result was that Mr. Benét brought them face to face in a famous short story. That story was made into an opera, then into a straight play, which you are about to read, and finally into a motion picture.

If you will use your imagination to see the two formidable antagonists, to develop a keen sympathy for Mary and Jabez Stone, to thrill with horror at the appearance of the miser's lost soul, to shudder at the awful jury of fiends and the inflexible Judge, you will be in the right mood for the smashing climax of the trial scene.

CHARACTERS

JABEZ STONE	JUSTICE HATHORNE'S CLERK
MARY STONE	KING PHILIP
DANIEL WEBSTER	TEACH
MR. SCRATCH	WALTER BUTLER
THE FIDDLER	SIMON GIRTY
JUSTICE HATHORNE	DALE

Men and Women of Cross Corners, New Hampshire

SCENE: JABEZ STONE's *farmhouse*
TIME: 1841

The SETTING *is the main room of a New Hampshire farmhouse in 1841, a big comfortable room that hasn't yet developed the stuffiness of a front parlor. A door, right, leads to the kitchen— a door, left, to the outside. There is a fireplace, right. Windows, in center, show a glimpse of summer landscape. Most of the furniture has been cleared away for the dance which follows the wedding of* JABEZ *and* MARY STONE, *but there is a settle or bench by the fireplace, a table, left, with some wedding presents upon it, at least three chairs by the table, and a cider barrel on which the* FIDDLER *sits, in front of the table. Near the table, against the side wall, there is a cupboard where there are glasses and a jug. There is a clock. (See Note A, p. 155, for production hints.) A country wedding has been in progress—the wedding of* JABEZ *and* MARY STONE. *He is a husky young farmer, around twenty-eight or thirty. The bride is in her early twenties. He is dressed in stiff store clothes, but not ridiculously—they are of good quality and he looks important. The bride is in a simple white or cream wedding dress and may carry a small, stiff bouquet of country flowers.*

Now the wedding is over and the guests are dancing. The FIDDLER *is perched on the cider barrel. He plays and calls square- dance figures. The guests include the recognizable types of a small New England town: doctor, lawyer, storekeeper, old maid, schoolteacher, farmer, etc. There is an air of prosperity and hearty country mirth about the whole affair.*

At rise, JABEZ *and* MARY *are up left center, receiving the con- gratulations of a few last guests, who talk to them and pass on to the dance. The others are dancing. There is a buzz of conver- sation that follows the tune of the dance music.*

FIRST WOMAN. Right nice wedding.
FIRST MAN. Handsome couple.
SECOND WOMAN. [*Passing through* CROWD *with dish of oyster stew.*] Oysters for supper!

SECOND MAN. [*Passing cake.*] And layer cake—layer cake—

AN OLD MAN. [*Hobbling toward cider barrel.*] Makes me feel young again! Oh, by jingo!

AN OLD WOMAN. [*Pursuing him.*] Henry, Henry, you've been drinking cider!

FIDDLER. Set to your partners! Dosy-do!

WOMEN. Mary and Jabez.

MEN. Jabez and Mary.

A WOMAN. Where's the State Senator?

A MAN. Where's the lucky bride?

[*With cries of "Mary—Jabez—strike it up, fiddler—make room for the bride and groom," the* CROWD *drags* MARY *and* JABEZ, *pleased but embarrassed, into the center of the room and* MARY *and* JABEZ *do a little solo dance, while the* CROWD *claps, applauds and makes various remarks.*]

A MAN. Handsome steppers!

A WOMAN. She's pretty as a picture.

A SECOND MAN. Cut your pigeon-wing, Jabez!

THE OLD MAN. Young again, young again, that's the way I feel! [*He tries to cut a pigeon-wing himself.*]

THE OLD WOMAN. Henry, Henry, careful of your rheumatiz!

A THIRD WOMAN. Makes me feel all teary—seeing them so happy.

[*The solo dance ends, the music stops for a moment.*]

THE OLD MAN. [*Gossiping to a neighbor.*] Wonder where he got it all—Stones was always poor.

HIS NEIGHBOR. Ain't poor now—makes you wonder just a mite.

A THIRD MAN. Don't begrudge it to him—but I wonder where he got it.

THE OLD MAN. [*Starting to whisper.*] Let me tell you something—

THE OLD WOMAN. [*Quickly.*] Henry, Henry, don't you start to gossip. [*She drags him away.*]

FIDDLER. [*Cutting in.*] Set to your partners! Scratch for corn! [*The dance resumes, but as it does so, the* CROWD *chants back and forth.*]

WOMEN. Gossip's got a sharp tooth.

MEN. Gossip's got a mean tooth.

WOMEN. She's a lucky woman. They're a lucky pair.

MEN. That's true as gospel. But I wonder where he got it.

WOMEN. Money, land and riches.

MEN. Just came out of nowhere.

WOMEN AND MEN. [*Together.*] Wonder where he got it all.— But that's his business.

FIDDLER. Left and right—grand chain!

[*The dance rises to a pitch of ecstasy with the final figure— the fiddle squeaks and stops. The dancers mop their brows.*]

FIRST MAN. Whew! Ain't danced like that since I was knee-high to a grasshopper!

SECOND MAN. Play us "The Portland Fancy," fiddler!

THIRD MAN. No, wait a minute, neighbor. Let's hear from the happy pair! Hey, Jabez!

FOURTH MAN. Let's hear from the State Senator!

[*They crowd around* JABEZ *and push him up on the settle.*]

OLD MAN. Might as well. It's the last time he'll have the last word!

OLD WOMAN. Now, Henry Banks, you ought to be ashamed of yourself!

OLD MAN. Told you so, Jabez!

THE CROWD. Speech!

JABEZ. [*Embarrassed.*] Neighbors—friends—I'm not much of a speaker—spite of your 'lecting me to State Senate—

THE CROWD. That's the ticket, Jabez. Smart man, Jabez. I voted for ye. Go ahead, Senator, you're doing fine.

JABEZ. But we're certainly glad to have you here—me and Mary. And we want to thank you for coming and—

A VOICE. Vote the Whig ticket!

ANOTHER VOICE. Hooray for Daniel Webster!

JABEZ. And I'm glad Hi Foster said that, for those are my sentiments, too. Mr. Webster has promised to honor us with his presence here tonight.

THE CROWD. Hurray for Dan'l! Hurray for the greatest man in the U.S.!

JABEZ. And when he comes, I know we'll give him a real New Hampshire welcome.

THE CROWD. Sure we will—Webster forever—and down with Henry Clay!

JABEZ. And meanwhile—well, there's Mary and me [*Takes her hand.*]—and, if you folks don't have a good time, well, we won't feel right about getting married at all. Because I know I've been lucky—and I hope she feels that way, too. And, well, we're going to be happy or bust a trace! [*He wipes his brow to terrific applause. He and* MARY *look at each other.*]

A WOMAN. [*In kitchen doorway.*] Come and get the cider, folks!

[*The* CROWD *begins to drift away—a few to the kitchen—a few toward the door that leads to the outside. They furnish a shifting background to the next little scene, where* MARY *and* JABEZ *are left alone by the fireplace.*]

JABEZ. Mary.

MARY. Mr. Stone.

JABEZ. Mary.

MARY. My husband.

JABEZ. That's a big word, husband.

MARY. It's a good word.

JABEZ. Are you happy, Mary?

MARY. Yes. So happy, I'm afraid.

JABEZ. Afraid?

MARY. I suppose it happens to every girl—just for a minute. It's like spring turning into summer. You want it to be summer. But the spring was sweet. [*Dismissing the mood.*] I'm sorry. Forgive me. It just came and went, like something cold. As if we'd been too lucky.

JABEZ. We can't be too lucky, Mary. Not you and me.

MARY. [*Rather mischievously.*] If you say so, Mr. Stone. But you don't even know what sort of housekeeper I am. And Aunt Hepsy says—

JABEZ. Bother your Aunt Hepsy! There's just you and me and that's all that matters in the world.

MARY. And you don't know something else—

JABEZ. What's that?

MARY. How proud I am of you. Ever since I was a little girl. Ever since you carried my books. Oh, I'm sorry for women who can't be proud of their men. It must be a lonely feeling.

JABEZ. [*Uncomfortably.*] A man can't always be proud of everything, Mary. There's some things a man does, or might do —when he has to make his way.

MARY. [*Laughing.*] I know—terrible things—like being the best farmer in the county and the best State Senator—

JABEZ. [*Quietly.*] And a few things, besides. But you remember one thing, Mary, whatever happens. It was all for you. And nothing's going to happen. Because he hasn't come yet— and he would have come if it was wrong.

MARY. But it's wonderful to have Mr. Webster come to us.

JABEZ. I wasn't thinking about Mr. Webster. [*He takes both her hands.*] Mary, I've got something to tell you. I should have told you before, but I couldn't seem to bear it. Only, now that it's all right, I can. Ten years ago—

A VOICE. [*From off stage.*] Dan'l! Dan'l Webster!

[JABEZ *drops* MARY's *hands and looks around. The* CROWD *begins to mill and gather toward the door. Others rush in from the kitchen.*]

ANOTHER VOICE. Black Dan'l! He's come!

ANOTHER VOICE. Three cheers for the greatest man in the U.S.!

ANOTHER VOICE. Three cheers for Daniel Webster!

[*And, to the cheering and applause of the* CROWD, DANIEL WEBSTER *enters and stands for a moment upstage, in the familiar pose, his head thrown back, his attitude leonine. He stops the cheering of the* CROWD *with a gesture.*]

WEBSTER. Neighbors—old friends—it does me good to hear you. But don't cheer me—I'm not running for President this summer. [*A laugh from the* CROWD.] I'm here on a better errand —to pay my humble respects to a most charming lady and her very fortunate spouse.

[*There is the twang of a fiddle-string breaking.*]

FIDDLER. 'Tarnation! Busted a string!

A VOICE. He's always bustin' strings.

[WEBSTER *blinks at the interruption but goes on.*]

WEBSTER. We're proud of State Senator Stone in these parts —we know what he's done. Ten years ago he started out with a patch of land that was mostly rocks and mortgages and now— well, you've only to look around you. I don't know that I've ever seen a likelier farm, not even at Marshfield—and I hope, before I die, I'll have the privilege of shaking his hand as Governor of this State. I don't know how he's done it—I couldn't have done it myself. But I know this—Jabez Stone wears no man's collar. [*At this statement there is a discordant squeak from the fiddle and* JABEZ *looks embarrassed.* WEBSTER *knits his brows.*] And what's more, if I know Jabez, he never will. But I didn't come here to talk politics—I came to kiss the bride. [*He does so amid great applause. He shakes hands with* JABEZ.] Congratulations, Stone—you're a lucky man. And now, if our friend in the corner will give us a tune on his fiddle—

[*The* CROWD *presses forward to meet the great man. He shakes hands with several.*]

A MAN. Remember me, Mr. Webster? Saw ye up at the State House at Concord.

ANOTHER MAN. Glad to see ye, Mr. Webster. I voted for ye ten times.

[WEBSTER *receives their homage politely, but his mind is still on music.*]

WEBSTER. [*A trifle irritated.*] I said, if our friend in the corner would give us a tune on his fiddle—

FIDDLER. [*Passionately, flinging the fiddle down.*] Hell's delight—excuse me, Mr. Webster. But the very devil's got into that fiddle of mine. She was doing all right up to just a minute ago. But now I've tuned her and tuned her and she won't play a note I want.

[*And, at this point,* MR. SCRATCH *makes his appearance. He has entered, unobserved, and mixed with the* CROWD *while all eyes were upon* DANIEL WEBSTER. *He is, of course, the devil—a New England devil, dressed like a rather shabby attorney but with something just a little wrong in clothes and appearance. For one thing, he wears black gloves on his hands. He carries a large black tin box, like a botanist's collecting-box, under one arm. Now he slips through the* CROWD *and taps the* FIDDLER *on the shoulder.*]

SCRATCH. [*Insinuatingly.*] Maybe you need some rosin on your bow, fiddler?

FIDDLER. Maybe I do and maybe I don't. [*Turns and confronts the stranger.*] But who are you? I don't remember seeing you before.

SCRATCH. Oh, I'm just a friend—a humble friend of the bridegroom's. [*He walks toward* JABEZ. *Apologetically.*] I'm afraid I came in the wrong way, Mr. Stone. You've improved the place so much since I last saw it that I hardly knew the front door. But, I assure you, I came as fast as I could.

JABEZ. [*Obviously shocked.*] It—it doesn't matter. [*With a great effort.*] Mary—Mr. Webster—this is a—a friend of mine from Boston—a legal friend. I didn't expect him today but—

SCRATCH. Oh, my dear Mr. Stone—an occasion like this—I wouldn't miss it for the world. [*He bows.*] Charmed, Mrs. Stone. Delighted, Mr. Webster. But—don't let me break up the merriment of the meeting. [*He turns back toward the table and the* FIDDLER.]

FIDDLER. [*With a grudge, to* SCRATCH.] Boston lawyer, eh?

SCRATCH. You might call me that.

FIDDLER. [*Tapping the tin box with his bow.*] And what have you got in that big tin box of yours? Law-papers?

SCRATCH. Oh—curiosities for the most part. I'm a collector, too.

FIDDLER. Don't hold much with Boston curiosities, myself. And you know about fiddling too, do you? Know all about it?

SCRATCH. Oh— [*A deprecatory shrug.*]

FIDDLER. Don't shrug your shoulders at me—I ain't no Frenchman. Telling me I needed more rosin!

MARY. [*Trying to stop the quarrel.*] Isaac—please—

FIDDLER. Sorry, Mary—Mrs. Stone. But I been playing the fiddle at Cross Corners weddings for twenty-five years. And now here comes a stranger from Boston and tells me I need more rosin!

SCRATCH. But, my good friend—

FIDDLER. Rosin indeed! Here—play it yourself then and see what you can make of it! [*He thrusts the fiddle at* SCRATCH. *The latter stiffens, slowly lays his black collecting-box on the table, and takes the fiddle.*]

SCRATCH. [*With feigned embarrassment.*] But really, I— [*He bows toward* JABEZ.] Shall I—Mr. Senator?

[JABEZ *makes a helpless gesture of assent.*]

MARY. [*To* JABEZ.] Mr. Stone—Mr. Stone—are you ill?

JABEZ. No—no—but I feel—it's hot—

WEBSTER. [*Chuckling.*] Don't you fret, Mrs. Stone. I've got the right medicine for him. [*He pulls a flask from his pocket.*] Ten-year-old Medford, Stone—I buy it by the keg down at Marshfield. Here— [*He tries to give some of the rum to* JABEZ.]

JABEZ. No—[*He turns.*]—Mary—Mr. Webster— [*But he cannot explain. With a burst.*] Oh, let him play—let him play! Don't you see he's bound to? Don't you see there's nothing we can do?

[*A rustle of discomfort among the guests.* SCRATCH *draws the bow across the fiddle in a horrible discord.*]

FIDDLER. [*Triumphantly.*] I told you so, stranger. The devil's in that fiddle!

SCRATCH. I'm afraid it needs special tuning. [*Draws the bow in a second discord.*] There—that's better. [*Grinning.*] And now for this happy—this very happy occasion—in tribute to the bride and groom—I'll play something appropriate—a song of young love—

MARY. Oh, Jabez—Mr. Webster—stop him! Do you see his hands? He's playing with gloves on his hands.

[WEBSTER *starts forward, but, even as he does so,* SCRATCH *begins to play and all freeze as* SCRATCH *goes on with the extremely inappropriate song that follows. At first his manner*]

is oily and mocking—it is not till he reaches the line "The devil took the words away" that he really becomes terrifying and the CROWD *starts to be afraid.*]
SCRATCH. [*Accompanying himself fantastically.*]

> Young William was a thriving boy.
> (Listen to my doleful tale.)
> Young Mary Clark was all his joy.
> (Listen to my doleful tale.)
>
> He swore he'd love her all his life.
> She swore she'd be his loving wife.
>
> But William found a gambler's den
> And drank with livery-stable men.
>
> He played the cards, he played the dice.
> He would not listen to advice,
>
> And when in church he tried to pray,
> The devil took the words away.

[SCRATCH, *still playing, starts to march across the stage.*]

> The devil got him by the toe,
> And so, alas, he had to go.
>
> "Young Mary Clark, young Mary Clark,
> I now must go into the dark."

[*These last two verses have been directed at* JABEZ. SCRATCH *continues, now turning on* MARY.]

> Young Mary lay upon her bed.
> "Alas my Will-i-am is dead."
>
> He came to her a bleeding ghost—

[*He rushes at* MARY, *but* WEBSTER *stands between them.*]
WEBSTER. Stop! Stop! You miserable wretch—can't you see

that you're frightening Mrs. Stone? [*He wrenches the fiddle out of* SCRATCH's *hands and tosses it aside.*] And now, sir—out of this house!

SCRATCH. [*Facing him.*] You're a bold man, Mr. Webster. Too bold for your own good, perhaps. And anyhow, it wasn't my fiddle. It belonged to— [*He wheels and sees the* FIDDLER *tampering with the collecting-box that has been left on the table.*] Idiot! What are you doing with my collecting-box? [*He rushes for the* FIDDLER *and chases him round the table, but the* FIDDLER *is just one jump ahead.*]

FIDDLER. Boston lawyer, eh? Well, I don't think so. I think you've got something in that box of yours you're afraid to show. And, by jingo— [*He throws open the lid of the box. The lights wink and there is a clap of thunder. All eyes stare upward. Something has flown out of the box. But what?* (*See Note B for production hints.*) FIDDLER, *with relief.*] Why, 'tain't nothing but a moth.

MARY. A white moth—a flying thing.

WEBSTER. A common moth—*telea polyphemus*—

THE CROWD. A moth—just a moth—a moth—

FIDDLER. [*Terrified.*] But it ain't. It ain't no common moth! I seen it! And it's got a death's-head on it! [*He strikes at the invisible object with his bow to drive it away.*]

VOICE OF THE MOTH. Help me, neighbors! Help me! (*See Note C for production hints.*)

WEBSTER. What's that? It wails like a lost soul.

MARY. A lost soul.

THE CROWD. A lost soul—lost—in darkness—in the darkness.

VOICE OF THE MOTH. Help me, neighbors!

FIDDLER. It sounds like Miser Stevens.

JABEZ. Miser Stevens!

THE CROWD. The Miser—Miser Stevens—a lost soul—lost.

FIDDLER. [*Frantically.*] It sounds like Miser Stevens—and you had him in your box. But it can't be. He ain't dead.

JABEZ. He ain't dead—I tell you he ain't dead! He was just as spry and mean as a woodchuck, Tuesday.

THE CROWD. Miser Stevens—soul of Miser Stevens—but he ain't dead.

SCRATCH. [*Dominating them.*] Listen!

[*A bell off stage begins to toll a knell, slowly, solemnly.*]

MARY. The bell—the church bell—the bell that rang at my wedding.

WEBSTER. The church bell—the passing bell.

JABEZ. The funeral bell.

THE CROWD. The bell—the passing bell—Miser Stevens— dead.

VOICE OF THE MOTH. Help me, neighbors, help me! I sold my soul to the devil. I'm not the first or the last. Help me. Help Jabez Stone!

SCRATCH. Ah, would you! [*He catches the moth in his red bandanna, stuffs it back into his collecting-box, and shuts the lid with a snap.*]

VOICE OF THE MOTH. [*Fading.*] Lost—lost forever, forever. Lost, like Jabez Stone.

[*The CROWD turns on JABEZ. They read his secret in his face.*]

THE CROWD. Jabez Stone—Jabez Stone—answer us—answer us.

MARY. Tell them, dear—answer them—you are good—you are brave—you are innocent.

[*But the CROWD is all pointing hands and horrified eyes.*]

THE CROWD. Jabez Stone—Jabez Stone. Who's your friend in black, Jabez Stone? [*They point to SCRATCH.*]

WEBSTER. Answer them, Mr. State Senator.

THE CROWD. Jabez Stone—Jabez Stone. Where did you get your money, Jabez Stone?

[*SCRATCH grins and taps his collecting-box. JABEZ cannot speak.*]

JABEZ. I—I— [*He stops.*]

THE CROWD. Jabez Stone—Jabez Stone. What was the price you paid for it, Jabez Stone?

JABEZ. [*Looking around wildly.*] Help me, neighbors! Help me!

[*This cracks the built-up tension and sends the* CROWD *over the edge into fanaticism.*]

A WOMAN's VOICE. [*High and hysterical.*] He's sold his soul to the devil! [*She points to* JABEZ.]

OTHER VOICES. To the devil!

THE CROWD. He's sold his soul to the devil! The devil himself! The devil's playing the fiddle! The devil's come for his own!

JABEZ. [*Appealing.*] But, neighbors—I didn't know—I didn't mean—oh, help me!

THE CROWD. [*Inexorably.*] He's sold his soul to the devil!

SCRATCH. [*Grinning.*] To the devil!

THE CROWD. He's sold his soul to the devil! There's no help left for him, neighbors! Run, hide, hurry, before we're caught! He's a lost soul—Jabez Stone—he's the devil's own! Run, hide, hasten! [*They stream across the stage like a flurry of bats, the cannier picking up the wedding-presents they have given to take along with them.*]

[MR. SCRATCH *drives them out into the night, fiddle in hand, and follows them.* JABEZ *and* MARY *are left with* WEBSTER. JABEZ *has sunk into a chair, beaten, with his head in his hands.* MARY *is trying to comfort him.* WEBSTER *looks at them for a moment and shakes his head, sadly. As he crosses to exit to the porch, his hand drops for a moment on* JABEZ's *shoulder, but* JABEZ *makes no sign.* WEBSTER *exits.* JABEZ *lifts his head.*]

MARY. [*Comforting him.*] My dear—my dear—

JABEZ. I—it's all true, Mary. All true. You must hurry.

MARY. Hurry?

JABEZ. Hurry after them—back to the village—back to your folks. Mr. Webster will take you—you'll be safe with Mr. Webster. You see, it's all true and he'll be back in a minute. [*With a shudder.*] The other one. [*He groans.*] I've got until twelve o'clock. That's the contract. But there isn't much time.

MARY. Are you telling me to run away from you, Mr. Stone?

JABEZ. You don't understand, Mary. It's true.

MARY. We made some promises to each other. Maybe you've

forgotten them. But I haven't. I said, it's for better or worse. It's for better or worse. I said, in sickness or in health. Well, that covers the ground, Mr. Stone.

JABEZ. But, Mary, you must—I command you.

MARY. "For thy people shall be my people and thy God my God." [*Quietly.*] That was Ruth, in the Book. I always liked the name of Ruth—always liked the thought of her. I always thought—I'll call a child Ruth, some time. I guess that was just a girl's notion. [*She breaks.*] But, oh, Jabez—why?

JABEZ. It started years ago, Mary. I guess I was a youngster then—guess I must have been. A youngster with a lot of ambitions and no way in the world to get there. I wanted city clothes and a big white house—I wanted to be State Senator and have people look up to me. But all I got on the farm was a crop of stones. You could work all day and all night but that was all you got.

MARY. [*Softly.*] It was pretty—that hill-farm, Jabez. You could look all the way across the valley.

JABEZ. Pretty? It was fever and ague—it was stones and blight. If I had a horse, he got colic—if I planted garden truck, the woodchucks ate it. I'd lie awake nights and try to figure out a way to get somewhere—but there wasn't any way. And all the time you were growing up, in the town. I couldn't ask you to marry me and take you to a place like that.

MARY. Do you think it's the place makes the difference to a woman? I'd—I'd have kept your house. I'd have stroked the cat and fed the chickens and seen you wiped your shoes on the mat. I wouldn't have asked for more. Oh, Jabez—why didn't you tell me?

JABEZ. It happened before I could. Just an average day—you know—just an average day. But there was a mean east wind and a mean small rain. Well, I was plowing, and the share broke clean off on a rock where there hadn't been any rock the day before. I didn't have money for a new one—I didn't have money to get it mended. So I said it and I said loud, "I'll sell my soul for about two cents," I said. [*He stops.* MARY *stares at him.*] Well, that's all there is to it, I guess. He came along that afternoon—that fellow from Boston—and the dog looked at him and ran away. Well, I had to make it more than two cents, but he was agreeable to that. So I pricked my thumb with a pin and signed the paper. It felt hot when you touched it, that paper. I keep remembering that. [*He pauses.*] And it's all come true and he's kept his part of the bargain. I got the riches and I've married you. And, oh, God Almighty, what shall I do?

MARY. Let us run away! Let us creep and hide!

JABEZ. You can't run away from the devil—I've seen his horses. Miser Stevens tried to run away.

MARY. Let us pray—let us pray to the God of Mercy that He redeem us.

JABEZ. I can't pray, Mary. The words just burn in my heart.

MARY. I won't let you go! I won't! There must be someone who could help us. I'll get the judge and the squire—

JABEZ. Who'll take a case against old Scratch? Who'll face the devil himself and do him brown? There isn't a lawyer in the world who'd dare do that.

[WEBSTER *appears in the doorway.*]

WEBSTER. Good evening, neighbors. Did you say something about lawyers—

MARY. Mr. Webster!

JABEZ. Dan'l Webster! But I thought—

WEBSTER. You'll excuse me for leaving you for a moment. I was just taking a stroll on the porch, in the cool of the evening. Fine summer evening, too.

JABEZ. Well, it might be, I guess, but that kind of depends on the circumstances.

WEBSTER. H'm. Yes. I happened to overhear a little of your conversation. I gather you're in trouble, Neighbor Stone.

JABEZ. Sore trouble.

WEBSTER. [*Delicately.*] Sort of law case, I understand.

JABEZ. You might call it that, Mr. Webster. Kind of a mortgage case, in a way.

MARY. Oh, Jabez!

WEBSTER. Mortgage case. Well, I don't generally plead now, except before the Supreme Court, but this case of yours presents some very unusual features and I never deserted a neighbor in trouble yet. So, if I can be of any assistance—

MARY. Oh, Mr. Webster, will you help him?

JABEZ. It's a terrible lot to ask you. But—well, you see, there's Mary. And, if you could see your way to it—

WEBSTER. I will.

MARY. [*Weeping with relief.*] Oh, Mr. Webster!

WEBSTER. There, there, Mrs. Stone. After all, if two New Hampshire men aren't a match for the devil, we might as well give the country back to the Indians. When is he coming, Jabez?

JABEZ. Twelve o'clock. The time's getting late.

WEBSTER. Then I'd better refresh my memory. The—er—mortgage was for a definite term of years?

JABEZ. Ten years.

WEBSTER. And it falls due—?

JABEZ. Tonight. Oh, I can't see how I came to be such a fool!

WEBSTER. No use crying over spilt milk, Stone. We've got to get you out of it, now. But tell me one thing. Did you sign this precious document of your own free will?

JABEZ. Yes, it was my own free will. I can't deny that.

WEBSTER. H'm, that's a trifle unfortunate. But we'll see.

MARY. Oh, Mr. Webster, can you save him? Can you?

WEBSTER. I shall do my best, madam. That's all you can ever say till you see what the jury looks like.

MARY. But even you, Mr. Webster—oh, I know you're Secretary of State—I know you're a great man—I know you've done wonderful things. But it's different—fighting the devil!

WEBSTER. [*Towering.*] I've fought John C. Calhoun, madam. And I've fought Henry Clay. And, by the great shade of Andrew Jackson, I'd fight ten thousand devils to save a New Hampshire man!

JABEZ. You hear, Mary?

MARY. Yes. And I trust Mr. Webster. But—oh, there must be some way that I can help!

WEBSTER. There is one, madam, and a hard one. As Mr. Stone's counsel, I must formally request your withdrawal.

MARY. No.

WEBSTER. Madam, think for a moment. You cannot help Mr. Stone—since you are his wife, your testimony would be prejudiced. And frankly, madam, in a very few moments this is going to be no place for a lady.

MARY. But I can't—I can't leave him—I can't bear it!

JABEZ. You must go, Mary. You must.

WEBSTER. Pray, madam—you can help us with your prayers. Are the prayers of the innocent unavailing?

MARY. Oh, I'll pray—I'll pray. But a woman's more than a praying machine, whatever men think. And how do I know?

WEBSTER. Trust me, Mrs. Stone.

[MARY *turns to go, and, with one hand on* JABEZ's *shoulder, as she moves to the door, says the following prayer.*]

MARY.

Now may there be a blessing and a light betwixt thee and me, forever.
For, as Ruth unto Naomi, so do I cleave unto thee.
Set me as a seal upon thy heart, as a seal upon thine arm, for love is strong as death.
Many waters cannot quench love, neither can the floods drown it.
As Ruth unto Naomi, so do I cleave unto thee.
The Lord watch between thee and me when we are absent, one from the other.
Amen. Amen.

[*She goes out.*]

WEBSTER. Amen.

JABEZ. Thank you, Mr. Webster. She ought to go. But I couldn't have made her do it.

WEBSTER. Well, Stone—I know ladies—and I wouldn't be surprised if she's still got her ear to the keyhole. But she's best out of this night's business. How long have we got to wait?

JABEZ. [*Beginning to be terrified again.*] Not long—not long.

WEBSTER. Then I'll just get out the jug, with your permission, Stone. Somehow or other, waiting's wonderfully shorter with a jug. [*He crosses to the cupboard, gets out jug and glasses, pours himself a drink.*] Ten-year-old Medford. There's nothing like it.

I saw an inch-worm take a drop of it once and he stood right up on his hind legs and bit a bee. Come—try a nip.

JABEZ. There's no joy in it for me.

WEBSTER. Oh, come, man, come! Just because you've sold your soul to the devil, that needn't make you a teetotaller. [*He laughs and passes the jug to* JABEZ, *who tries to pour from it. But at that moment the clock whirs and begins to strike the three-quarters, and* JABEZ *spills the liquor.*]

JABEZ. Oh, God!

WEBSTER. Never mind—it's a nervous feeling, waiting for a trial to begin. I remember my first case—

JABEZ. 'Tain't that. [*He turns to* WEBSTER.] Mr. Webster— Mr. Webster—for God's sake harness your horses and get away from this place as fast as you can!

WEBSTER. [*Placidly.*] You've brought me a long way, neighbor, to tell me you don't like my company.

JABEZ. I've brought you the devil's own way. I can see it all, now. He's after both of us—him and his collecting-box! Well, he can have me, if he likes—I don't say I relish it but I made the bargain. But you're the whole United States! He can't get you, Mr. Webster—he mustn't get you!

WEBSTER. I'm obliged to you, Neighbor Stone. It's kindly thought of. But there's a jug on the table and a case in hand. And I never left a jug or a case half-finished in my life. [*There is a knock at the door.* JABEZ *gives a cry.*] Ah, I thought your clock was a trifle slow, Neighbor Stone. Come in!

[SCRATCH *enters from the night.*]

SCRATCH. Mr. Webster! This *is* a pleasure!

WEBSTER. Attorney of record for Jabez Stone. Might I ask your name?

SCRATCH. I've gone by a good many. Perhaps Scratch will do for the evening. I'm often called that in these regions. May I? [*He sits at the table and pours a drink from the jug. (See Note D for production hints.) The liquor steams as it pours into the glass while* JABEZ *watches, terrified.* SCRATCH *grins, toasting* WEBSTER *and* JABEZ *silently in the liquor. Then he becomes business-*

like. To WEBSTER.] And now I call upon you, as a law-abiding citizen, to assist me in taking possession of my property.

WEBSTER. Not so fast, Mr. Scratch. Produce your evidence, if you have it.

[SCRATCH *takes out a black pocketbook and examines papers.*]

SCRATCH. Slattery—Stanley—Stone. [*Takes out a deed.*] There, Mr. Webster. All open and aboveboard and in due and legal form. Our firm has its reputation to consider—we deal only in the one way.

WEBSTER. [*Taking deed and looking it over.*] H'm. This appears—I say, it appears—to be properly drawn. But, of course, we contest the signature. [*Tosses it back, contemptuously.*]

SCRATCH. [*Suddenly turning on* JABEZ *and shooting a finger at him.*] Is that your signature?

JABEZ. [*Wearily.*] You know very well it is.

WEBSTER. [*Angrily.*] Keep quiet, Stone. [*To* SCRATCH.] But that is a minor matter. This precious document isn't worth the paper it's written on. The law permits no traffic in human flesh.

SCRATCH. Oh, my dear Mr. Webster! Courts in every state in the Union have held that human flesh is property and recoverable. Read your Fugitive Slave Act. Or, shall I cite Brander versus McRae?

WEBSTER. But, in the case of the State of Maryland versus Four Barrels of Bourbon—

SCRATCH. That was overruled, as you know, sir. North Carolina versus Jenkins and Co.

WEBSTER. [*Unwillingly.*] You seem to have an excellent acquaintance with the law, sir.

SCRATCH. Sir, that is no fault of mine. Where I come from, we have always gotten the pick of the Bar.

WEBSTER. [*Changing his note, heartily.*] Well, come now, sir. There's no need to make hay and oats of a trifling matter when we're both sensible men. Surely we can settle this little difficulty out of court. My client is quite prepared to offer a compromise. [SCRATCH *smiles.*] A very substantial compromise. [SCRATCH *smiles more broadly, slowly shaking his head.*] Hang it, man, we offer ten thousand dollars! [Scratch *signs "No."*] Twenty thousand—thirty—name your figure! I'll raise it if I have to mortgage Marshfield!

Scratch. Quite useless, Mr. Webster. There is only one thing I want from you—the execution of my contract.

Webster. But this is absurd. Mr. Stone is now a State Senator. The property has greatly increased in value!

Scratch. The principle of *caveat emptor* [1] still holds, Mr. Webster. [*He yawns and looks at the clock.*] And now, if you have no further arguments to adduce—I'm rather pressed for time— [*He rises briskly as if to take* Jabez *into custody.*]

Webster. [*Thundering.*] Pressed or not, you shall not have this man. Mr. Stone is an American citizen and no American citizen may be forced into the service of a foreign prince. We fought England for that, in '12, and we'll fight for it again!

Scratch. Foreign? And who calls me a foreigner?

Webster. Well, I never yet heard of the dev—of your claiming American citizenship.

Scratch. And who with better right? When the first wrong was done to the first Indian, I was there. When the first slaver put out for the Congo, I stood on her deck. Am I not in your books and stories and beliefs, from the first settlements on? Am I not spoken of, still, in every church in New England? 'Tis true, the North claims me for a Southerner and the South for a Northerner, but I am neither. I am merely an honest American like yourself—and of the best descent—for, to tell the truth, Mr. Webster, though I don't like to boast of it, my name is older in the country than yours.

Webster. Aha! Then I stand on the Constitution! I demand a trial for my client!

Scratch. The case is hardly one for an ordinary jury—and indeed, the lateness of the hour—

Webster. Let it be any court you choose, so it is an American judge and an American jury. Let it be the quick or the dead, I'll abide the issue.

[1] *caveat emptor* = "let the buyer beware."

SCRATCH. The quick or the dead! You have said it! [*He points his finger at the place where the jury is to appear. There is a clap of thunder and a flash of light. The stage blacks out completely. All that can be seen is the face of* SCRATCH, *lit with a ghastly green light as he recites the invocation that summons the* JURY. *As, one by one, the important* JURYMEN *are mentioned, they appear. (See Note E for production hints.)*]

I summon the jury Mr. Webster demands.
From churchyard mould and gallows grave,
Brimstone pit and burning gulf,
I summon them!
Dastard, liar, scoundrel, knave,
I summon them! Appear!
There's Simon Girty, the renegade,
The haunter of the forest glade
Who joined with Indian and wolf
To hunt the pioneer.
The stains upon his hunting-shirt
Are not the blood of the deer.
There's Walter Butler, the loyalist,
Who carried a firebrand in his fist
Of massacre and shame.
King Philip's eye is wild and bright.
They slew him in the great Swamp Fight,
But still, with terror and affright,
The land recalls his name.
Blackbeard Teach, the pirate fell,
Smeet the strangler, hot from hell,
Dale, who broke men on the wheel,
Morton, of the tarnished steel,
I summon them, I summon them
From their tormented flame!
Quick or dead, quick or dead,
Broken heart and bitter head,
True Americans, each one,
Traitor and disloyal son,
Cankered earth and twisted tree,
Outcasts of eternity,
Twelve great sinners, tried and true,

For the work they are to do!
I summon them, I summon them!
Appear, appear, appear!

[*The* JURY *has now taken its place in the box*—WALTER BUT-
LER *in the place of foreman. They are eerily lit and so made
up as to suggest the unearthly. They sit stiffly in their box.
At first, when one moves, all move, in stylized gestures. It is
not till the end of* WEBSTER'S *speech that they begin to show
any trace of humanity. They speak rhythmically, and, at
first, in low, eerie voices.*]

JABEZ. [*Seeing them, horrified.*] A jury of the dead!

JURY. Of the dead!

JABEZ. A jury of the damned!

JURY. Of the damned!

SCRATCH. Are you content with the jury, Mr. Webster?

WEBSTER. Quite content. Though I miss General Arnold from
the company.

SCRATCH. Benedict Arnold is engaged upon other business. Ah,
you asked for a justice, I believe. [*He points his finger and* JUS-
TICE HATHORNE, *a tall, lean, terrifying Puritan, appears, followed
by his* CLERK.] Justice Hathorne is a jurist of experience. He pre-
sided at the Salem witch trials. There were others who repented
of the business later. But not he, not he!

HATHORNE. Repent of such notable wonders and undertak-
ings? Nay, hang them, hang them all! [*He takes his place on the
bench.*]

[*The* CLERK, *an ominous little man with clawlike hands, takes
his place. The room has now been transformed into a courtroom.*]

CLERK. [*In a gabble of ritual.*] Oyes, oyes, oyes. All ye who
have business with this honorable court of special session this
night, step forward!

HATHORNE. [*With gavel.*] Call the first case.

CLERK. The World, the Flesh, and the Devil versus Jabez
Stone.

HATHORNE. Who appears for the plaintiff?

SCRATCH. I, Your Honor.

HATHORNE. And for the defendant?

WEBSTER. I.

JURY. The case—the case—he'll have little luck with this case.

HATHORNE. The case will proceed.

WEBSTER. Your Honor, I move to dismiss this case on the grounds of improper jurisdiction.

HATHORNE. Motion denied.

WEBSTER. On the grounds of insufficient evidence.

HATHORNE. Motion denied.

JURY. Motion denied—denied. Motion denied.

WEBSTER. I will take an exception.

HATHORNE. There are no exceptions in this court.

JURY. No exceptions—no exceptions in this court. It's a bad case, Daniel Webster—a losing case.

WEBSTER. Your Honor—

HATHORNE. The prosecution will proceed—

SCRATCH. Your Honor—gentlemen of the jury. This is a plain, straightforward case. It need not detain us long.

JURY. Detain us long—it will not detain us long.

SCRATCH. It concerns one thing alone—the transference, barter and sale of a certain piece of property, to wit, his soul, by Jabez Stone, farmer, of Cross Corners, New Hampshire. That transference, barter, or sale is attested by a deed. I offer that deed in evidence and mark it Exhibit A.

WEBSTER. I object.

HATHORNE. Objection denied. Mark it Exhibit A.

[SCRATCH *hands the deed—an ominous and impressive document—to the* CLERK, *who hands it to* HATHORNE. HATHORNE *hands it back to the* CLERK, *who stamps it. All very fast and with mechanical gestures.*]

JURY. Exhibit A—mark it Exhibit A. [SCRATCH *takes the deed from the* CLERK *and offers it to the* JURY, *who pass it rapidly among them, hardly looking at it, and hand it back to* SCRATCH.] We know the deed—the deed—it burns in our fingers—we do not have to see the deed. It's a losing case.

SCRATCH. It offers incontestable evidence of the truth of the prosecution's claim. I shall now call Jabez Stone to the witness-stand.

JURY. [*Hungrily.*] Jabez Stone to the witness-stand, Jabez Stone. He's a fine, fat fellow, Jabez Stone. He'll fry like a batter-cake, once we get him where we want him.

WEBSTER. Your Honor, I move that this jury be discharged for flagrant and open bias!

HATHORNE. Motion denied.

WEBSTER. Exception.

HATHORNE. Exception denied.

JURY. His motion's always denied. He thinks himself smart and clever—lawyer Webster. But his motion's always denied.

WEBSTER. Your Honor! [*He chokes with anger.*]

CLERK. [*Advancing.*] Jabez Stone to the witness-stand!

JURY. Jabez Stone—Jabez Stone.

[WEBSTER *gives* JABEZ *an encouraging pat on the back, and* JABEZ *takes his place in the witness-stand, very scared.*]

CLERK. [*Offering a black book.*] Do you solemnly swear—testify—so help you—and it's no good, for we don't care what you testify?

JABEZ. I do.

SCRATCH. What's your name?

JABEZ. Jabez Stone.

SCRATCH. Occupation?

JABEZ. Farmer.

SCRATCH. Residence?

JABEZ. Cross Corners, New Hampshire.

[*These three questions are very fast and mechanical on the part of* SCRATCH. *He is absolutely sure of victory and just going through a form.*]

JURY. A farmer—he'll farm in hell—we'll see that he farms in hell.

SCRATCH. Now, Jabez Stone, answer me. You'd better, you know. You haven't got a chance and there'll be a cooler place by the fire for you.

WEBSTER. I protest! This is intimidation! This mocks all justice!

HATHORNE. The protest is irrelevant, incompetent, and immaterial. We have our own justice. The protest is denied.

JURY. Irrelevant, incompetent, and immaterial—we have our own justice—oh, ho, Daniel Webster! [*The* JURY's *eyes fix upon* WEBSTER *for an instant, hungrily.*]

SCRATCH. Did you or did you not sign this document?

JABEZ. Oh, I signed it! You know I signed it. And, if I have to go to hell for it, I'll go!

[*A sigh sweeps over the* JURY.]

JURY. One of us—one of us now—we'll save a place by the fire for you, Jabez Stone.

SCRATCH. The prosecution rests.

HATHORNE. Remove the prisoner.

WEBSTER. But I wish to cross-examine—I wish to prove—

HATHORNE. There will be no cross-examination. We have our own justice. You may speak, if you like. But be brief.

JURY. Brief—be very brief—we're weary of earth—incompetent, irrelevant, and immaterial—they say he's a smart man, Webster, but he's lost his case tonight—be very brief—we have our own justice here.

[WEBSTER *stares around him like a baited bull. Can't find words.*]

MARY'S VOICE. [*From off stage.*] Set me as a seal upon thy heart, as a seal upon thine arm, for love is strong as death—

JURY. [*Loudly.*] A seal!—ha, ha—a burning seal!

MARY'S VOICE. Love is strong—

JURY. [*Drowning her out.*] Death is stronger than love. Set the seal upon Daniel Webster—the burning seal of the lost. Make him one of us—one of the damned—one with Jabez Stone!

[*The* JURY's *eyes all fix upon* WEBSTER. *The* CLERK *advances as if to take him into custody. But* WEBSTER *silences them all with a great gesture.*]

WEBSTER.

Be still!
I was going to thunder and roar. I shall not do that.

I was going to denounce and defy. I shall not do that.

You have judged this man already with your abominable justice.
  See that you defend it. For I shall not speak of this man.

You are demons now, but once you were men. I shall speak to
  every one of you.

Of common things I speak, of small things and common.

The freshness of morning to the young, the taste of food to the
  hungry, the day's toil, the rest by the fire, the quiet sleep.

These are good things.

But without freedom they sicken, without freedom they are nothing.

Freedom is the bread and the morning and the risen sun.

It was for freedom we came in the boats and the ships. It was for
  freedom we came.

It has been a long journey, a hard one, a bitter one.

But, out of the wrong and the right, the sufferings and the starva-
  tions, there is a new thing, a free thing.

The traitors in their treachery, the wise in their wisdom, the valiant in their courage—all, all have played a part.

It may not be denied in hell nor shall hell prevail against it.

Have you forgotten this? [*He turns to the* JURY.] Have you forgotten the forest?

GIRTY. [*As in a dream.*] The forest, the rustle of the forest, the
free forest.

WEBSTER. [*To* KING PHILIP.] Have you forgotten your lost nation?

KING PHILIP. My lost nation—my fires in the wood—my warriors.

WEBSTER. [*To* TEACH.] Have you forgotten the sea and the way
of ships?

TEACH. The sea—and the swift ships sailing—the blue sea.

JURY. Forgotten—remembered—forgotten yet remembered.

WEBSTER. You were men once. Have you forgotten?

JURY. We were men once. We have not thought of it nor remembered. But we were men.

WEBSTER.

Now here is this man with good and evil in his heart.

Do you know him? He is your brother. Will you take the law
of the oppressor and bind him down?

It is not for him that I speak. It is for all of you.

There is sadness in being a man, but it is a proud thing, too.

There is failure and despair on the journey—the endless journey
of mankind.

We are tricked and trapped—we stumble into the pit—but, out
of the pit, we rise again.

No demon that was ever foaled can know the inwardness of that
—only men—bewildered men.

They have broken freedom with their hands and cast her out from
the nations—yet shall she live while man lives.

She shall live in the blood and the heart—she shall live in the earth
of this country—she shall not be broken.

When the whips of the oppressors are broken and their names forgotten and destroyed,

I see you, mighty, shining, liberty, liberty! I see free men walking and talking under a free star.

God save the United States and the men who have made her free.

The defense rests.

JURY. [*Exultantly.*] We were men—we were free—we were
men—we have not forgotten—our children—our children shall follow and be free.

HATHORNE. [*Rapping with gavel.*] The jury will retire to consider its verdict.

BUTLER. [*Rising.*] There is no need. The jury has heard Mr.
Webster. We find for the defendant, Jabez Stone!

JURY. Not guilty!

SCRATCH. [*In a screech, rushing forward.*] But, Your Honor—
[*But, even as he does so, there is a flash and a thunderclap,
the stage blacks out again, and when the lights come on,
JUDGE and JURY are gone. The yellow light of dawn lights
the windows.*]

JABEZ. They gone and it's morning—Mary, Mary!

MARY. [*In doorway.*] My love—my dear. [*She rushes to him.*]
[*Meanwhile SCRATCH has been collecting his papers and trying to sneak out. But WEBSTER catches him.*]

WEBSTER. Just a minute, Mr. Scratch. I'll have that paper first, if you please. [*He takes the deed and tears it.*] And, now, sir, I'll have *you!*

SCRATCH. Come, come, Mr. Webster. This sort of thing is ridic —ouch—is ridiculous. If you're worried about the costs of the case, naturally, I'd be glad to pay.

WEBSTER. And so you shall! First of all, you'll promise and covenant never to bother Jabez Stone or any other New Hampshire man from now till doomsday. For any hell we want to raise in this State, we can raise ourselves, without any help from you.

SCRATCH. Ouch! Well, they never did run very big to the barrel but—ouch—I agree!

WEBSTER. See you keep to the bargain! And then—well, I've got a ram named Goliath. He can butt through an iron door. I'd like to turn you loose in his field and see what he could do to you. [SCRATCH *trembles.*] But that would be hard on the ram. So we'll just call in the neighbors and give you a shivaree.[2]

SCRATCH. Mr. Webster—please—oh—

WEBSTER. Neighbors! Neighbors! Come in and see what a long-barrelled, slab-sided, lantern-jawed, fortune-telling note-shaver I've got by the scruff of the neck! Bring on your kettles and your pans! [*A noise and murmur outside.*] Bring on your muskets and your flails!

JABEZ. We'll drive him out of New Hampshire!

MARY. We'll drive old Scratch away!

[The CROWD *rushes in, with muskets, flails, brooms, etc. They pursue* SCRATCH *around the stage, chanting.*]

THE CROWD.

> We'll drive him out of New Hampshire!
> We'll drive old Scratch away!
> Forever and a day, boys;
> Forever and a day!

[*They finally catch* SCRATCH *between two of them and fling him out of the door, bodily.*]

A MAN. Three cheers for Dan'l Webster!

[2] *shivaree* is a corruption of the word *charivari*, which means a mock serenade of discordant noises, made with kettles, tin horns, etc.

ANOTHER MAN. Three cheers for Daniel Webster! He's licked the devil!

WEBSTER. [*Moving to center stage, and joining* JABEZ's *hands and* MARY's.] And whom God hath joined let no man put asunder. [*He kisses* MARY *and turns, dusting his hands.*] Well, that job's done. I hope there's pie for breakfast, Neighbor Stone.

[*And, as some of the women, dancing, bring in pies from the kitchen,*

The Curtain Falls]

UNDERSTANDING AND APPRECIATING THE PLAY

1. What events that happened before Jabez's wedding day is it especially necessary for us to know? By what means is this exposition given?

2. "I was going to thunder and roar. I was going to denounce and defy," Daniel Webster tells the jury. "I shall not do that." How else, then, does he sway the jury?

3. What crimes were committed by those of the jury who were named? Suggest other members who might have served on such a jury.

4. What elements of fantasy do we encounter in this play?

5. What does the play have to say about the conflict between the good and the evil in man?

6. What does the play say about freedom and democracy?

7. Stephen Vincent Benét holds high rank among American poets. Point out passages which are particularly poetic.

8. The theme most frequently found in the writings of Stephen Vincent Benét is best expressed in the following poetic lines from this play:

"There is sadness in being a man but it is a proud thing, too.

There is failure and despair on the journey—the endless journey of mankind.

We are tricked and trapped—we stumble into the pit—but out of the pit, we rise again."

(a) Explain the meaning of the passage in your own worls; (b) Apply the thought expressed in the passage to Jabez Stone and to mankind in general.

VOCABULARY BUILDING

1. Explain in your own words—the meanings of the following phrases: an *ominous* little man; it offers *incontestable* evidence; *flagrant* and open *bias;* Scratch replied *inexorably;* a *deprecatory* shrug; I want the *execution* of my contract; *eerily* lit; Webster spoke *placidly;* the *quick* and the dead.

2. Synonyms rarely mean exactly the same thing. Can you show the variations of meaning in the following synonyms: *odious, nefarious, villainous, flagrant, atrocious, outrageous, monstrous?*

THINGS TO DO

1. Develop one of these topics into a story, or a play: A Strange Dream; A Never-to-Be-Forgotten Incident in My Childhood; Long Ago and Far Away; A Hundred Years from Now; Yesterday and Today; A Trip to Mars; The Value of a Dream; Of Course It Didn't Happen; After Life; Autobiography of a Dollar Bill; A Fantasy; How Shall We Cross the Atlantic in the Future?

2. What movie fantasies have you seen? Discuss ways in which the movie is freer than the play on a stage. Consider action, setting, fantasy.

3. Some of the most appealing fantasies have been based on the idea of a dying person's being snatched from the jaws of death. For the most part, such plays consist of a fanciful account of what the characters dreamed or experienced while on their journey to the other world. Write a scenario for a play based on this idea or on any other supernatural subject in which you may be interested.

4. Another interesting possibility for a play or a story may be found in taking a person out of one century and placing him in another. Mark Twain had his Connecticut Yankee see King Arthur's Court with the eyes of a modern man. In the play *Berkeley Square,* Peter Standish, while retaining his twentieth-century point of view, is placed in another era. He is so greatly impressed with his eighteenth-century sweetheart that he breaks his engagement with his modern fiancée. By bringing a character out of the past into the present or taking him out of the present into either the past or the future, you have unlimited opportunity for examining and commenting on changing customs and beliefs.

5. Read the short-story version of *The Devil and Daniel Webster*. Compare it with the play and comment upon the technical problems that Mr. Benét had to handle in dramatizing the story. These are points which you may well discuss: Of the many scenes in the story, which setting did he select for the play? Was Mr. Benét wise in his choice? How did he handle the problem of exposition? What part of the action did he decide to portray on the stage? How did he use and expand the dialogue? How well did he succeed in retaining the spirit and the style of the story?

6. Most of us sooner or later encounter personal crises in which we have to act on or reject an ambitious impulse. If you have encountered such a crisis in your life, write a narrative theme relating the decision you had to make, how you made it, and the consequences of your choice.

7. Choose some piece of literature with which you are familiar, and dramatize it either as a stage play or as a radio drama: *e.g.*, the Biblical story of Joseph and His Brethren, *Tom Sawyer*, *Penrod*, *Treasure Island*, *The Pied Piper of Hamelin*.

PRODUCTION NOTES

Producing *The Devil and Daniel Webster* will tax the ingenuity of any amateur director. In the first place, the play calls for a very large cast. Then there is a great variety of theatrical effects and tricks—the dance-narrative, the chanting crowd, the moth in the Devil's box, the queer behavior of the fiddle, the weird and sudden appearance and black-out of the jury. If you can handle these effects, you have learned much about staging.

Mr. Benét's own production notes for this play follow. They will help you in presenting this difficult play.

Note A. The set must be arranged so that it can be transformed, in short notice, from the living room of a farmhouse into a courtroom. In an elaborate production, the back-wall of the set, between the two windows, can be flown during the first black-out and a practical jury box, with the jurors concealed within it, can be rolled on. The fireplace can also revolve and turn into the judge's stand. In a simpler production, a pair of long benches, one higher than the other, at the back of the set, can be used as a jury box and the jurors steal on during the black-out, to be gradually lit at the end of Scratch's invocation, while the Judge enters and takes his seat on the high settle by the fireplace, his Clerk sitting on a stool below him. The

The Devil and Daniel Webster

table, left, becomes the lawyer's table, where Scratch and Webster sit. There is no need of an actual dock or witness box—Jabez, during his interrogation, merely stands to the right of the jury, lit by a spot.

Note B. As a practical moth-effect would be difficult, the whole business of the moth can be suggested by the Crowd turning, staring and pointing, first up, then right, then left, following the flight of an imaginary moth. The stage begins to darken at the first letting of the moth out of the box, and the following scene is played in dim light.

Scratch can recite his song instead of singing it, though music for this song, if desired, can be obtained by special arrangement with Brandt and Brandt, 101 Park Avenue, New York City. The fiddle accompaniment can be faked, off stage, if necessary. All it needs is to be eerie and discordant.

Note C. The speeches of the Moth should come in a high, shrill voice from somebody concealed among the Crowd where he will not be seen by the audience. If desired, the speeches can be spoken from off stage. But the words are important and must be heard. During this scene, the Crowd speaks in a definite, beating rhythm.

Note D. Alka-seltzer or dry ice—or a combination of both, will make the devil's glass steam. But, if dry ice is used, Mr. Scratch must be careful not to try to drink from the glass.

Note E. The moment the stage blacks out, Mr. Scratch removes a flashlight with a green bulb from the inside pocket of his voluminous coat and, holding it carefully in his black-gloved hands, lets the green light play on his face during the invocation. On the last line, he switches off the flashlight and sticks it back in his pocket. This can be done so the audience does not see it.

We should also like to add that though music and dancing are unquestioned contributions to its production, the play can be done without either.

LIST OF PROPERTIES

Glasses	Dish (with cake)
Jug	Black tin box
Clock	Flask
Violin and bow	Gavel
Bouquet of flowers (optional)	Black book
Dish (for oyster stew)	Pies

A few wedding presents of various kinds
Black pocketbook with a few documents and other papers, including a large and impressive deed

Television Drama: The Theater of the People

A MORE SUITABLE TITLE for this brief discussion would be Television Drama: The Theater or the Opiate of the People. For at times our television set appears to be the electronic marvel of our age, bringing to us so much enlightenment and wonderful entertainment; at other times it is a kind of idiot box into which some people stare undiscriminatingly for hours on end until they are stupefied and—to borrow a phrase from teenagers of another era—slightly "mogo in the gogo." This is to say until their emotional balance and sense of values become distorted.

Consider the implications of these facts: there is a television set in nine American homes out of ten; on an average day about a hundred and thirty million people watch television; and in the average household television is viewed for six hours a day. So far as drama is concerned, here is a medium in which one performance of a play may be viewed by millions upon millions of people. A single TV performance of a Shakespearean play, for instance, may have an audience many times the total number of people who attended the play in all the three and a half centuries since it was written. And there is probably more dramatic activity in one week in just the New York television studios than may be found in three seasons on Broadway.

What kind of dramatic fare does television provide? In length, TV plays run from short sketches to elaborate productions of full-length plays. In quality, TV dramas range from the occasionally excellent—superior productions of the best plays of our time and of the past—to the generally mediocre and to the sometimes very bad.

157

How good is the taste of the American television-viewing public? It's hard to tell, but it's probably not so low as the executives of our principal TV networks seem to think. Recently, when critics objected, among other things, to the plethora of far-fetched Westerns and violent gangster and private-eye shows flooding the channels, the executives of one of the three major networks replied, "This is cultural democracy in action: The programming obligations of the broadcasters must therefore be based on a democratic concept of cultural freedom—that is, the rights of the people to want what they want when they want it." And when the critics of TV programming expressed their dissatisfaction with this explanation, an executive of the network asked, "Can we legislate taste? Can we make it a criminal offense to be mediocre? Shall we set up a commissar of taste?" In effect, the networks are saying that they know just what the people want, and that they're giving the public exactly what it wants. But the networks leave two vital questions unanswered: (1) how they can be so certain that they know what the public wants and (2) whether they are doing all they can to improve the taste of their vast audiences.

Before we can get TV shows of better quality, we must convince the networks that we want and can appreciate such shows. The best way to do that is for us to develop a genuine sense of discrimination between the good and the bad or the mediocre, as well as a desire for the good. Incidentally, that kind of discrimination applies not only to television but also to other public media of communication, such as books, newspapers, magazines, and radio. The major responsibility for improving taste falls upon the home and, even in larger measure, upon the school.

She Walks in Beauty *

JAMES TRUEX

When young Hawkins was called to the principal's office, he was in for one surprise after another. So will you be in for surprises—and for a television play that has humor and charm, kindliness and warmth, young love and love in later years.

She Walks in Beauty is probably best described as a television sketch or vignette—a word picture which portrays something subtly and delicately. It was originally presented as part of the Kate Smith Hour and featured Sir Cedric Hardwicke in the role of Mr. Bernard, the school principal.

You will note that the stage directions include only a minimum of television production notes. Most television directors react unfavorably to scripts which contain too many directions for camera angles and suggestions for actors; the directors prefer to do much of their own thinking and planning.

CHARACTERS

MR. BERNARD
MISS INGERSOLL
ROBERT HAWKINS
MISS MARY ALICE RILEY

It is spring in the suburbs. MR. BERNARD, *high school principal, is gazing dreamily out of the window of his office. He is in his early fifties and his hair is growing thin.*

SOUND: *Background spring noises, which are broken into abruptly by a sharp knocking on the door.*

[MR. BERNARD *goes to his desk, hastily slides a paper into an upper desk drawer.*]

MR. BERNARD. Come in.

* Reprinted by permission of the author and his representative, Blanche Gaines. Permission to produce *She Walks in Beauty* in any form must be obtained from Blanche Gaines, 350 West 57th Street, New York 16, N.Y.

[SOUND: *Door open and close.*]

[MISS INGERSOLL, *a tweedy teacher in low-heel shoes, strides into the room.*]

MISS INGERSOLL. Mr. Bernard . . .

MR. BERNARD. Yes, Miss Ingersoll?

MISS INGERSOLL. There's something going on in this school that I feel it my duty to call to your attention.

MR. BERNARD. Go right ahead, Miss Ingersoll. What is it this time?

MISS INGERSOLL. Read this! [*She tosses a piece of paper on the desk. He reads it, then looks up.*] Well, what do you think of it?

MR. BERNARD. I think it's a love poem, Miss Ingersoll. Did you write it?

MISS INGERSOLL. Please, Mr. Bernard. This is a serious matter. This piece of obscenity was written by one of my students . . . right in the middle of my geometry class.

MR. BERNARD. Oh, now, I wouldn't call it obscene, Miss Ingersoll. Passionate, perhaps, but not obscene. We must not forget that it's spring. Didn't you ever write this sort of thing when you were young?

MISS INGERSOLL. That's neither here nor there, Mr. Bernard. The important thing to notice is the dedication: "To M.A.R." They are the initials of the new English instructor, Miss Mary Alice Riley.

MR. BERNARD. Then obviously the poem is intended for her. What are we doing with it?

MISS INGERSOLL. Mr. Bernard, as the new principal, you should really try to be more aware of what's going on in this school. That young lady has caused dissension and trouble ever since she joined our staff. She's a disturbing influence on the young . . . this poem proves it. She doesn't dress like a teacher, act like a teacher . . .

MR. BERNARD. Or look like a teacher. You've pointed these things out to me before, Miss Ingersoll. Go on.

MISS INGERSOLL. I know you seem to regard it lightly, but when students begin writing lewd verses in honor of Miss Riley in my geometry class, I feel that something drastic should be done.

MR. BERNARD. What do you want me to do, Miss Ingersoll? The young lady in question has a contract to teach high school English until June of this year. She is pretty; she dresses well; and at least one young member of the junior class seems to have fallen in love with her. But don't you see that none of these things can possibly be construed as a breach of contract?

MISS INGERSOLL. I can see that my twenty years of service here in this school means nothing to you, Mr. Bernard. When the late Mr. Green was principal, he welcomed my advice.

MR. BERNARD. I welcome it, too, Miss Ingersoll. But in this instance, I'm at a loss to know what steps I should take to satisfy both yourself and my conscience.

MISS INGERSOLL. Would it be too much for me to ask you to speak to the author of this . . . poem and see that he is properly disciplined? He's waiting outside.

MR. BERNARD. Then show the culprit in.

MISS INGERSOLL. Thank you. [*She goes to door.*]

[SOUND: *Door open.*]

[HAWKINS *enters reluctantly.*]

Mr. Bernard will take care of you.

HAWKINS. Yes, ma'am.

[MISS INGERSOLL *exits.* HAWKINS *stands, head down.*]

[SOUND: *Door close.*]

MR. BERNARD. Come over here, Hawkins.

[HAWKINS *shuffles toward the desk.* MR. BERNARD *holds out poem.*]

Did you write this?

HAWKINS. Yes, sir.

MR. BERNARD. In Miss Ingersoll's geometry class?

HAWKINS. Yes, sir. I'm sorry.

MR. BERNARD. That you wrote the poem?

HAWINS. No, sir . . . that I wrote it in Miss Ingersoll's geometry class.

MR. BERNARD. [*Rising.*] I see. Hawkins, while writing poetry is not altogether reprehensible as a pastime, I should advise you in the future not to indulge in it during school hours. In that way you can make more certain that the poem reaches the person for whom it is intended, and no one else.

HAWKINS. [*Puzzled.*] Yes, sir.

MR. BERNARD. [*Walking to window.*] As for the poem itself, I think it has considerable merit. But that line: [*Reading.*] "She walks in beauty like the night." Didn't Lord Byron write that one?

HAWKINS. Yes, sir. But it seemed to fit in so well.

MR. BERNARD. I know it's tempting, Hawkins, but we poets must be careful not to borrow too much from the past. We must create our own images.

HAWKINS. Yes, sir. Did you say "we" poets, sir?

MR. BERNARD. Why, yes. I've tried my hand at poetry myself from time to time.

HAWKINS. No kidding, sir!

MR. BERNARD. No kidding. As a matter of fact, I was working on one today. [*Going to desk and taking paper from drawer.*] I'd be grateful if you'd glance at it and give me your opinion of it. [*Hands paper to* HAWKINS.] Unfortunately, I was interrupted before I was able to finish the last line.

HAWKINS. [*Reading poem.*] Gee, Mr. Bernard, you're a real poet! This is terrific. It's a sonnet, isn't it?

MR. BERNARD. It hopes to be. If I can ever find anything suitable to rhyme with "gazelle."

HAWKINS. [*Staring at paper.*] But Mr. Bernard! The dedication! "Lines written to M.A.R."!

MR. BERNARD. Mary Alice Riley.

HAWKINS. You, too, huh?

MR. BERNARD. Me, too, Hawkins.

HAWKINS. Gosh, Mr. Bernard, isn't she a pip!

MR. BERNARD. She is all of that, Hawkins, and more. It is my privilege to watch her every morning as she travels across the lawn to her classroom. That journey is a sonnet in itself.

HAWKINS. I'm taking her course in the Romantic Period . . . Eighteen hundred to eighteen hundred thirty-two.

MR. BERNARD. You're a lucky fellow.

HAWKINS. Say, this makes us rivals, doesn't it?

MR. BERNARD. In a way, Hawkins, though youth is on your side.

HAWKINS. I've got too much youth, Mr. Bernard. When you're fifteen years old, nobody takes you seriously.

MR. BERNARD. When you're fifty, you can't take yourself seriously. I don't know which is worse.

HAWKINS. Gosh, Mr. Bernard, I had a hunch you were pretty human for a school principal, but I never dreamed you were *this* human!

MR. BERNARD. Some people regard it as a failing, Hawkins. You'd better get back to class. I think we should keep this poetry business a secret between ourselves, don't you?

HAWKINS. Yes, sir. And may the best man win!

MR. BERNARD. Oh, and Hawkins . . . no more poetizing in Miss Ingersoll's geometry class. Understand?

HAWKINS. Absolutely!

MR. BERNARD. In a way, Miss Ingersoll suffers from your complaint and mine . . . a lack of reciprocal affection. She is caught on the horns of an isosceles triangle. We must be kind to her.

HAWKINS. Yes, sir. [HAWKINS *turns to go.*]

[SOUND: *Door knock and open and close.*]

[MARY ALICE RILEY *enters.*]

MISS RILEY. [*Angrily.*] I see I've arrived just in time. Don't go, Hawkins. What I have to say concerns you.

MR. BERNARD. Miss Riley! Won't you sit down?

MISS RILEY. No, thank you. A moment ago in the faculty room, Miss Ingersoll announced that she had reported this young man for writing a poem dedicated to me. Is that so?

MR. BERNARD. It is.

MISS RILEY. She seems to feel that it was immoral and that I singlehandedly am the cause of a general moral collapse in the student body.

MR. BERNARD. [*Going to desk.*] Miss Ingersoll gets unduly ruffled, Miss Riley. The poem is hardly immoral . . . if you would care to read it . . . [*He holds out paper.*]

Miss Riley. [*Taking it.*] Has it ever occurred to you and Miss Ingersoll that if Hawkins has a desire to express himself in verse, he has a perfect right to, without the entire school faculty passing judgment on him?

Hawkins. Miss Riley!

Miss Riley. Mr. Bernard, in the midst of the oppressive atmosphere of this dreary school, you should thank your stars that there is at least one young man with imagination and a soul. Instead of punishing him, you should reward him!

Hawkins. [*Going to* Miss Riley.] Miss Riley! I'm not being punished!

Miss Riley. What's that?

Hawkins. I'm not being punished! Mr. Bernard is on our side!

Miss Riley. How do you mean?

Hawkins. [*Grabbing* Mr. Bernard's *poem off desk.*] Here. Here's the proof. He wrote this poem this morning . . . to you. He's in love with you, too, Miss Riley!

[Miss Riley *takes poem, reads it, then turns to* Mr. Bernard.]

Mr. Bernard. Now, Hawkins! I hardly think we need lay all our cards on the table at once. I, uh . . . things seem to have gotten a little out of hand, don't they! The truth is, that Hawkins and I discovered a while ago that we had a number of interests in common.

Hawkins. And you're most of them, Miss Riley.

Miss Riley. May I sit down?

Mr. Bernard. Certainly.

Miss Riley. [*Sitting.*] I'm sorry, Mr. Bernard. It begins to look as though Miss Ingersoll is right . . . I *am* a troublemaker.

Mr. Bernard. You forget that Miss Ingersoll started the whole thing.

Hawkins. [*Standing beside* Mr. Bernard.] I guess you'll just have to choose between us, Miss Riley.

Miss Riley. Must I?

Hawkins. It's what they always do in the movies.

MR. BERNARD. Forgive my friend Hawkins, Miss Riley. He speaks with the impetuosity of youth. Contrary to popular tradition, it's when we are old that we are willing to wait.

MISS RILEY. [*Rising and going between them.*] Dear Hawkins, dear Mr. Bernard, believe me when I say that I am deeply touched by these evidences of your regard. But in the interests of fairness, I must confess that I cannot choose between you, because I have already chosen.

[*Both look at her hopefully.*]

On this coming Saturday, at eight p.m., my engagement will be announced to Mr. Horace Braisted.

HAWKINS. You mean Mr. Braisted, the chemistry teacher?

MISS RILEY. Yes, Hawkins. Since Mr. Braisted doesn't wish for me to continue as a teacher, I shall be relinquishing my post this June.

MR. BERNARD. Braisted's a lucky man. We'll miss you.

MISS RILEY. And I shall miss you. [*Holding up poems.*] May I keep these?

HAWKINS. Sure.

MR. BERNARD. Certainly. If Mr. Braisted won't mind.

MISS RILEY. I'll not be engaged until Saturday, Mr. Bernard. Good afternoon. [*She throws a kiss to them both and leaves.*]

[SOUND: *Door open and close.*]

MR. BERNARD. Well, Hawkins, that's that.

HAWKINS. Mr. Braisted is a dope.

MR. BERNARD. [*Going toward door.*] There is no accounting for tastes.

HAWKINS. And I had ideas of becoming a poet.

MR. BERNARD. Don't give up, Hawkins. The world's finest poems have been written by rejected suitors.

HAWKINS. Gee, I never thought of that.

MR. BERNARD. The Cavalier poets made a specialty out of unrequited love . . . Robert Herrick, Richard Lovelace . . . How do you feel?

HAWKINS. [*Thinking for a moment.*] Hungry!

MR. BERNARD. [*Going to hatrack.*] You're recovering already. I wish I could say the same of myself.

HAWKINS. Cheer up, Mr. Bernard. I guess she isn't the only pebble on the beach.

MR. BERNARD. I'm no longer at my best in a bathing suit. Come, Hawkins, let's take a stroll and sublimate our feelings in the miracle of spring's return.

HAWKINS. O.K., Mr. Bernard.

MR. BERNARD. Perhaps we'll stop at the drug store and drown our sorrows in an ice cream soda. [*They go off arm in arm.*]
[*Fade out.*]

[*The End*]

UNDERSTANDING AND APPRECIATING THE PLAY

1. "I've got too much youth, Mr. Bernard," Hawkins complains. Why does he feel that way?

2. As far as Miss Riley is concerned, why is Mr. Bernard at a disadvantage? What references does he make to his shortcomings in this respect?

3. How good a principal do you think Mr. Bernard is? For example, does he understand young people? Explain.

4. Much of the appeal of the play is in the whimsically humorous remarks made by Mr. Bernard. Which of his observations do you especially like?

5. Is Miss Ingersoll treated entirely unsympathetically? Discuss.

6. Is *She Walks in Beauty* a comedy or a farce? Why?

7. Mr. Bernard says, "Forgive my friend Hawkins, Miss Riley. He speaks with the impetuosity of youth." Are young people more hasty and less patient than older folk? Discuss.

8. How did you expect the "infatuation" triangle to turn out? Were you surprised when Miss Riley announced her engagement? Why?

9. Mr. Bernard comforts Hawkins by telling the boy that some of the world's finest poems have been written by rejected suitors. Do you think that something good may come out of disappointment, loss, and suffering? What good, for example?

THINGS TO DO

1. Topics for themes or discussion: Called to the Principal's Office; On Being Too Young; Qualities Students Admire in a Teacher; Qualities Teachers Admire in a Student; A Good Principal; Was It Love or Infatuation?; A Favorite Teacher; A Favorite Television Program; A Favorite Television Personality.

2. For a period of time specified by your teacher, view one or more of the following kinds of television programs: one that offers a series of worthwhile plays; a discussion, debate, or interview show; a news report show; an educational program; a show featuring good music; a documentary series. Take notes on what you see and hear. Then, either orally or in writing, present a report. Suggested form of the report: first, tell what each program in the series was about; then discuss why each program was good or bad and why it either appealed or failed to appeal to you; finally, give an over-all analysis of the entire series.

3. For discussion: Television Programs, Trash or Treasure? Those in charge of television programming have been accused of showing too many inferior programs, of catering to the less intelligent and the less discriminating among their millions of viewers. The broadcasters reply that they're giving their audiences what the people want. What do you think of television programming? How good or how bad do you think TV programs are? How can a demand for better programs be developed? What can be done to persuade the television industry to improve the caliber of its programs?

4. In a glossary of television terms, look up the explanations of such terms as the following and explain them to the class: audio, background, bridge, closeup, dissolve, fade in, fade out, live mike, monitor, pan, segue, shot, simulcast, video.

5. For discussion: Career versus Marriage. After their marriage, Mr. Braisted did not want his wife to continue with her career as a teacher. How do you feel about a woman's combining a career with marriage? Do you approve of a married woman's working? If so, under what circumstances, and for how long?

6. For discussion: Each period in life has its advantages and disadvantages. What are the advantages and disadvantages of adolescence? Of middle-age? You may decide to discuss only adolescence. First define your terms, of course.

7. Review a television play you have seen. Do not devote a large part of your review to a recounting of plot; story isn't everything,

and you certainly should not tell how the plot turns out. Be certain to discuss, also, such matters as acting skill, camera work, and the dramatist's skill in characterization, dialogue, sustaining interest or suspense, and handling of theme and other ideas.

8. The Cavalier poets made a specialty of unrequited love, Mr. Bernard told Hawkins; and the principal mentioned the seventeenth-century soldier-poets Robert Herrick and Richard Lovelace. Read aloud to the class your favorite lyrics by these and other Cavalier poets. Tell the class why the poems appeal to you.

VOCABULARY BUILDING

In the contexts in which they appear, explain the meaning of the italicized words: has caused *dissension* and trouble; I wouldn't call it *obscene;* can possibly be *construed* as a *breach* of contract; not *reprehensible* as a pastime; suffers from a lack of *reciprocal* affection; gets *unduly ruffled;* the *oppressive* atmosphere of the school; speaks with the *impetuosity* of youth; *relinquishing* my past; *unrequited* love; *sublimate* our feelings.

PRODUCTION NOTES

Because it is a ten-minute vignette, She Walks in Beauty is a desirable fill-in, either on a one-act play bill or in a variety show.

Grouping, movement, business are relatively simple; yet the very lack of complication poses the challenge of avoiding monotony. Fortunately, there is variety in characterization and in tempo.

The script calls for two character actors to play the mature roles of Mr. Bernard and Miss Ingersoll and for two "straight" parts in which young people portray characters close to their own age. Each character is, of course, individualized. Mr. Bernard's sympathetic understanding, kindliness, warmth, and humor dominate the emotional tone of the play. The agitated entrances and disturbed emotional states of Miss Ingersoll and also of Miss Riley, before the latter calms down, are in contrast to the gawky, uncertain entrance and wistful behavior of Hawkins.

MORE GOOD TELEVISION PLAYS

Television Plays. Paddy Chayefsky. [Simon and Schuster]
Six Television Plays. Reginald Rose. [Simon and Schuster]
Patterns: Four Television Plays. Rod Serling. [Simon and Schuster]
These are full-length television plays by three of the most eminent
television dramatists.
The Best Television Plays of the Year. Edited by William I. Kaufman.
[Harcourt-Brace]   Winners of the annual Harcourt-Brace Awards as
the best television plays of the year.
Radio and Television Plays. Edited by Lawrence H. Feigenbaum.
[Globe]   A good collection for use in schools.

BOOKS ON WRITING FOR TELEVISION
AND RADIO

Handbook of Radio Writing. Erik Barnouw. [Little, Brown]
Television Plays for Writers. A. S. Burack. [The Writer, Inc.]
Television and Radio Writing. Stanley Field. [Houghton Mifflin]
Close-up on Writing for Television. Arthur Hailey. [Doubleday]
Pointers on Radio Writing. Josefina Niggli. [The Writer, Inc.]
Writing for Television. Gilbert V. Seldes. [Doubleday]

Further Experiences with and through Plays

Further Experiences

IN PART TWO you will continue to have experiences with various types of plays; but here the kind of life experience to be gained through the plays has suggested an arrangement not by types but by themes and problems.

To help you better to understand yourself and others, to help you face and solve personal and social problems: these are among the purposes of the selection and arrangement of plays in the second part of the book. How should young people face disappointment and frustration? How should a boy overcome shyness and make a favorable impression upon others? Why are some young people who come from good families tempted into wrongdoing? What are the big, the important things in life? If you are faced with any problem such as one of these, perhaps the reading and discussion of these plays will furnish the inspiration to lift you out of your difficulty. The plays and their related activities will certainly help you to a broader understanding of life and of your own experiences.

The Sounds of Triumph *

WILLIAM INGE

As individuals, are we capable of facing times of adversity? Can we face the times of disappointment and frustration, pain and suffering, and personal loss which life holds for all of us? Or do we imagine that the "bad breaks" are reserved for others, and never for us?

Are we such bad losers, in love or in anything else of personal importance, that we go to pieces or vent resentment and hatred on the fortunate winner?

Are we such over-active, thoughtless participants in the game of life that we fail to take the time occasionally to evaluate what we are doing and where we are heading? On the other hand, are some of us too much withdrawn from life?

William Inge, one of America's outstanding playwrights, affords us perceptive insights into these vital problems. He does so in a serious play, the setting of which is near a college athletic field. Against the background of a track meet, the principal characters reveal their innermost feelings.

CHARACTERS

OLD MAN	FIRST ATHLETE
ANN	SECOND ATHLETE
TOM	VOICES
BEN	

The scene is laid at the side of a small hillock behind which lies an open field. In the far background are bright colored pennants flying in the breeze, and we hear the distant sound of strident band music, proclaiming victory. Mixed with the music is the sound of cheering voices.

An OLD MAN, *bent over his cane, comes walking onto the scene, drawn by the music and voices. He goes to the top of the hillock and stands, his back to the audience, watching the games in the distance.*

> VOICES. Give 'em the axe, the axe, the axe!
> Give 'em the axe, the axe, the axe!
>
> Yeh for Simpson!
>
> Simpson won the 50-yard dash!
>
> Next event!
>
> Ready for the next event!
>
> Give 'em the axe, the axe, the axe!
> Give 'em the axe, the axe, the axe!

[*Now a young girl,* ANN, *comes running, laughing onto the scene. She is about 19, pretty, dressed simply in sweater and skirt, her hair free. Following fast behind her is* TOM, *a young athlete, dressed in the gray sweatsuit and track shoes provided by his college. He catches up with* ANN, *grabs her in his arms and kisses her. Then* THEY *laugh lovingly together.* ANN *suddenly notices the* OLD MAN, *who thus far has not turned to watch the young people but still stands, his back to the audience, looking off into the distance.*]

ANN. He'll see.

TOM. What if he does? [*Thoughtless but not cruel.*] He's just an old man.

ANN. Still, he can see us.

TOM. What if he does see us? What if he does? [*He grabs her in his arms and kisses her again. Then he proclaims loudly, attracting the* OLD MAN's *attention.*] Look, everybody! I'm kissing Ann. Ann and I are in love. I'm kissing her. See? [ANN *in his arms, he looks closely into her eyes.*] Now, I've told the whole world, and the whole world may be watching. Does that keep me from kissing you?

ANN. Tom, Ben will be coming along any minute, and I don't want Ben to know.

TOM. [*Recklessly.*] To hell with Ben!

ANN. But I like Ben!

TOM. You like Ben, but you're in love with me. Admit it.

ANN. I do admit it, Tom.

TOM. Then forget about Ben. That's the only thing you can do. Forget him.

ANN. I don't want to hurt his feelings.

TOM. But you've got to hurt his feelings.

ANN. I mustn't. Ben and I grew up together. I know how deeply he feels things, much more than he shows.

TOM. I've had my feelings hurt, fer crying out loud! Before I came to college, I was nuts about a girl in high school, and she gave me the air. Yah! For a long time after that, I couldn't eat, I couldn't study, I didn't wanta see anyone. But I got over it. I learned to take it. It's just part of growing up.

ANN. I know. The same thing happened to me in high school. I was awfully fond of a boy and he started dating my best friend. I cried and cried and cried. I sulked around the house until Mother took me to see a doctor. Do you know what he did? He gave me vitamin shots. Honestly! [THEY *laugh.*]

TOM. But you got over it, didn't you?

ANN. [*Their mood is still jovial. Their present love is too much with them for the past to cast a gloom.*] Yes, I got over it.

TOM. And that's what Ben has got to do. Get over it. Even if he *is* my buddy, I gotta admit, he's spoiled. He's gotta learn to take his medicine like everyone else.

ANN. [*Troubledly.*] I think he's suspected something already.

TOM. After the races, we'll tell him.

ANN. Both of us?

TOM. Why not? We'll go to him together and say, "Ben, Ann and I are in love. She's going to wear my fraternity pin. Sorry, old man. These things are tough, but human beings always get over 'em. It's just part of growing up."

ANN. I dread telling him. But I'll feel better about it, if we're together.

TOM. Just think, Ann. We'll always be together *now*. [*He takes her in his arms.*]

ANN. [*Truly in love.*] Oh Tom!

[*He kisses her.*]

TOM. We're as one person already. Aren't we?

ANN. Yes, Tom. I feel it, too.

TOM. It's a magical process, love, isn't it? One day, two people are separate individuals, each going his own way; on another day, they meet and fall in love, and they become like one. Without you now, I'd feel just half a man.

ANN. I feel the same, but I never realized, before we met, that I was incomplete in any way.

TOM. [*Taking her in his arms again.*] Oh, Ann!

ANN. Tom!

[*He kisses her again, while the* VOICES *and music come up from the background. The* OLD MAN *watches, his back still to the audience. He jumps up and down with enthusiasm.*]

VOICES. Yeh! Yeh! [*In a chant.*] V-I-C-T-O-R-Y!
That's the way to spell it!
Here's the way to yell it! [*A bombastic shout.*]
VICTORY!

Yeh! Yeh!

Pin a medal on Cutler! Cutler won the hurdles. Yeh! Yeh!

TOM. [*Releasing* ANN *in his arms.*] Did you hear that? Cutler won the hurdles. This is a big day for us. We better go back.

ANN. Can't we sit together until your event?

TOM. Somehow. We'll manage somehow.

[THEY *run off together arm in arm. Slowly* BEN *comes on from behind the hillock, where he stands for a few moments, watching* ANN *and* TOM *disappear. One must get the feeling that he has been watching them and knows in his heart what has happened. First there is a look of intense anguish on his face and he stands rigid with bitterness and rage.*]

Then gradually the intensity subsides, his features and his body relax into sad resignation, and he lopes down the hillock, getting to the bottom, letting himself fall to the ground, lying sprawled there. Slowly, the OLD MAN *takes cognizance of him and, still standing at the top of the hillock, speaks.*]

OLD MAN. [*In the gentlest voice.*] Have you been hurt?

BEN. [*Lifting his head.*] I'm all right.

OLD MAN. Is there anything the matter?

BEN. [*A pause elapses while he considers the question and decides to avoid answering. Instead he asks directly.*] Who are you?

OLD MAN. I recently heard myself referred to as "just an old man." That's true, of course, but my students refer to me as Professor Benoit, Associate in the Department of Ancient Languages.

BEN. I apologize for not recognizing you, Professor.

OLD MAN. No one ever recognizes a professor. Don't apologize.

[*There is a long pause.* BEN *is trying to hold back tears. The* OLD MAN, *perhaps sensing* BEN's *despair, tries to sound diverting.*]

OLD MAN. There's such a crowd there, isn't there? I honestly believe I never saw so many people. Wouldn't the Board of Regents be pleased if my classes started filling up that way?

[*Suddenly* BEN *bursts out in uncontrollable tears. The* OLD MAN *is very concerned, hurrying down to* BEN's *side.*]

My boy! My boy!

BEN. [*Fighting off the* OLD MAN's *almost motherly protection.*] Go away, Old Man. Go away!

OLD MAN. [*He seems to understand, withdraws, going back to the top of the hillock.*] Very well. I'm sorry I interfered. I shall mind my business and continue watching the games.

[*Now he stands as he did before, his back to* BEN, *who lies face down on the ground, all but writhing with the pain of his rejection. Background* VOICES *and music come up again. The band starts off with Boola Boola, and the cheering squad in unison, the voices sounding vindictive.*]

VOICES. Give 'em the axe, the axe, the axe,
Give 'em the axe! Give 'em the axe!
Give 'em the axe! Where?
Right in the neck, the neck, the neck!
Right in the neck, the neck, the neck!
Right in the neck! Right in the neck!
Right in the neck there!

[*Now the voices seem to explode into a vocal shower of calls, whistles, shrieks, etc.*]

OLD MAN. [*His back to the audience, speaking for himself and anyone who cares to listen.*] I look forward to the games all year long. Last October I bought my season ticket to the Student Activity Program and have attended all the events during the year. I happened upon this little knoll a few years ago when I was out on one of my walks, and I saw what a splendid view it offers of the stadium, so I've been coming here, where I enjoy being a solitary spectator. You see, I'm rather a childish old man, and I get so excited watching the games that I'm embarrassed for others to see me, particularly my students, who surely would think I had taken leave of my senses, if they saw me jumping up and down and pounding the air with my fists. [*He gives a little chuckle.*] So I gave my ticket to the cleaning woman. And it pleased me to do that, for I can't afford to pay her much and she loves the games, too. Everyone loves the games. Although not everyone cares to contend in them. I never did care to. I was studious even as a child. And I was frail. I was always getting the nose-bleed. So I made myself content to watch and not participate. I suppose all people are divided into two groups, those who participate and those who watch and observe. Sometimes, in my more melancholy moments, I wonder if I have lived life at all, if my life has not been, rather, a period of observation on earth, watching others live, studying the way they live and commenting on their success or failure in the process. Being very moved by them at times, but still detached so that my envy of their success is fleeting, and my sadness at their failure passes when I sit down at a good meal or take a glass of sherry. Once I was in love, and it terrified me. She was so beautiful, so tender, so fine that I trembled in her mere proximity. The reality of her seemed too much for me to bear, and I fled. I could not accept the responsibility of loving her. [*He sighs.*] Alas! sometimes I am very lonely, of course. I go to bed, some nights, despondent, but I always awake feeling free. But I must admit, I always hurry to my office to become involved in my research as quickly as possible, for if I remain idle very long, I sometimes become very depressed.

[*A rousing cheer comes from the stadium.*]

> VOICES. V-I-C-T-O-R-Y!
> That's the way to spell it.
> Here's the way to yell it!
> VICTORY! Yeh! Yeh!
>
> Hopkins won the discus! Yeh, Hopkins!
>
> He's our boy! Yeh, Hopkins!

OLD MAN. They're putting Ronnie Hopkins up on their shoulders now, carrying him through the stadium. I had the lad in class last year. I found him at times almost belligerent about learning, or about not learning. "What do I care about ancient history?" he used to bellow. "Why should I spend my time worrying about what happened in the past? I'm living now." "True," I always replied to him, "but sometimes the present means more to us if we see it in terms of what has been before." He would shake his head then and mumble some incoherent protest. After grave consideration, I finally passed him in the course, but with a very low grade. He never even learned to spell Nebuchadnezzar.

> VOICES. Yeh, Hopkins!
>
> He's our boy!
>
> Trot him round the field again!

OLD MAN. [*Turns his back on the scene in the stadium and looks down at* BEN, *who still lies sprawled at the foot of the hillock, his face in his hands.*] Where do you come from, young man?

BEN. [*Lifting his face, wiping away a few tears with the back of his hand.*] A little town . . . in Iowa.

OLD MAN. I was through Iowa once on a train.

BEN. I wish to God I was back there.

OLD MAN. It never does any good to go back. Our memory always idealizes the past. If we return to it, we never find there what we're seeking.

BEN. Maybe.

OLD MAN. What are you studying here at the university?

BEN. I . . . I hope to become an architect.

OLD MAN. And you're an athlete, too? Remarkable.

BEN. I'm supposed to run in the relays.

OLD MAN. But aren't you going to?

BEN. I . . . I don't think so.

OLD MAN. But they'll be waiting for you at the stadium.

BEN. Let them.

OLD MAN. They're counting on you.

BEN. What if they are!

OLD MAN. I should think you'd be eager to start your race.

BEN. I was . . . until a few minutes ago.

OLD MAN. And now?

BEN. [*Slowly, with bitter distaste.*] Races suddenly seem . . . *disgusting.*

OLD MAN. Why?

BEN. I never knew before . . . what it is to lose.

[*Another shout of victory goes up.*]

VOICES. Yeh Pomeroy!

Give 'em the axe, the axe, the axe!
Give 'em the axe, the axe, the axe!

Yeh! Yeh!

OLD MAN. [*Still in thought, responding to* BEN.] Yes, it's terrifying, to lose.

[Two YOUNG ATHLETES, BEN's *age, run on together.*]

FIRST ATHLETE. Hey, Ben, we been lookin' all over for you.

SECOND ATHLETE. You're in the next event. Get goin'.

OLD MAN. [*Gently urging him.*] Go on, young man.

BEN. [*To the other athletes.*] Why should I?

FIRST ATHLETE. What?

SECOND ATHLETE. For crying out loud, Ben, you can't let us down.

BEN. I'm not going to run in the race.

FIRST ATHLETE. Well . . . I'll be a . . .

SECOND ATHLETE. Have you gone nuts?

OLD MAN. Young man, think carefully about this. Try to persuade yourself . . .

BEN. I've made up my mind. [*There is a long pause.*]

FIRST ATHLETE. What'll we tell the coach, Ben?

BEN. Whatever you like.

SECOND ATHLETE. Who'll he put in your place?

BEN. He'll find someone.

FIRST ATHLETE. [*Angrily.*] You're a lousy sport.

SECOND ATHLETE. I agree.

BEN. I suppose I am.

FIRST ATHLETE. [*With a look at* SECOND ATHLETE.] Well . . . let's go back and give 'em the news.

SECOND ATHLETE. O.K.

[*The* TWO ATHLETES *run off together.* BEN *stands rigid. The* OLD MAN *watches with keen and sympathetic interest. The cheering and the music resume in the background.*]

OLD MAN. [*Finally.*] It shouldn't frighten you so . . . to lose.

BEN. No . . . it *shouldn't.*

[TOM *and* ANN *come running on together.* ANN *calls.*]

ANN. Ben!

[BEN *turns as if trying to escape them.*]

TOM. Ben, we have to talk to you.

[BEN *waits. They come to his side.*]

ANN. You know? I'm wearing Tom's pin?

[BEN *nods.*]

I wanted to be the one to tell you, Ben.

TOM. We were *both* gonna tell you, Ben.

ANN. Ben . . .

[BEN *stands attentive but keeps his eyes off both of them.*]
I just wanted to tell you . . . I really like you an awful lot.

TOM. Ann still thinks the world of you, Ben . . . and I guess
you know how *I* feel, don't you? I feel we'll always be friends.
[*He puts an arm around* BEN's *shoulder.*]

ANN. Tom says you're the best friend he ever had.

TOM. And I mean it.

ANN. I don't see any reason why we can't still be friends, Ben.
Maybe better friends than before.

TOM. Ben . . . why don't you come to the Varsity Dance with
us tonight? If you don't have a date, you can dance with Ann all
you want to . . .

ANN. I'd love it, Ben.

TOM. Come on, Ben. You'll get over this eventually. Why not
now?

BEN. [*Words come with difficulty.*] I hadn't planned . . . to
go to the Varsity.

VOICES. [*Calling from the stadium.*] Tom! Hey, Tom! Where
are you, Tom? Your event is next, Tom!

TOM. Golly, I'm next. I gotta beat it. Wait for me at the gate,
Ann. [TOM *starts but* BEN *holds him.*]

BEN. [*Grasping* TOM's *sleeve.*]
Tom! [*He is trembling with rage.*]

TOM. Hey, Ben, I gotta go.

BEN. [*Sobbing in rage.*] Damn you, Tom! Damn you! I hate
you now . . . hate you enough to kill. [*He seizes* TOM *by the
throat.*] You were my friend, and you've filled me with a hate
I've never known.

TOM. [*Forcing himself from* BEN's *hold.*] Ben!

ANN. Ben, you can't hate Tom. He's your friend.

TOM. [*Going to* BEN.] I don't want you to hate me, Ben. I
don't want you to.

BEN. [*Realizing the futility of his gesture.*] Go on.

TOM. I don't want you to hate me, Ben.

BEN. Go on. They're waiting.
[TOM *runs off.*]

ANN. You mustn't blame Tom for what happened, Ben. It's my

fault as much as his. We've fallen in love. Don't you see? It wasn't something that we did intentionally. It . . . just happened.

BEN. I don't feel much like talking, Ann.

ANN. I understand. Please try to look on us as friends, Ben. Please.

BEN. I'm not sure I know how to look on anyone any more, Ann.

ANN. Just remember that we do like you. We do.

BEN. Like is such a pale word.

ANN. You'll find another girl in time, Ben. A girl who'll love you just as much as I love Tom.

BEN. Some people . . . don't find love . . . very easily, Ann.

ANN. You didn't love me, Ben. Not really. You were just used to me, and I was used to you, because we've known each other so long.

BEN. But I did love you, Ann.

ANN. Not like Tom does, Ben. A girl knows when she is really loved, Ben.

BEN. Are you going to be married?

ANN. This summer.

BEN. I feel like an outsider already.

ANN. Oh Ben, we want you as best man, and we want you as our friend forever.

BEN. Goodbye, Ann.

ANN. You'll get over it, Ben. In another few weeks, you'll find another girl and wonder what you ever saw in me.

BEN. I'd like to be alone a while now, Ann.

ANN. [*Kisses him on the cheek.*] Goodbye Ben.

[*She runs off.* BEN *slips to the ground, his body convulsed with groaning sobs, writhing in mortal agony. The* OLD MAN, *who has stood withdrawn on his hillock throughout all this scene, now makes a tentative gesture as though hoping to console* BEN, *but then decides it might be better not to interfere, and so returns his attention to the field below where trumpets are sounding for a new event and the band plays* Boola Boola. *But he cannot help recalling* BEN's *pros-*

trate body on the ground, and so he turns again from the games and goes to him, speaking softly.]

OLD MAN. Young man . . .

[BEN *does not move.*]

You mustn't let yourself feel so deeply. You will only make your own life very unhappy.

BEN. Now I know why people go mad and kill.

OLD MAN. Yes. Some people go mad and kill.

BEN. And all the hatred I feel . . . is wasted, isn't it?

OLD MAN. Yes. It's a lot of powerful feeling . . . you feel it's powerful enough to propel a great machine . . . but it has no use at all. It blackens the very sky above and blinds you to everything lovely you might see.

BEN. [*In a fury of protest.*] I don't want to hate. I don't want to.

OLD MAN. No. Hatred will destroy you.

BEN. [*Jumps to his feet, runs to the right, calling into distance.*] Tom, come back! I won't hate you, Tom. I won't hate you.

[*Down in the stadium, a gun is fired, starting the race.*]

OLD MAN. He won't hear you now. He's in the race.

BEN. [*In a weak voice, returning Center.*] Tom!

OLD MAN. Young man, maybe you'd like to come up on my hillock and watch.

BEN. No.

OLD MAN. Oh, the games are most exciting. Come and watch. Here beside me.

BEN. I've always played in the games. I feel humiliated just to stand and watch.

OLD MAN. Oh, come now. One doesn't have to run in the races to enjoy them. Sometimes I think I enjoy the relays more than anyone, standing up here on my lonely hillside. And I can spell Nebuchadnezzar, too. [*He chuckles.*]

[BEN *is still reluctant.*]

Come along.

[BEN *slowly rises and starts up the hillside, as though trying an unheard-of experiment.*]

BEN. The games . . . will look different . . . from here.

OLD MAN. [*Displaying the view as though it were a great painting.*] Up here, you can see them all, and the view gives them perspective. Isn't it a magnificent sight.

[BEN *looks intently into the distance.*]

And when the games are over, you don't have to fight your way through all the crowd.

BEN. [*Beginning to sound interested.*] Look! Tom won his race, didn't he?

OLD MAN. Yes. He won. He won.

BEN. I'm glad . . . he won.

OLD MAN. And now they're starting a new event. Oh, listen to the trumpets and the bumptious band. And see the cheer leaders jumping up and down.

[*We hear those sounds.*]

BEN. [*Smiling.*] Yes. It's like something happening in another world, from up here.

OLD MAN. But it's beautiful, isn't it? And fascinating?

BEN. Yes, yes. Oh, I'll want to watch the games forever.

[*Curtain*]

UNDERSTANDING AND APPRECIATING THE PLAY

1. By referring to characters and situations, discuss what this play has to say about the following problems:

A. How one should face times of adversity or misfortune.

B. The need to take time out occasionally to take stock of what we're doing and where we're heading.

C. The need, on the other hand, for some people to be more active participants in the game of life.

2. Does this play show evidence of Inge's gift for writing very accurate and convincing dialogue? Do Ben, Ann, and Tom speak the way young people do in real life? Discuss.

3. How did you react to the principal characters' baring their hearts to you so frankly and completely?

4. Is *The Sounds of Triumph* worthy of William Inge, who is regarded as one of America's outstanding dramatists? How good or

how bad is the play? What did you like or dislike about it? Would it be a wise choice for a public performance at your school? Why?

5. How helpful was the professor to Ben? Explain.

6. Do you approve of the way in which Tom and Ann broke the news of their engagement to Ben? Why?

7. Do you think that Ben's reaction to what Tom and Ann told him was typical of most boys in such a situation? What would you have done if you were in Ben's place?

8. Could Ann have been certain that Ben didn't love her as much as Tom did? Does a person really know how strongly he or she is loved? Explain. In this connection, do you think that Ben might have been hurt not so much because he loved Ann but because his pride was hurt?

9. Why should Ben not have hated Tom and possibly Ann? What reasons did the professor give for Ben not to hate? How convincing are these reasons?

10. Discuss the following quotations, first in the context of the play and then in their application to situations and problems encountered in life:

A. Tom: "Sorry, old man. These things are tough, but human beings always get over'em. It's just part of growing up."

B. Ben: "Some people don't find love . . . very easily, Ann."

C. Old Man: "It never does any good to go back. Our memory always idealizes the past. If we return to it, we never find there what we're seeking."

D. Ben (the last line of the play): "Yes, yes. Oh, I'll want to watch the games forever!"

E. Ronnie Hopkins: "What do I care about ancient history? Why should I spend time worrying about what happened in the past? *I'm* living now."

F. Old Man: "I suppose all people are divided into two groups, those who participate, and those who watch and observe. . . . I wonder if I have lived life at all, if my life has not been . . . a period of observation."

VOCABULARY BUILDING

Explain the following phrases or clauses in your own words: *strident* band music; Their mood is still *jovial;* The old man *takes cognizance* of him; tries to sound *diverting;* all but *writhing* with the pain of his *dejection;* the voices sounding *vindictive;* I trembled in her mere

proximity; mumble some *incoherent* protest; after *grave* consideration; a look of *intense* anguish.

THINGS TO DO

1. Develop one of the following topics: How to Face Times of
Adversity, A Trying Time for Me, A Great Disappointment, Learning
"How to Take It," It's Part of Growing Up, If I Had It to Do Over
Again, A Fear (or a Handicap) Which I Overcame.

2. Work up and act out in sociodrama fashion another way or
other ways in which Tom and Ann might have told Ben about their
being in love, and how Ben might have reacted to what they told him.

3. Do research on a time of crisis, danger, or adversity faced by a
nation, by an individual, or by a racial, religious, or other group.
Write an essay, story, or dramatization based upon your research.

4. Discuss your ideas of what is meant "by being in love" or of
the qualities that make for a good husband or wife.

5. For speech or writing:

A. Do you approve of early marriages? Do you approve of young
people marrying while one or both are in college?

B. In sports, are we a nation of spectators? Do we devote far too
much time in watching others compete and far too little time in
our own participation in sports?

C. Should colleges give athletic scholarships and subsidize athletes
in other ways?

D. Should interscholastic and/or intercollegiate athletics (that is,
varsity teams) be abolished?

6. Just as Ronnie Hopkins questioned the value of studying ancient history, so do many students object to subjects which do not
seem to them to be directly related to the vocation or profession
which they intend to enter. Thus a student will say, "I want to be a
secretary, why should I study science or read Shakespeare?" Another
will inquire, "I am going to be an engineer. Why should I study
foreign languages?" What do you think of such statements? How important are such general-education subjects as literature, foreign
languages, and history?

PRODUCTION NOTES

Before an appropriate audience and with a capable cast, *The Sounds of Triumph* is an excellent choice for staging. But you must be certain that you have the right kinds of viewers and cast. Your audience should be mature enough, emotionally and intellectually, to enjoy and appreciate a serious play in which utterly frank, highly dramatic revelations of emotion alternate with longer incidents of quiet reflection. Then you must have someone sufficiently skilled and uninhibited to express the wide range of emotions which the actor playing Ben is required to portray. Furthermore, you should have someone capable of interpreting the personality of the professor: his age and physical infirmity, his academic knowledge and philosophic wisdom, his concern for others, his introverted withdrawal from much of life. Fortunately, it is not so difficult to find actors who can play the parts of Tom and Ann convincingly.

In directing the play, it is important to highlight the contrasts between the quiet scenes and the dynamic ones. It is, of course, essential to "build" properly in the dramatic incidents. With certain audiences, it may be preferable to reduce the number of romantic scenes between Tom and Ann and to eliminate some of Ben's emotional postures and reactions. The noise and cheers of the crowd need not be reproduced with absolute fidelity; instead, the sounds may merely be suggested. You may wish to experiment with recording the sounds of the crowd on tape. Make certain, however, that you can reproduce the sound on cue.

Jacob Comes Home *

WILLIAM KOZLENKO

In *Jacob Comes Home,* William Kozlenko takes us to the Germany of the Nazi era, in the late 1930's, and with great power and poetic insight he tells us a tragic story. It is a story which shows how brutalized and degraded a nation can become when racial and religious hatred poisons the mind and hardens the heart.

To understand this play fully, one should know something about the period with which it deals. In 1933 Hitler and his Nazi Party turned Germany into a police state, openly proclaiming their contempt for democratic ideals and scoffing at those who believed in the dignity and worth of all mankind. They insisted on the right of the strong to rule the weak, on the absolute subordination of the individual to the state, and on the need for unquestioning obedience to Hitler and the leaders he appointed. Glorifying hatred and force, the Nazis made brutality and conquest a way of life. For those who were different or who disagreed, a knock at the door might well mean torture and death. Whether it was because of race, creed, or political beliefs, many people suffered under Hitler, but the chief symbol of Nazi oppression was the Jew. "The art of truly great popular leaders in all ages," Hitler had written in his autobiography *Mein Kampf,* "consisted in not detracting the attention of the people, but in concentrating always on a single adversary." For the Nazi, the Jew was a convenient "adversary," and the story of *Jacob Comes Home* was repeated, in various ways, not once or twice but six million times.

The play is, accordingly, a human record of a particularly tragic period in history. It is also more than that. The oppression of the individual because of his race or his belief did not stop with Hitler's death. Around the world there are still men, whether of fascist or communist persuasion, who use Hitler's ideas and methods in their attack on personal dignity and freedom. So, in a way, the tragedy of the Braun family we are about to meet in the play is a tragedy of our century.

CHARACTERS

LIESE BRAUN
MAGDA BRAUN, *her mother*
JOSEPH BRAUN, *her grandfather*
HULDA, *Magda's sister*
RUDOLF HUBER, *Jacob's friend*

SYNOPSIS

TIME: 1939
PLACE: Berlin, Germany

The scene is a home in Berlin, Germany. It is evening. At C. in the back wall is a window, looking out onto the street. U.R. is a door leading outside. At L. is a table, with a chair on either side. There is another chair U.R.C., and one D.L., and still another at R. The room is dimly lighted, as if darkness were far more welcome than light. A candelabrum with three flickering candles [1] stands on the table at L.

As the curtain rises, LIESE BRAUN, *a girl in her early twenties, is standing by the window, peering out from behind the drawn curtains.* HULDA *is at L.,* RUDOLPH *sits in the chair U.R.,* JOSEPH *is in the chair at R. of table, and* MAGDA *is at L. of table. There is a note of strange suspense and anticipation in the room. The long silences between speeches are like heavy rests in music— or else like the weighing of words when life and death hang in the balance.*

MAGDA. [*Looking up at* LIESE.] Any sign yet, Liese?
LIESE. No, Mother. Not yet.

[1] Since the Brauns are a Jewish family, they have observed the religious custom of ushering in the Jewish Sabbath by lighting candles on Fridays at sundown.

MAGDA. What can be keeping him?

HULDA. [*Slowly crossing to R.C.*] How can you see when the street is so dark?

JOSEPH. She has young eyes, Hulda, and her senses have been sharpened by fear.

HULDA. [*Her back to the audience; speaking to* JOSEPH.] I know, Father, but, still . . . when all the lights are turned off . . .

LIESE. Faces are hard to recognize—but I can make out the figures.

HULDA. Even without the uniforms?

LIESE. Both.

MAGDA. Why should I tremble so with fright?

JOSEPH. Do we know else but fear and terror these days?

MAGDA. It's like a chill.

[HULDA *sits in the chair D.R.*]

RUDOLF. When I was taken by the—when I left . . . they were still searching houses. Have they ceased, already?

LIESE. There are still many Jews left in Germany, Rudolf.

JOSEPH. Too many for the— [2]

LIESE. [*Frightened.*] Grandfather, please—

JOSEPH. Who can hear me, child? We are among friends.

RUDOLF. Joseph, please, never dare say that word.

JOSEPH. Even here—in my own house?

LIESE. Yes—even here.

HULDA. You frighten me. I must go.

JOSEPH. Of what are you frightened, Hulda? A word?

HULDA. Of that word, Father—of that word.

JOSEPH. This is my house. I was born here. Walls and the lips of friends do not betray.

LIESE. Not even walls. They listen and when they—they come . . . they speak.

MAGDA. [*Coming D.L.*] I am frightened. I don't know why, but I'm frightened.

HULDA. I must leave. My children are alone in the house.

JOSEPH. Stay, Hulda. We are waiting . . .

[2] When he was interrupted by Liese, Joseph meant to say, "Too many for the Nazis."

MAGDA. [*Approaching* RUDOLF, *a few steps at a time.*] Rudolf, please remember. . . . Think hard. . . . Are you sure it's today?

RUDOLF. That's what I heard. Magda, would I lie to you?

MAGDA. You wouldn't, but they—

RUDOLF. They said, "On Friday your Jacob can go home."

HULDA. Which Friday?

RUDOLF. Today. I heard the news myself on Monday.

MAGDA. Why didn't they release Jacob on Monday, too?

JOSEPH. Monday is yesterday. Friday is today. We are waiting for today.

MAGDA. Did they say when today?

RUDOLF. Would they say such a thing? Friday, that's all.

LIESE. But he isn't here yet.

JOSEPH. We must wait.

MAGDA. How can we be sure? It may have been a lie. [*She goes to chair L.*]

RUDOLF. There were two hundred men in the prison . . . from this neighborhood.

JOSEPH. All Jews?

RUDOLF. Not all.

HULDA. How many?

RUDOLF. About a hundred—young and old. The warden called off a list of names. Ten names on Monday—my name was in that. Ten names on Tuesday. Ten names on Wednesday . . . and so on. And in the ten names for Friday . . . he called out Jacob Braun.

MAGDA. Our Jacob?

RUDOLF. Jacob Braun from Wiengasse.[3]

HULDA. That's our Jacob.

MAGDA. Did you see him?

RUDOLF. He was standing beside me.

MAGDA. What did he do?

RUDOLF. He began to weep.

LIESE. Did my father say anything?

RUDOLF. He wasn't allowed to speak.

MAGDA. And then . . . ?

[3] Vienna Avenue; pronounced Vēn' gäss ĕ.

RUDOLF. [*Rising and coming downstage.*] But, Magda, I told you all this already.

MAGDA. [*Going toward* RUDOLF *D.R.*] I know, Rudolf, I know. Please forgive me. Tell me again . . . again. . . .

RUDOLF. He clutched my hand.

MAGDA. Warmly?

RUDOLF. As a friend would clutch a friend's hand. [*He takes* MAGDA's *hand.*]

MAGDA. Was he happy that you were leaving?

RUDOLF. Very happy. He said I should come to see you and tell you. . . .

MAGDA. And then?

RUDOLF. He whispered. . . .

LIESE. No one saw him?

RUDOLF. No one. His breath brushed my ear. "On Friday I shall be home," he said, "home . . ."

MAGDA. He said it just that way? Home?

RUDOLF. He was choking—the tears stuck in his throat. . . . If they saw him cry, they'd—

MAGDA. And then, Rudolf? Then? Tell me.

RUDOLF. The Monday prisoners were discharged. [*He drops* MAGDA's *hand, and crosses to D.L.*]

LIESE. Is that when you last saw him?

RUDOLF. He was standing off, by himself, trying to smile. He wanted to cry, but he smiled. He waved me a greeting, and then they took him away.

HULDA. And now we are waiting for him.

LIESE. [*Coming down to back of* JOSEPH's *chair.*] They let you go out quietly? They said or did nothing?

RUDOLF. They said little and did much.

JOSEPH. I hear stories. . . . Are they true?

RUDOLF. True.

JOSEPH. What?

RUDOLF. They exercise what they call small formalities to discourage opposition when you leave.

MAGDA. Did Jacob always weep? Did he always choke with tears in his throat?

RUDOLF. He never smiled.

JOSEPH. Formalities, Rudolf?

RUDOLF. Yes. Liese, is anybody coming this way?

[LIESE *goes U.C. to the window.*]

LIESE. The street is empty.

JOSEPH. You can speak.

[LIESE *turns back to the group.*]

HULDA. How can you see when it's so dark?

[MAGDA *goes to* HULDA.]

RUDOLF. [*Going to the table and speaking directly to* JOSEPH.]
They took me into a small room . . . four men with steel whips
stood with feet apart . . . two stripped me naked. . . .

HULDA. They beat you?

RUDOLF. [*Terror-stricken.*] Oh, God! I am afraid! Even here!
I am afraid.

JOSEPH. Say it softly, my son, very softly . . . as if you were
saying it to yourself.

RUDOLF. Such fear and terror they bring into a man's heart.

JOSEPH. Speak, Rudolf, speak. . . . Do not be afraid.

RUDOLF. The flesh remembers—

JOSEPH. Whisper it.

RUDOLF. —and cries out in pain even here—even here.

JOSEPH. Whisper it, as Jacob brushed your ear with a whisper.

RUDOLF. I can't! I can't!

JOSEPH. Courage, Rudolf. Give your thoughts a voice and—

RUDOLF. Oh, merciful God! To have lived through such suffering! To be thrown bleeding dead to the ground! Not to be able
to shriek out: "What have I done? What have I done? Are you
living men that you stand unmoved by a living man's pain? Are
you living men that you stand unshaken by a living man's cries?"
God, what is this beast that came from a father and mother and
still calls itself—a man! Who is this judge that proclaims: "You,
Jew, shall die! You, Jew, shall live!" [*He slumps into the chair at
L.* JOSEPH *rises and goes to* RUDOLF. *After a moment, he speaks.*]

JOSEPH. Oh, Rudolf, my son, there are no words in a man's heart
that can appease the burning pain in his body. You have suffered
in your helplessness, and we have suffered in ours. Because your

body and your spirit have felt torture, does that mean that we, who have not yet been tortured, feel this torture the less? Must we be whipped into bleeding shreds to learn the pain a body can endure? Is there not a 'greater pain in waiting and not knowing who will be next? Our hearts throb in our chests like knuckles beating frantically on a door. And unspoken voices shriek in our ears: It's your turn now! Your turn! And if a day passes that they are not at our doors, there is the dread of the morrow, when the knuckles will be on the hand of a man, and the voice the voice of torture come to make us dead!

RUDOLF. Where is the fury of this righteous world that allows living flesh to be so degraded?

JOSEPH. No, Rudolf, not the fury of a righteous world! But the righteousness of fury!

MAGDA. And Jacob? Must he, too—

RUDOLF. None is spared. The strong may survive. But the weak will perish.

MAGDA. But if they see he is sick and kind, would they still—

RUDOLF. [*Rising and turning downstage.*] Are they physicians that they seek to cure the ill? If you are strong, they make you weak. If you walk erect, they make you lame. If you love life, they make you want death. And if you refuse to die—

MAGDA. They . . . ?

RUDOLF. Make you dead!

LIESE. [*Looking out of the window.*] Shshsh! . . . Quiet. . . . I see two men coming down the street.

MAGDA. [*Moving a few steps U.C.*] Two?

HULDA. Are they in uniform?

LIESE. They're still too far away. I can't make out.

MAGDA. Are they walking slowly or—

LIESE. Slowly.

MAGDA. [*Standing by the chair U.C.*] One must be Jacob! [*She turns toward C.*] Oh, God, Jacob has come home! Jacob has returned to us—alive!

JOSEPH. Are they approaching closer? [*He goes to the window and looks over* LIESE's *right shoulder.*]

LIESE. Yes . . . but they do not speak to each other.

JOSEPH. They are afraid of the wind that would catch their words and drop them on hostile ears.

HULDA. Who can the other man be?

RUDOLF. Perhaps a friend who has also been befriended.

LIESE. One is tall, the other short.

JOSEPH. [*To* MAGDA.] The tall man must be Jacob.

MAGDA. There will be happiness in another home tonight.

HULDA. They must also be sitting like us, or standing by the window, watching and waiting. . . .

MAGDA. Where are they now?

LIESE. Crossing the street.

JOSEPH. If my eyes were not so dim, I would stand here and count the number of steps that would bring Jacob to this door.

RUDOLF. I would do it; but I dare not show my face at the window.

LIESE. I would say they are about fifty feet away. . . .

HULDA. You still can't see their faces?

LIESE. They have hats pulled down low.

JOSEPH. They must either be ashamed or afraid.

RUDOLF. If they are Jews, they are afraid. If—

LIESE. Rudolf, quiet!

MAGDA. Jacob will soon be here. [*Going to* JOSEPH *U.L.C.*] Do I look well? Are my eyes red?

JOSEPH. He will welcome you as you are.

MAGDA. [*Looking around to include the others.*] No, no, I must look my best! He is returning home. When he opens the door, let us start to sing. . . .

RUDOLF. Sing softly, or they will think we have feasted on wine.

JOSEPH. Or that we are too happy.

MAGDA. [*At C.*] I *am* happy. Why should I deny it? Jacob has returned home!

JOSEPH. He must not speak of his suffering. His silence will be more eloquent. But we—we must talk of everything else but the things that have given him so much pain.

RUDOLF. He will look at you with strange, fearful eyes.

MAGDA. He will be home!

RUDOLF. There will be dread in them. . . . Words will falter on his tongue . . .

LIESE. We promise not to stare at him.

RUDOLF. Each here will ask himself: "Can this be the same living Jacob who left this house ten days ago?"

JOSEPH. He will return as if he had arisen from the grave.

RUDOLF. Remember to let your eyes tell lies. When he looks into them, let him not see what you see.

LIESE. [*Taking* MAGDA's *arm.*] We will laugh, and our eyes will laugh with us!

MAGDA. He will be home! That's all I know! That's all I care! [*She goes near the door.*]

RUDOLF. [*Going to the chair L. of table.*] But you must make him smile! Must make him laugh! Must—

LIESE. [*At the window.*] Softer, Rudolf. They are coming toward the house.

RUDOLF. —make him forget even for an hour.

JOSEPH. The hour will begin in a moment.

LIESE. They are nearer . . .

MAGDA. Sixty more seconds and we shall hear his step . . .

LIESE. They are looking around.

MAGDA. Strangers look around. Jacob is no stranger.

RUDOLF. [*Taking a step toward C.*] It must be—

LIESE. Shshsh!

HULDA. If the bell should suddenly ring—

LIESE. [*Turning to C.*] Why couldn't I make out the faces?

HULDA. —I would faint.

RUDOLF. Your eyes must be wet, Liese.

HULDA. How can you see when the night is so dark?

JOSEPH. He is walking up the stairs . . . step by step . . .

RUDOLF. They walk very slowly after they come back.

MAGDA. Now he's on the first landing . . .

JOSEPH. He has stopped to catch his breath.

MAGDA. Now he is turning . . .

HULDA. Is there a light in the hallway?

JOSEPH. One more flight and—

MAGDA. Shshsh!

[*They are all turned toward the door, paralyzed. Waiting,*

*waiting: a great deep silence is being ticked away by un-
heard seconds.* RUDOLF *leans forward across the table.* JOSEPH
rises, tense. MAGDA *takes a step R. then pauses. Suddenly
from the other room comes a* CRASH *of glass, as if a rock had
been hurled through the window.*]

HULDA. [*Jumping up.*] My God!

JOSEPH. [*Rising.*] Of the two, neither was Jacob. [*He starts to
walk slowly into the other room.*]

MAGDA. Father! Father, don't go in!

JOSEPH. Of what are you afraid—a dead stone?

RUDOLF. Of the living hand that threw it.

HULDA. I am frightened! I must go!

[JOSEPH *goes into the other room.*]

LIESE. [*Almost in tears.*] If there were only a little bit more
light. I could have seen; and seen right; would not have hoped.

JOSEPH. [*Returning with the rock in his hand.*] Once, this may
have been part of a man—a head, perhaps, or a heart . . .

RUDOLF. Our country beats with the tread of uniformed men
who have hearts such as this . . .

HULDA. The stone was a warning. . . . First, windows; then,
heads.

JOSEPH. No, Hulda, a symbol of how little separates this rock
from the throbbing heart of a pitiless man.

LIESE. Shsh! . . . I see somebody walking.

RUDOLF. Slow or fast?

LIESE. Fast.

MAGDA. It cannot be Jacob.

LIESE. He wears his hat high on his head.

JOSEPH. He is either a proud or a fearless man.

LIESE. And he's coming this way.

RUDOLF. Many men live on this street. Why hope and tremble?

JOSEPH. We shall wait.

MAGDA. I know Jacob's walk. It is slow and heavy.

LIESE. This man is looking at our house.

HULDA. Can you see his face?

LIESE. He has gone.

RUDOLF. He was not looking for us.

MAGDA. The candles have burned low, Father.

JOSEPH. Within the hour they will have burned out. When Jacob returns, we will light three others. For Jacob, too, is a pious man.

[*A* RING. LIESE *jumps away from the window. They all come together, huddling close, fear and dread on their faces.*]

MAGDA. Lord in Heaven, can it be—

JOSEPH. Shall I go?

[*Strong* KNOCKING *on the door.*]

MAN. [*From off R.*] Open up!

HULDA. [*Whimpering.*] For whom has he come? For whom?

JOSEPH. Hulda, quiet! Show no fear.

MAN. Open up!

MAGDA. [*Opening the door.*] My name is—

VOICE. Is this the Braun residence?

MAGDA. Yes.

MAN. Your name?

MAGDA. Magda Braun.

MAN. Wife—

MAGDA. —of Jacob Braun.

MAN. [*Handing her a small, carefully wrapped parcel.*] Package . . .

MAGDA. Package?

MAN.[4] Addressed to you. Three marks charge, please.

MAGDA. Three—

MAN. For the ashes of your husband! [5]

MAGDA. My . . . !

JOSEPH. [*Bending his head; softly.*] Jacob *has* come home. . . .
[MAGDA, *dazed, digs into her dress pocket for the money, as the curtain slowly falls.*]

The End

[4] The man was a member of the Gestapo, the secret police of Nazi Germany.

[5] The three marks charge was not taken out of thin air by the playwright. The Nazis burned the bodies of thousands of Jews whom they had killed in concentration camps. For a period of time in Berlin, when a Jewish woman was permitted to collect the remains of her husband, in the form of an urn of ashes, the Nazis charged her three and a half marks.

UNDERSTANDING AND APPRECIATING THE PLAY

1. Why was the rock hurled through the window of the Braun home? What kind of persons might have thrown the rock? What do you think of people who commit acts of this kind? What can be done to reduce such incidents?

2. What is the final outcome of the play? Did you expect the play to end in this manner? Is it a credible ending or an impossible one? Why?

3. Justify classifying the play as a tragedy.

4. It has been said that prejudice and hatred are two-edged swords —that those who are guilty of prejudice or hatred are also harmed. Do you agree with this belief? Why? Do you think that the Nazis were hurt by their own brutality? Why?

5. What is the climax of the play?

6. Discuss the use of suspense in *Jacob Comes Home*.

7. This is a play of tragic power and poetic impulse. Select parts of the play that have a beauty of language or a distinct lift in style, and be prepared to read them aloud as effectively as you can.

8. Part of the problem of exposition is to establish the mood, or emotional tone, of the drama. Usually, the mood and atmosphere are established at the very beginning by the setting and lighting and by what the characters who open the play do and say. How soon and in what ways is the emotional tone of *Jacob Comes Home* established?

VOCABULARY BUILDING

Jacob Comes Home is an example of how effective something stated in simple language can be. With the exception of the German expressions, there is scarcely a word in the play with which you are not familiar. Name and discuss some outstanding writings and speeches which are noted for the simplicity of their language and style.

THINGS TO DO

1. For discussion or written expression: Religious and racial prejudice. What are the causes—that is, why are some people prejudiced

against those of another religion or race? How can prejudice be reduced?

2. Read the poems "Ozymandias," by Percy Bysshe Shelley, and
"Four Preludes," by Carl Sandburg. Comment in writing or orally on
what these poems have to say about the vanity of absolute rulers and
of chauvinistic nations.

3. During the depression years of the 1930's, various radical and
totalitarian movements and personalities—including Communists,
Fascists, and Nazis—tried to influence Americans to follow them.
Hate mongers tried to blame unemployment and other economic dis-
location upon religious or political groups which they disliked. Study
and report upon one movement or personality of this kind. Point
out how this group or leader constituted a threat to our American
democracy and to the civil rights of American citizens.

4. For discussion or written expression: How can we best combat
communism in America? How can we best combat Fascism or Naziism
in America?

5. Theme topic: Man's Inhumanity to Man.

PRODUCTION NOTES

Jacob Comes Home is reprinted here in an acting edition based
on productions in the Northwestern University Studio Theater. There
are therefore many helpful directions for all concerned with the
staging of the play.

Stage movement and grouping are very specifically delineated.
The director is nevertheless advised to supplement the directions
provided in the script by blocking out the action in a prompt book,
modifying the groupings and movements as he sees fit. In addition,
he must see to it that the actors do full justice to the poetic dialogue
and that the prevailing mood of "strange suspense and anticipation"
is established and maintained. As an aid to achieving effective contrasts in emotional intensity and variety in suspense, consult Figure 1,
the plot-suspense chart for *Jacob Comes Home* in the chapter on
Staging the Plays.

Suggestions to the technical staff: The sound of breaking glass is
generally simulated by placing pieces of old window glass in a sack
and smashing the glass by hurling the sack on to the floor. A note of
caution to the lighting technician: although the key to success in
lighting the play is in the direction "The room is dimly lighted, as if
darkness were far more welcome than light," be certain to provide

sufficient illumination for easy visibility of the action. Effective spot-lighting, moreover, can enhance the emotional impact of the play. The technical staff may consider the possibility of using music as a background. The *Jacob Comes Home* booklets published by Row, Peterson and Company provide a cue sheet for music.

The Valiant*

HOLWORTHY HALL AND ROBERT MIDDLEMASS

Why do people act as they do? How can we explain the quirks of human behavior?

Very few one-act plays have achieved a popularity equal to that enjoyed by *The Valiant*, and even fewer have been performed as frequently. A survey of the reading interests of thousands of students in the State of New York revealed that this play was the most popular literary selection read in the high schools of that state. Since 1921 it has been played thousands of times on television and radio and in schools, colleges, Little Theaters, and vaudeville; it has served as a starring vehicle for several famous actors, among them Paul Muni. If it is true that the dramatist's main aim is to arouse an emotional response, then this play richly succeeds, and its great popularity is no mystery. Intensely gripping, and exerting a marked emotional appeal, it is certain to thrill an audience. As a reader, your problem is to imagine the action so vividly that you will react with as much emotion as the audience in the theater.

Unusually well planned, *The Valiant* is an almost perfect example of the closely-knit plot so essential in a play in which the interest lies mainly in the outcome of the conflict. The dialogue, too, is written with consummate skill.

CHARACTERS

WARDEN HOLT, *about sixty*
FATHER DALY, *the prison chaplain*
JAMES DYKE, *the prisoner*
JOSEPHINE PARIS, *the girl, about eighteen*
DAN, *a jailer*
AN ATTENDANT

SCENE: *The* WARDEN'S *office in the State's Prison at Wethersfield,*
   Connecticut
TIME: *About half-past eleven on a rainy night*

The Curtain rises upon the WARDEN'S *office in the State's Prison
at Wethersfield, Connecticut. It is a large, cold, unfriendly apart-
ment, with bare floors and staring, whitewashed walls; it is furnished only with the* WARDEN'S *flat-topped desk, and swivel-chair,
with a few straight-backed chairs, one beside the desk and others
against the walls, with a water-cooler and an eight-day clock. On
the* WARDEN'S *desk. are a telephone instrument, a row of electric
push-buttons, and a bundle of forty or fifty letters. At the back
of the room are two large windows, crossed with heavy bars; at the
left there is a door to an anteroom, and at the right there are two
doors, of which the more distant leads to the office of the deputy
warden, and the nearer is seldom used.*

WARDEN HOLT, *dressed in a dark brown sack suit, with a negligee shirt and black string-tie, carelessly knotted in a bow, is seated
at his desk, reflectively smoking a long, thin cigar. He is verging
toward sixty, and his responsibilities have printed themselves in
italics upon his countenance. His brown hair and bushy eye-
brows are heavily shot with gray; there is a deep parenthesis of
wrinkles at the corners of his mouth and innumerable fine lines
about his eyes. His bearing indicates that he is accustomed to
rank as a despot, and yet his expression is far from that of an un-
reasoning tyrant. He is no sentimentalist, but he believes that
in each of us there is a constant oscillation of good and evil; and
that all evil should be justly punished in this world, and that all
good should be generously rewarded—in the next.*

Behind the WARDEN, *the prison* CHAPLAIN *stands at one of the
barred windows, gazing steadily out into the night.* FATHER DALY
*is a slender, white-haired priest of somewhat more than middle
age; he is dressed in slightly shabby clericals. His face is calm,
intellectual and inspiring; but just at this moment, it gives evidence of a peculiar depression.*

The WARDEN *blows a cloud of smoke to the ceiling, inspects the
cigar critically, drums on the desk, and finally peers over his*

shoulder at the CHAPLAIN. *He clears his throat and speaks brusquely.*

THE WARDEN. Has it started to rain?

FATHER DALY. [*Answers without turning.*] Yes, it has.

THE WARDEN. [*Glaring at his cigar and impatiently tossing it aside.*] It *would* rain tonight. [*His tone is vaguely resentful, as though the weather had added a needless fraction to his impatience.*]

FATHER DALY. [*Glances at a big silver watch.*] It's past eleven o'clock. [*He draws a deep breath and comes slowly to the center of the room.*] We haven't much longer to wait.

THE WARDEN. No, thank God! [*He gets up, and goes to the water-cooler; with the glass half-way to his lips he pauses.*] Was he quiet when you left him?

FATHER DALY. [*A trifle abstractedly.*] Yes, yes, he was perfectly calm and I believe he'll stay so to the very end.

THE WARDEN. [*Finishes his drink, comes back to his desk, and lights a fresh cigar.*] You've got to hand it to him, Father; I never saw such nerve in all my life. It isn't bluff, and it isn't a trance, either, like some of 'em have—it's plain nerve. You've certainly got to hand it to him. [*He shakes his head in frank admiration.*]

FATHER DALY. [*Sorrowfully.*] That's the pity of it—that a man with all his courage hasn't a better use for it. Even now, it's very difficult for me to reconcile his character, as I see it, with what we know he's done.

THE WARDEN. [*Continues to shake his head.*] He's got my goat, all right.

FATHER DALY. [*With a slight grimace.*] Yes, and he's got mine, too.

THE WARDEN. When he sent for you tonight, I hoped he was going to talk.

FATHER DALY. He did talk, very freely.

THE WARDEN. What about?

FATHER DALY. [*Smiles faintly, and sits beside the desk.*] Most everything.

THE WARDEN. [*Looks up quickly.*] Himself?

FATHER DALY. No. That seems to be the only subject he isn't interested in.

THE WARDEN. [*Sits up to his desk, and leans upon it with both elbows.*] He still won't give you any hint about who he really is?

FATHER DALY. Not the slightest. He doesn't intend to, either. He intends to die as a man of mystery to us. Sometimes I wonder if he isn't just as much of a mystery to himself.

THE WARDEN. Oh, he's trying to shield somebody, that's all. James Dyke isn't his right name—we know that; and we know all the rest of his story is a fake, too. Well, where's his motive? I'll tell you where it is. It's to keep his family and his friends, wherever they are, from knowing what's happened to him. Lots of 'em have the same idea but I never knew one to carry it as far as this, before. You've certainly got to hand it to him. All we know is that we've got a man under sentence; and we don't know who he is, or where he comes from, or anything else about him, any more than we did four months ago.

FATHER DALY. It takes moral courage for a man to shut himself away from his family and his friends like that. They would have comforted him.

THE WARDEN. Not necessarily. What time is it?

FATHER DALY. Half-past eleven.

THE WARDEN. [*Rises and walks over to peer out of one of the barred windows.*] I guess I'm getting too old for this sort of thing. A necktie party didn't use to bother me so much; but every time one comes along nowadays, I've got the blue devils beforehand and afterward. And this one is just about the limit.

FATHER DALY. It certainly isn't a pleasant duty even with the worst of them.

THE WARDEN. [*Wheels back abruptly.*] But what gets *me* is why I should hate this one more than any of the others. The boy is guilty as hell.

FATHER DALY. Yes, he killed a man. "Wilfully, feloniously, and with malice aforethought."

THE WARDEN. And he pleaded guilty. So he deserves just what he's going to get.

FATHER DALY. That is the law. But has it ever occurred to you,

Warden, that every now and then when a criminal behaves in a
rather gentlemanly fashion to us, we instinctively think of him
as just a little less of a criminal?

THE WARDEN. Yes, it has. But, all the same, this front of his
makes me as nervous as the devil. He pleaded guilty all right, but
he don't *act* guilty. I feel just as if tonight I was going to do
something every bit as criminal as he did. I can't help it. And
when I get to feeling like that, why, I guess it's pretty nearly
time I sent in my resignation.

FATHER DALY. [*Reflectively.*] His whole attitude has been very
remarkable. Why, only a few minutes ago I found myself com-
paring it with the fortitude that the Christian martyrs carried to
their death, and yet—

THE WARDEN. He's no martyr.

FATHER DALY. I know it. And he's anything in the world but
a Christian. That was just what I was going to say.

THE WARDEN. Has he got any religious streak in him at all?

FATHER DALY. I'm afraid he hasn't. He listens to me very at-
tentively, but— [*He shrugs his shoulder.*] It's only because I
offer him companionship. Anybody else would do quite as well
—and any other topic would suit him better.

THE WARDEN. Well, if he wants to face God as a heathen, *we*
can't force him to change his mind.

FATHER DALY. [*With gentle reproach.*] No, but we can never
give up trying to save his immortal soul. And his soul tonight
seems as dark and foreboding to me as a haunted house would
seem to the small boys down in Wethersfield. But I haven't given
up hope.

THE WARDEN. No—you wouldn't.

FATHER DALY. Are you going to talk with him again yourself?

THE WARDEN. [*Opens a drawer of his desk, and brings out a
large envelope.*] I'll have to. I've still got some Liberty Bonds
that belong to him. [*He gazes at the envelope, and smiles grimly.*]
That was a funny thing—when the newspaper syndicate offered
him twenty-five hundred for his autobiography, he jumped at it
so quick I was sure he wanted the money for something or other.
[*He slaps the envelope on the desk.*] But now the bonds are here,

waiting for him, he won't say what to do with 'em. Know why? [FATHER DALY *shakes his head.*] Why, of course you do! Because the story he wrote was pure bunk from start to finish and the only reason he jumped at the chance of writing it was so's he could pull the wool over everybody's head a little farther. He don't want the bonds, but I've got to do *something* with 'em. [*He pushes a button on the desk.*] And besides, I want to make one more try at finding out who he is.

FATHER DALY. Shall I go with you to see him or do you want to see him alone?

THE WARDEN. [*Sits deliberating with one hand at his forehead, and the other hand tapping the desk.*] Father, you gave me a thought—I believe I'm going to do something tonight that's never been done before in this prison—that is to say—not in all the twenty-eight years that *I've* been warden.

FATHER DALY. What's that?

THE WARDEN. [*Who has evidently come to an important decision, raps the desk more forcibly with his knuckles.*] Instead of our going to see him, I'll have that boy brought into this office and let him sit here with you and me until the time comes for us all to walk through that door to the execution room.

FATHER DALY. [*Startled.*] What on earth is your idea in doing a thing like that?

THE WARDEN. Because maybe if he sits here awhile with just you and me, and we go at him right, he'll loosen up and tell us about himself. It'll be different from being in his cell; it'll be sort of free and easy, and maybe he'll weaken. And then, besides, if we take him to the scaffold through this passage-way, maybe I can keep the others quiet. If they don't know when the job's being done, they may behave 'emselves. I don't want any such yelling and screeching tonight as we had with that Greek. [*A* JAILER *in blue uniform enters from the deputy's room and stands waiting.*] Dan, I want you to get Dyke and bring him to me here. [*The* JAILER *stares blankly at him and the* WARDEN's *voice takes on an added note of authority.*] Get Dyke and bring him in here to me.

THE JAILER. Yes, sir. [*He starts to obey the order but halts in the doorway and turns as the* WARDEN *speaks again. It is apparent that the* WARDEN *is a strict disciplinarian of the prison staff.*]

THE WARDEN. Oh, Dan!

THE JAILER. Yes, sir?

THE WARDEN. How nearly ready are they?

THE JAILER. They'll be all set in ten or fifteen minutes, sir. Twenty minutes at the outside.

THE WARDEN. [*Very sharp and magisterial.*] Now, I don't want any hitch or delay in this thing tonight. If there is, somebody's going to get in awful Dutch with me. Pass that along.

THE JAILER. There won't be none, sir.

THE WARDEN. When everything's ready—not a second before —you let me know.

THE JAILER. Yes, sir.

THE WARDEN. I'll be right here with Dyke and Father Daly.

THE JAILER. [*Eyes widening.*] Here?

THE WARDEN. [*Peremptorily.*] Yes, here!

THE JAILER. [*Crushes down his astonishment.*] Yes, sir.

THE WARDEN. When everything and everybody is ready, you come from the execution room through the passage [*He gestures toward the nearer door on the right.*]—open that door quietly— and stand there.

THE JAILER. Yes, sir.

THE WARDEN. You don't have to say anything, and I don't *want* you to say anything. Just stand there. That all clear?

THE JAILER. Yes, sir.

THE WARDEN. That'll be the signal for us to start—understand?

THE JAILER. Yes, sir.

THE WARDEN. [*Draws a deep breath.*] All right. Now bring Dyke to me.

THE JAILER. Yes, sir. [*He goes out dazedly.*]

FATHER DALY. What about the witnesses and the reporters?

THE WARDEN. They're having their sandwiches and coffee now —the deputy'll have 'em seated in another ten or fifteen minutes. Let 'em wait. [*His voice becomes savage.*] I'd like to poison the

lot of 'em. Reporters! Witnesses! [*The telephone bell rings.*] Hello
—yes—yes—what's that?—Yes, yes, right here—who wants him?
[*To* FATHER DALY.] Father, it's the Governor! [*His expression is
tense.*]

FATHER DALY. [*His voice also gives evidence of incredulity and
hope.*] What! [*He walks swiftly over to the desk.*] Is it about
Dyke?

THE WARDEN. Ssh. [*He turns to the telephone.*] Yes, this is
Warden Holt speaking. Hello—oh, hello, Governor Fuller, how
are you? Oh, I'm between grass and hay, thanks. Well, this isn't
my idea of a picnic exactly—yes—yes— Oh, I should say in
about half an hour or so—everything's just about ready. [*His
expression gradually relaxes, and* FATHER DALY, *with a little sigh
and shake of the head, turns away.*] Oh, no, there won't be any
slip-up—yes, we made the regular tests, one this afternoon and
another at nine o'clock tonight— Oh, no, Governor, nothing can
go wrong— Well, according to the law I've got to get it done as
soon as possible after midnight, but you're the Governor of the
state— How long?—Certainly, Governor, I can hold it off as long
as you want me to— What say?—A *girl!*—You're going to send
her to me?—You *have* sent her!—She ought to be here by this
time?—All right, Governor, I'll ring you up when it's over.
Good-bye. [*He hangs up the receiver, mops his forehead with his
handkerchief, and turns to* FATHER DALY *in great excitement.*]
Did you get *that?* Some girl thinks Dyke's her long-lost brother,
and she's persuaded the old man to let her come out here tonight
—he wants me to hold up the job until she's had a chance to see
him. She's due here any minute, he says—in his own car—es-
corted by his own private secretary! Can you beat it?

FATHER DALY. [*Downcast.*] Poor girl!

THE WARDEN. [*Blots his forehead vigorously.*] For a minute
there I thought it was going to be a reprieve at the very least.
Whew!

FATHER DALY. So did I.

[*The door from the deputy's room is opened, and* DYKE
comes in, followed immediately by the JAILER. DYKE *halts
just inside the door and waits passively to be told what to*

do next. He has a lean, pale face, with a high forehead, good eyes, and a strong chin; his mouth is ruled in a firm straight line. His wavy hair is prematurely gray. His figure has the elasticity of youth, but he might pass among strangers either as a man of forty, or as a man of twenty-five, depending upon the mobility of his features at a given moment. He is dressed in a dark shirt open at the throat, dark trousers without belt or suspenders, and soft slippers. The JAILER *receives a nod from the* WARDEN, *and goes out promptly, closing the door behind him.*]

THE WARDEN. [*Swings half-way around in his swivel-chair.*] Sit down, Dyke. [*He points to the chair at the right of his desk.*]

DYKE. Thanks. [*He goes directly to the chair and sits down.*]

THE WARDEN. [*Leans back, and surveys him thoughtfully.* FATHER DALY *remains in the background.*] Dyke, you've been here under my charge for nearly four months and I want to tell you that from first to last you've behaved yourself like a gentleman.

DYKE. [*His manner is vaguely cynical without being in the least impertinent.*] Why should I make you any trouble?

THE WARDEN. Well, you *haven't* made me any trouble, and I've tried to show what I think about it. I've made you every bit as comfortable as the law would let me.

DYKE. You've been very kind to me. [*He glances over his shoulder at the* CHAPLAIN.] And you, too, Father.

THE WARDEN. I've had you brought in here to stay from now on. [DYKE *looks inquiringly at him.*] No, you won't have to go back to your cell again. You're to stay right here with Father Daly and me.

DYKE. [*Carelessly.*] All right.

THE WARDEN. [*Piqued by this cool reception of the distinguished favor.*] You don't seem to understand that I'm doing something a long way out of the ordinary for you.

DYKE. Oh, yes, I do, but maybe *you* don't understand why it doesn't give me much of a thrill.

FATHER DALY. [*Comes forward.*] My son, the Warden is only trying to do you one more kindness.

DYKE. I know he is, Father, but the Warden isn't taking very much of a gamble. From now on, one place is about the same as another.

THE WARDEN. What do you mean?

DYKE. [*His voice is very faintly sarcastic.*] Why, I mean that I'm just as much a condemned prisoner here as when I was in my cell. That door [*He points to it.*] leads right *back* to my cell. Outside those windows are armed guards every few feet. You yourself can't get through the iron door in that anteroom [*He indicates the door to the left.*] until somebody on the outside unlocks it; and I know as well as you do where *that* door [*He points to the nearer door on the right.*] leads to.

THE WARDEN. [*Stiffly.*] Would you rather wait in your cell?

DYKE. Oh, no, this is a little pleasanter. Except—

THE WARDEN. Except what?

DYKE. In my cell, I could smoke.

THE WARDEN. [*Shrugs his shoulders.*] What do you want— cigar or cigarette?

DYKE. A cigarette, if it's all the same.

[*The* WARDEN *opens a drawer of his desk, takes out a box of cigarettes, removes one and hands it to* DYKE. *The* WARDEN, *striking a match, lights* DYKE's *cigarette, and then carefully puts out the match.*]

DYKE. [*Smiles faintly.*] Thanks. You're a good host.

THE WARDEN. Dyke, before it's too late I wish you'd think over what Father Daly and I've said to you so many times.

DYKE. I've thought of nothing else.

THE WARDEN. Then—as man to man—and this is your last chance—who are you?

DYKE. [*Inspects his cigarette.*] Who am I? James Dyke—a murderer.

THE WARDEN. That isn't your real name and we know it.

DYKE. You're not going to execute a name—you're going to execute a *man*. What difference does it make whether you call me Dyke or something else?

THE WARDEN. You had another name once. What was it?

DYKE. If I had, I've forgotten it.

FATHER DALY. Your mind is made up, my son?

DYKE. Yes, Father, it is.

THE WARDEN. Dyke.

DYKE. Yes, sir?

THE WARDEN. Do you see this pile of letters? [*He places his hand over it.*]

DYKE. Yes, sir.

THE WARDEN. [*Fingers them.*] Every one of these letters is about the same thing and all put together we've got maybe four thousand of 'em. These here are just a few samples.

DYKE. What about them?

THE WARDEN. We've had letters from every State in the Union and every province in Canada. We've had fifteen or twenty from England, four or five from France, two from Australia, and one from Russia.

DYKE. Well?

THE WARDEN. [*Inclines toward him.*] Do you know what every one of those letters says—what four thousand different people are writing to me about?

DYKE. No, sir.

THE WARDEN. [*Speaks slowly and impressively.*] Who *are* you—and are you the missing son—or brother—or husband—or sweetheart?

DYKE. [*Flicks his cigarette ashes to the floor.*] Have you answered them?

THE WARDEN. No, I couldn't. I want you to.

DYKE. How's that?

THE WARDEN. I want you to tell me who you are.

[DYKE *shakes his head.*]

Can't you see you *ought* to do it?

DYKE. No, sir, I can't exactly see that. Suppose you explain it to me.

THE WARDEN. [*Suddenly.*] You're trying to shield somebody, aren't you?

DYKE. Yes—no, I'm not!

THE WARDEN. [*Glances at* FATHER DALY *and nods with elation.*] Who is it? Your family?

DYKE. I said I'm not.

THE WARDEN. But first, you said you were.

DYKE. That was a slip of the tongue.

THE WARDEN. [*Has grown persuasive.*] Dyke, just listen to me a minute. Don't be narrow, look at this thing in a big, broad way. Suppose you should tell me your real name, and I publish it, it'll bring an awful lot of sorrow, let's say, to *one* family, *one* home, and that's your own. That's probably what you're thinking about. Am I right? You want to spare your family and I don't blame you. On the surface, it sure would look like a mighty white thing for you to do. But look at it *this* way: suppose you came out with the truth, flat-footed, why, you might put all that sorrow into *one* home—your own—but at the same time you'd be putting an immense amount of relief in four thousand—others. Don't you get that? Don't you figure you owe something to all these other people?

DYKE. Not a thing.

FATHER DALY. [*Has been fidgeting.*] My boy, the Warden is absolutely right. You do owe something to the other people—you owe them peace of mind—and for the sake of all those thousands of poor, distressed women, who imagine God knows what, I beg of you to tell us who you are.

DYKE. Father, I simply can't do it.

FATHER DALY. Think carefully, my boy, think very carefully. We're not asking out of idle curiosity.

DYKE. I know that, but please don't let's talk about it any more. [*To the* WARDEN.] You can answer those letters whenever you want to, and you can say I'm not the man they're looking for. That'll be the truth, too. Because I haven't any mother—or father—or sister—or wife—or sweetheart. That's fair enough, isn't it?

FATHER DALY. [*Sighs wearily.*] As you will, my son.

THE WARDEN. Dyke, there's one more thing.

DYKE. Yes?

THE WARDEN. Here are the Liberty Bonds [*He takes up the large envelope from his desk.*] that belong to you. Twenty-five hundred dollars in real money.

DYKE. [*Removes the bonds and examines them.*] Good-looking, aren't they?

THE WARDEN. [*Casually.*] What do you want me to do with them?

DYKE. Well, I can't very well take them with me, so, under the circumstances, I'd like to put them where they'll do the most good.

THE WARDEN. [*More casually yet.*] Who do you want me to send 'em to?

DYKE. [*Laughs quietly.*] Now, Warden Holt, you didn't think you were going to catch me that way, did you?

THE WARDEN. [*Scowls.*] Who'll I send 'em to? I can't keep 'em here, and I can't destroy 'em. What do you want to do with 'em?

DYKE. [*Ponders diligently and tosses the envelopes to the desk.*] I don't know. I'll think of something to do with them. I'll tell you in just a minute. Is there anything else?

THE WARDEN. Not unless you want to make some sort of statement.

DYKE. No, I guess I've said everything. I killed a man and I'm not sorry for it—that is, I'm not sorry I killed that particular person. I—

FATHER DALY. [*Raises his hand.*] Repentance—

DYKE. [*Raises his own hand in turn.*] I've heard that repentance, Father, is the sickbed of the soul—and mine is very well and flourishing. The man deserved to be killed; he wasn't fit to live. It was my duty to kill him, and I did it. I'd never struck a man in anger in all my life, but when I knew what that fellow had done, I knew I had to kill him, and I did it deliberately and intentionally—and carefully. I knew what I was doing, and I haven't any excuse—that is, I haven't any excuse that satisfies the law. Now, I learned pretty early in life that whatever you do in this world you have to pay for in one way or another. If you kill a man, the price you have to pay is this [*He makes a gesture which sweeps the entire room.*] and that [*He points to the nearer door on the right.*], and I'm going to pay it. That's all there is to that. And an hour from now, while my body is lying in there, if a couple of angel policemen grab my soul and haul it up before God—

FATHER DALY. [*Profoundly shocked.*] My boy, my boy, please—

DYKE. I beg your pardon, Father. I don't mean to trample on anything that's sacred to you, but what I do mean to say is this: If I've got to be judged by God Almighty for the crime of murder, I'm not afraid, because the other fellow will certainly be there, too, won't he? And when God hears the whole story and both sides of it, which *you* never heard and never will—and they never heard it in the court room, either—why, then, if he's any kind of a God at all, I'm willing to take my chances with the other fellow. That's how concerned I am about the hereafter. And, if it'll make you feel any better, Father, why I *do* rather think there's going to be a hereafter. I read a book once that said a milligram of musk will give out perfume for seven thousand years, and a milligram of radium will give out light for *seventy* thousand. Why shouldn't a soul—mine, for instance— live more than twenty-seven? But if there *isn't* any hereafter —if we just die and are dead and that's all—why, I'm still not sorry and I'm not afraid, because I'm quits with the other fellow —the law is quits with me, and it's all balanced on the books. And that's all there is to that. [*An* ATTENDANT *enters from the anteroom.*]

THE WARDEN. Well? What is it?

THE ATTENDANT. Visitor to see you, sir. With note from Governor Fuller. [*He presents it.*]

THE WARDEN. [*Barely glances at the envelope.*] Oh! A young woman?

THE ATTENDANT. Yes, sir.

THE WARDEN. Is Mrs. Case there?

THE ATTENDANT. Yes, sir.

THE WARDEN. Have the girl searched, and then take her into the anteroom and wait till I call you.

THE ATTENDANT. Yes, sir. [*He goes out.*]

THE WARDEN. Dyke, a young woman has just come to see you—do you want to see her?

DYKE. I don't think so. What does she want?

THE WARDEN. She thinks maybe she's your sister, and she's come a thousand miles to find out.

DYKE. She's wrong. I haven't any sister.

THE WARDEN. [*Hesitates.*] Will I tell her that, or do you want to tell it to her yourself?

DYKE. Oh, you tell her.

THE WARDEN. All right. [*He starts to rise but resumes his seat as* DYKE *speaks.*]

DYKE. Just a second—she's come a thousand miles to see me, did you say?

THE WARDEN. Yes, and she's got special permission from the Governor to talk to you—that is, with my O.K.

DYKE. A year ago, nobody'd have crossed the street to look at me, and now they come a thousand miles!

FATHER DALY. This is one of your debts to humanity, my boy. It wouldn't take you two minutes to see her, and, if you don't, after she's made that long journey in hope and dread and suffering—

DYKE. Where can I talk with her—here?

THE WARDEN. Yes.

DYKE. Alone? [*The* WARDEN *is doubtful.*] Why, you don't need to be afraid. I haven't the faintest idea who the girl is, but if she happens to be some poor misguided sentimental fool, with a gun or a pocket full of cyanide of potassium, she's wasting her time. I wouldn't cheat the sovereign state of Connecticut for anything in the world—not even to please a young lady.

THE WARDEN. Dyke, there's something about you that gets everybody.

DYKE. How about the jury?

THE WARDEN. You've got a sort of way with you—

DYKE. How about that spread-eagle district attorney?

THE WARDEN. I'm going to let you talk with that girl in here —alone.

DYKE. Thanks.

THE WARDEN. It's a sort of thing that's never been done before, but if I put you on your honor—

DYKE. [*Cynically.*] My honor! Thank you, so much.

FATHER DALY. Warden, are you sure it's wise?

DYKE. Father, I'm disappointed in you. Do you imagine I'd do anything that could reflect on Warden Holt—or you—or the young lady—or *me?*

THE WARDEN. Father, will you take Dyke into the deputy's room? I want to speak to the young lady first.

FATHER DALY. Certainly. Come, my boy. [FATHER DALY *and* DYKE *start toward the deputy's room.*]

THE WARDEN. I'll call you in just a couple of minutes.

DYKE. We promise not to run away. [*They go out together.*]

THE WARDEN. [*Calls.*] Wilson! [*The* ATTENDANT *enters from the left.*]

THE ATTENDANT. Yes, sir.

THE WARDEN. Is the girl there?

THE ATTENDANT. Yes, sir.

THE WARDEN. Frisked?

THE ATTENDANT. Yes, sir.

THE WARDEN. Everything all right?

THE ATTENDANT. Yes, sir.

THE WARDEN. [*Throws away his cigar.*] Bring her in.

THE ATTENDANT. Yes, sir. [*He speaks through the door at the left.*] Step this way, Miss. This here's the Warden.

[*A young girl appears on the threshold, and casts about in mingled curiosity and apprehension. She is fresh and wholesome, and rather pretty; but her manner betrays a certain spiritual aloofness from the ultra-modern world—a certain delicate reticence of the flesh—which immediately separates her from the metropolitan class. Indeed, she is dressed far too simply for a metropolitan girl of her age; she wears a blue tailored suit with deep white cuffs and a starched white sailor-collar, and a small blue hat which fits snugly over her fluffy hair. Her costume is not quite conservative enough to be literally old-fashioned, but it hints at the taste and repression of an old-fashioned home.*

She is neither timid nor aggressive; she is unself-conscious. She looks at the WARDEN *squarely, but not in boldness, and*

yet not in feminine appeal; she has rather the fearlessness
of a girl who has lost none of her illusions about men in general. Her expression is essentially serious; it conveys, however, the idea that her seriousness is due to her present mission, and that ordinarily she takes an active joy in the mere
pleasure of existence.]

THE WARDEN. [*He had expected a very different type of
visitor, so that he is somewhat taken aback.*] All right, Wilson.

THE ATTENDANT. Yes, sir. [*He goes out.*]

THE WARDEN. [*With grave deference, half rises.*] Will you
sit down?

THE GIRL. Why—thank you very much. [*She sits in the chair
beside the desk and regards him trustfully.*]

THE WARDEN. [*He is palpably affected by her youth and in-
nocence, and he is not quite sure how best to proceed, but eventually he makes an awkward beginning.*] You've had an interview with the Governor, I understand?

THE GIRL. Yes, sir. I was with him almost an hour.

THE WARDEN. And you want to see Dyke, do you?

THE GIRL. Yes, sir. I *hope* I'm not—too late.

THE WARDEN. No, you're not too late. [*He is appraising her
carefully.*] But I want to ask you a few questions beforehand.
[*Her reaction of uncertainty induces him to soften his tone.*]
There isn't anything to get upset about. I just want to make it
easier for you, not harder. Where do you live?

THE GIRL. In Ohio.

THE WARDEN. [*Very kindly.*] What place?

THE GIRL. In Pennington, sir. It's a little town not far from
Columbus.

THE WARDEN. And you live out there with your father and
mother?

THE GIRL. No, sir—just my mother and I. My father died
when I was a little baby.

THE WARDEN. Why didn't your mother come here herself, instead of sending you?

THE GIRL. She couldn't. She's sick.

THE WARDEN. I see. Have you any brothers or sisters?

THE GIRL. [*Slightly more at ease.*] Just one brother, sir—this one. He and I were the only children. We were very fond of each other.

THE WARDEN. He was considerably older than you?

THE GIRL. Oh, yes. He's ten years older.

THE WARDEN. Why did he leave home?

THE GIRL. I don't really know, sir, except he just wanted to be in the city. Pennington's pretty small.

THE WARDEN. How long is it since you've seen him?

THE GIRL. It's eight years.

THE WARDEN. [*His voice is almost paternal.*] As long as that? Hm! And how old are you now?

THE GIRL. I'm almost eighteen.

THE WARDEN. [*Repeats slowly.*] Almost eighteen. Hm! And are you sure after all this time you'd recognize your brother if you saw him?

THE GIRL. Well—[*She looks down, as if embarrassed to make the admission.*]—of course I *think* so, but maybe I couldn't. You see, I was only a little girl when he went away—he wasn't a bad boy, sir, I don't think he could ever be really bad—but if this *is* my brother, why he's been in a great deal of trouble and you know that trouble makes people look different.

THE WARDEN. Yes, it does. But what makes you think this man Dyke may be your brother—and why didn't you think of it sooner? The case has been in the papers for the last six months.

THE GIRL. Why, it wasn't until last Tuesday that Mother saw a piece in the *Journal*—that's the Columbus paper—that he'd written all about himself, and there was one little part of it that sounded so like Joe—like the funny way he used to say things—and then there was a picture that looked the least little *bit* like him—well, Mother just wanted me to come East and find out for sure.

THE WARDEN. It's too bad she couldn't come herself. She'd probably know him whether he'd changed or not.

THE GIRL. Yes, sir. But I'll do the best I can.

THE WARDEN. When was the last time you heard from him, and where was he, and what was he doing?

THE GIRL. Why, it's about five or six years since we had a letter from Joe. He was in Seattle, Washington.

THE WARDEN. What doing?

THE GIRL. I don't remember. At home, though, he worked in the stationery store. He liked books.

THE WARDEN. [*Suspiciously.*] Why do you suppose he didn't write home?

THE GIRL. I—couldn't say. He was just—thoughtless.

THE WARDEN. Wasn't in trouble of any kind?

THE GIRL. Oh, *no!* Never. That is—unless he's—here now.

THE WARDEN. [*Deliberates.*] How are you going to tell him?

THE GIRL. I don't know what you mean.

THE WARDEN. Why, you say maybe you wouldn't know him even if you saw him—and I'll guarantee this man Dyke won't help you out very much. How do you think you're going to tell? Suppose he don't want to be recognized by you or anybody else? Suppose he's so ashamed of himself he—

THE GIRL. I'd thought of that. I'm just going to talk to him —ask him questions—about things he and I used to do together —I'll watch his face, and if he's my brother, I'm sure I can tell.

THE WARDEN. [*With tolerant doubt.*] What did you and your brother ever used to do that would help you out now?

THE GIRL. He used to play games with me when I was a little girl, and tell me stories—that's what I'm counting on mostly— the stories.

THE WARDEN. I'm afraid—

THE GIRL. Especially Shakespeare stories.

THE WARDEN. Shakespeare!

THE GIRL. Why, yes. He used to get the plots of the plays —all the Shakespeare plays—out of a book by a man named Lamb, and then he'd tell me the stories in his own words. It was wonderful!

THE WARDEN. I'm certainly afraid he—

THE GIRL. But best of all he'd learn some of the speeches from the plays themselves. He liked to do it—he was sure he was going to be an actor or something—he was in all the high school plays, always. And then he'd teach some of the speeches to me, and we'd say them to each other. And one thing—every night he'd sit at the side of my bed, and when I got sleepy there were two speeches we'd always say to each other, like good-night —two speeches out of *Romeo and Juliet,* and then I'd go to sleep. I can see it all. [*The* WARDEN *shakes his head.*] Why do you do that?

THE WARDEN. This boy isn't your brother.

THE GIRL. Do you think he isn't?

THE WARDEN. I *know* he isn't.

THE GIRL. How do you?

THE WARDEN. This boy never heard of Shakespeare—much less learned him. [*He presses a button on his desk.*] Oh, I'll let you see him for yourself, only you might as well be prepared. [*The* ATTENDANT *enters from the anteroom.*] Tell Dyke and Father Daly to come in here—they're in the deputy's room.

THE ATTENDANT. Yes, sir. [*He crosses behind the* WARDEN, *and goes off to the right.*]

THE WARDEN. If he turns out to be your brother—which he won't—you can have, say, an hour with him. If he don't, you'll oblige me by cutting it as short as you can.

THE GIRL. You see, I've got to tell Mother something perfectly definite. She's worried so long about him, and—and *now* the suspense is perfectly terrible for her.

THE WARDEN. I can understand that. You're a plucky girl.

THE GIRL. Of course, it would be awful for us if this *is* Joe, but even that would be better for Mother than just to stay awake nights, and wonder and wonder, and never *know* what became of him. [*The* ATTENDANT *opens the door of the deputy's room, and when* DYKE *and* FATHER DALY *have come in, he crosses again behind the* WARDEN, *and is going out at the left when the* WARDEN *signs to him and he stops.*]

THE WARDEN. [*Gets to his feet.*] Dyke, this is the young lady that's come all the way from Pennington, Ohio, to see you.

DYKE. [*Who has been talking in an undertone to* FATHER DALY, *raises his head quickly.*] Yes, sir?

THE WARDEN. I've decided you can talk with her here—alone. [*The* GIRL *has risen, breathless, and stands fixed;* DYKE *inspects her coldly from head to foot.*]

DYKE. Thank you. It won't take long.

THE WARDEN. [*Has been scanning the* GIRL's *expression; now, as he sees that she has neither recognized* DYKE *nor failed to recognize him, he makes a little grimace in confirmation of his own judgment.*] Father Daly and I'll stay in the deputy's office. We'll leave the door open. Wilson, you stand in the anteroom with the door open.

DYKE. [*Bitterly.*] My honor!

THE WARDEN. What say?

DYKE. I didn't say anything.

THE WARDEN. [*To the* GIRL.] Will you please remember what I told you about the time?

THE GIRL. Oh, yes, sir.

THE WARDEN. Come, Father. [*They go off into the deputy's room, and the* ATTENDANT, *at a nod from the* WARDEN, *goes off at the left.*]

[DYKE *and the* GIRL *are now facing each other;* DYKE *is well-poised and insouciant and gives the impression of complete indifference to the moment. The* GIRL, *on the other hand, is deeply agitated and her agitation is gradually increased by* DYKE's *own attitude.*]

THE GIRL. [*After several efforts to speak.*] Mother sent me to see you.

DYKE. [*Politely callous.*] Yes?

THE GIRL. [*Compelled to drop her eyes.*] You see, we haven't seen or heard of my brother Joe for ever so long, and Mother thought—after what we read in the papers—

DYKE. That I might be your brother Joe?

THE GIRL. [*Obviously relieved.*] Yes, that's it.

DYKE. Well, you can easily see that I'm not your brother, can't you?

THE GIRL. [*Stares at him again.*] I'm not sure. You look a little like him, just as the picture in the paper did, but then again, it's so long—[*She shakes her head dubiously.*] and I'd thought of Joe so differently—

DYKE. [*His manner is somewhat indulgent, as though to a child.*] As a matter of fact, I couldn't be *your* brother, or anybody else's brother, because I never had a sister. So that rather settles it.

THE GIRL. Honestly?

DYKE. Honestly.

THE GIRL. [*Unconvinced, becomes more appealing.*] What's your real name?

DYKE. Dyke—James Dyke.

THE GIRL. That's sure enough your name?

DYKE. Sure enough. You don't think I'd tell a lie at this stage of the game, do you?

THE GIRL. [*Musing.*] No, I don't believe you would. Where do you come from—-I mean where were you born?

DYKE. In Canada, but I've lived all over.

THE GIRL. Didn't you ever live in Ohio?

DYKE. No. Never.

THE GIRL. What kind of work did you do—what was your business?

DYKE. Oh, I'm sort of Jack-of-all-trades. I've been everything a man *could* be—except a success.

THE GIRL. Do you like books?

DYKE. Books?

THE GIRL. Yes—books to read.

DYKE. I don't read when there's anything better to do. I've read a lot here.

THE GIRL. Did you ever sell books—for a living, I mean?

DYKE. Oh, no.

THE GIRL. [*Growing confused.*] I hope you don't mind my asking so many questions. But I—

DYKE. No—go ahead, if it'll relieve your mind any.

THE GIRL. You went to school somewhere, of course—high school?

DYKE. No, I never got that far.

THE GIRL. Did you ever want to be an actor? Or *were* you ever?

DYKE. No, just a convict.

THE GIRL. [*Helplessly.*] Do you know any poetry?

DYKE. Not to speak of.

THE GIRL. [*Delays a moment, and then, watching him very earnestly, she recites just above her breath.*]

> Thou knowst the mask of night is on my face
> Else would a maiden blush bepaint my cheek
> For that which— [1]

[*Realizing that* DYKE's *expression is one of utter vacuity she falters, and breaks off the quotation, but she continues to watch him unwaveringly.*]
Don't you know what that is?

DYKE. No, but to tell the truth, it sounds sort of silly to *me*. Doesn't it to you?

THE GIRL. [*Her intonation has become slightly forlorn, but she gathers courage, and puts him to one more test.*]

> Good-night, good-night, parting is such sweet sorrow
> That I shall say good-night till it be morrow. [2]

DYKE. [*His mouth twitches in amusement.*] Eh?

THE GIRL. What comes next?

DYKE. Good Lord, *I* don't know.

THE GIRL. [*Gazes intently, almost imploringly, at him as though she is making a struggle to read his mind. Then she relaxes and holds out her hand.*] Good-bye. You—you're *not* Joe, are you? I—had to come and find out, though. I hope I've not made you too unhappy.

DYKE. [*Ignores her hand.*] You're not going now?

THE GIRL. [*Spiritless.*] Yes. I promised the—is he the Warden, that man in there?—I said I'd go right away if you weren't my brother. And you aren't, so—

[1] From Shakespeare's *Romeo and Juliet*, in the famous balcony scene (Act II, scene 2). Juliet is speaking to Romeo.
[2] From the same scene. Juliet calls out to Romeo as he is about to leave the orchard.

Dyke. You're going back to your mother?

The Girl. Yes.

Dyke. I'm surprised that she sent a girl like you on a sorry errand like this, instead of—

The Girl. She's very sick.

Dyke. Oh, that's too bad.

The Girl. [*Twisting her handkerchief.*] No, she's not well at all. And most of it's from worrying about Joe.

Dyke. Still, when you tell her that her son isn't a murderer —at least, that he isn't *this* one—that'll comfort her a good deal, won't it?

The Girl. [*Reluctantly.*] Yes, I think maybe it will, only—

Dyke. Only what?

The Girl. I don't think Mother'll ever be *really* well again until she finds out for certain where Joe is and what's become of him.

Dyke. [*Shakes his head compassionately.*] Mothers ought not to be treated like that. I wish I'd treated *mine* better. By the way, you didn't tell me what your name is.

The Girl. Josephine Paris.

Dyke. [*Is suddenly attentive.*] Paris? That's an unusual name. I've heard it somewhere, too.

The Girl. Just like the name of the city—in France.

Dyke. [*Knitting his brows.*] And your brother's name was Joseph?

The Girl. Yes—they used to call us Joe and Josie—that's funny, isn't it?

Dyke. [*Thoughtfully.*] No, I don't think it's so very funny. I rather like it. [*He passes his hand over his forehead as if trying to coerce his memory.*]

The Girl. What's the matter?

Dyke. [*Frowning.*] I was thinking of something—now, what on earth was that boy's name! Wait a minute, don't tell me— wait a minute—I've got it! [*He punctuates his triumph with one fist in the palm of the other hand.*] Joseph Anthony Paris!

The Girl. [*Amazed.*] Why, that's his name! That's Joe! How did you ever—

DYKE. [*His manner is very forcible and convincing.*] Wait! Now listen carefully to what I say, and don't interrupt me, because we've only got a minute, and I want you to get this all straight, so you can tell your mother. When the war came along I enlisted and I was overseas for four years—with the Canadians. Early one morning we'd staged a big trench raid, and there was an officer who'd been wounded coming back, and was lying out there in a shell-hole under fire. The Jerries [3] were getting ready for a raid of their own, so they were putting down a box barrage with light guns and howitzers and a few heavies. This officer was lying right in the middle of it. Well, all of a sudden a young fellow dashed out of a trench not far from where I was, and went for that officer. He had to go through a curtain of shells and, more than that, they opened on him with rifles and machine guns. The chances were just about a million to one against him, and he must have known it, but he went out just the same. He got the officer in his arms and started back, but he'd only gone a few yards when a five-point-nine landed right on top of the two of them. Afterward, we got what was left—the identification tag was still there—and that was the name—Joseph Anthony Paris!

THE GIRL. [*Carries both hands to her breast.*] Oh!

DYKE. If that was your brother's name, then you can tell your mother that he died like a brave man and a soldier, three years ago, in France.

THE GIRL. Joe—my brother Joe—is dead?

DYKE. On the field of battle. It was one of the wonderful, heroic things that went almost unnoticed, as so many of them did. If an officer had seen it, there'd have been a decoration for your mother to keep and remember him by.

THE GIRL. And you were there—and saw it?

DYKE. I was there and saw it. It was three years ago. That's why you and your mother haven't heard from him. And if you don't believe what I've said, why, you just write up to Ottawa and get the official record. Of course [*He shrugs his shoulders contemptuously*], those records are in terribly poor shape, but at least they can tell you what battalion he fought with, when he

[3] *Jerries:* one of the names given the Germans by the allied soldiers.

went overseas. Only you mustn't be surprised no matter whether they say he was killed in action, or died of wounds, or is missing, or even went through the whole war with his outfit, and was honorably discharged. They really don't know what happened to half the men. But I've told you the truth. And it certainly ought to make your mother happy when she knows that her boy died as a soldier, and not as a criminal.

THE GIRL. [*Is transfigured.*] Yes, yes, it will!

DYKE. And does it make you happy, too?

THE GIRL. [*Nods repeatedly.*] Yes. So happy—after what we were both afraid of—I can't even cry—yet. [*She brushes her eyes with her handkerchief.*] I can hardly wait to take it to her.

DYKE. [*Struck by a sudden inspiration.*] I want to give you something else to take to her. [*He picks up from the desk the envelope containing the Liberty Bonds and seals it.*] I want you to give this to your mother from me. Tell her it's from a man who was at Vimy Ridge and saw your brother die, so it's a sort of memorial for him. [*He touches her arm as she absently begins to tear open the envelope.*] No, don't you open it—let *her* do it.

THE GIRL. What is it? Can't I know?

DYKE. Never mind now, but give it to her. It's all I've got in the world and it's too late now for me to do anything else with it. And have your mother buy a little gold star to wear for her son—and you get one, too, and wear it—here— [*He touches his heart.*] Will you?

THE GIRL. Yes—I will. And yet somehow I'll almost feel that I'm wearing it for you, too.

DYKE. [*Shakes his head soberly.*] Oh, no! You mustn't ever do that. I'm not fit to be mentioned in the same breath with a boy like your brother, and now I'm afraid it *is* time for you to go. I'm sorry, but—you'd better. I'm glad you came before it was too late, though.

THE GIRL. [*Gives him her hand.*] Good-bye, and thank you. You've done more for me—and Mother—than I could possibly tell you. And—and I'm so sorry for you—so *truly sorry*—I wish I could only do something to make you a tiny bit happier, too. Is there anything I could do?

DYKE. [*Stares at her and by degrees he becomes wistful.*] Why—yes, there is. Only I— [*He leaves the sentence uncompleted.*]

THE GIRL. What is it?

DYKE. [*Looks away.*] I can't tell you. I never should have let myself think of it.

THE GIRL. Please tell me. I want you to. For—for Joe's sake, tell me what I can do.

DYKE. [*His voice is low and desolate.*] Well—in all the months I've been in this hideous place, you're the first girl I've seen. I didn't ever expect to see one again. I'd forgotten how much like angels women look. I've been terribly lonesome tonight, especially, and if you really do want to do something for me—for your brother's sake—you see, you're going to leave me in just a minute and—and I haven't any sister of my own, or anybody else, to say good-bye to me—so, if you could—*really* say good-bye—* [*She gazes at him for a moment, understands, flushes, and then slowly moves into his outstretched arms. He holds her close to him, touches his lips to her forehead twice, and releases her.*]

DYKE. [*Thickly.*] Good-bye, my dear.

THE GIRL. Good night. [*She endeavors to smile, but her voice catches in her throat.*] Good-bye.

DYKE. [*Impulsively.*] What is it?

THE GIRL. [*Shakes her head.*] N-nothing.

DYKE. Nothing?

THE GIRL. [*Clutches her handkerchief tight in her palm.*] I was thinking—I was thinking what I used to say to my brother —for good night. [*She very nearly breaks down.*] If I *only* could have—have said it to him just once more—for good-bye.

DYKE. What was it?

THE GIRL. I—I told it to you once, and you said it was silly.

DYKE. [*Softly.*] Say it again.

THE GIRL. [*She cannot quite control her voice.*]

> Good-night, good-night, parting is such sweet sorrow
> That I shall say good-night till it be morrow.

[*She goes uncertainly toward the anteroom, hesitates, almost turns back, and then with a choking sob she hurries
through the door and closes it behind her. For several seconds* DYKE *stands rigidly intent upon that door; until at
length, without changing his attitude or his expression, he
speaks very tenderly and reminiscently.*]

> Sleep dwell upon thine eyes, peace in thy breast;
> Would *I* were sleep and peace, so sweet to rest.[4]

[*The* WARDEN *and* FATHER DALY *come in quietly from the
deputy's room; and as they behold* DYKE, *how rapt and
unconscious of them he is, they look at each other, ques-
tioningly. The* WARDEN *glances at the clock and makes as
though to interrupt* DYKE's *solitary reflections but* FATHER
DALY *quietly restrains him.*
The CHAPLAIN *sits down in one of the chairs at the back
wall; the* WARDEN *crosses on tip-toe and sits at his desk;
he is excessively nervous and he continually refers to the
clock.* DYKE *turns, as though unwillingly, from the door;
there are depths in his eyes, and his thoughts are evidently
far away. He sits in the chair to the right of the* WARDEN's
*desk and leans outward, his right hand on his knee. He puts
his left hand to his throat as though to protect it from a
sudden pain. He gazes straight ahead into the unknown and
speaks in reverie.*]

> Of all the wonders that I yet have heard,
> It seems to me most strange that men should fear;
> Seeing that death, a necessary end,
> Will come when it will come.[5]

[*He stops and muses for a time, while the* WARDEN *glances
perplexedly at* FATHER DALY *to discover if the priest can interpret what* DYKE *is saying.* FATHER DALY *shakes his head.*

[4] Romeo's reply to Juliet as he leaves from beneath her balcony.
[5] From Shakespeare's *Julius Caesar*, Act II, scene 4. Caesar speaks in reply
to his wife's plea that his life would be endangered if he leaves his house
that day to go to the capitol. He does go, and is assassinated.

Abruptly DYKE's *face is illumined by a new and welcome recollection; and again he speaks, while the* WARDEN *tries in vain to comprehend him.*]

> Cowards die many times before their death;
> The valiant never taste of death but once.[6]

[*He stops again and shudders a trifle; his head droops and he repeats, barely above a whisper.*]

> The valiant never taste of death but once.

[*The nearer door on the right is opened noiselessly and the* JAILER, *in obedience to his instructions, steps just inside the room and stands there mute.* FATHER DALY *and the* WARDEN *glance at the* JAILER, *and with significance at each other, and both rise, tardily. The* WARDEN's *hand, as it rests on his desk, is seen to tremble. There is a moment of dead silence; presently* DYKE *lifts his head and catches sight of the motionless* ATTENDANT *at the open door. With a quick intake of his breath, he starts half out of his seat and stares, fascinated; he sinks back slowly, and turns his head to gaze first at* FATHER DALY *and then at the* WARDEN. *The* WARDEN *averts his eyes, but* FATHER DALY's *expression is of supreme pity and encouragement. Involuntarily,* DYKE's *hand again goes creeping upward toward his throat, but he arrests it. He grasps the arms of his chair and braces himself; he rises then, and stands very erect, in almost the position of a soldier at attention.*]

THE WARDEN. [*Swallows hard.*] Dyke!

FATHER DALY. [*Brushes past the* WARDEN, *his right hand lifted as though in benediction.*] My son!

DYKE. [*Regards them fixedly; his voice is low and steady.*] All right, let's go.

[*He faces about, and with his head held proud and high, and his shoulders squared to the world, he moves slowly toward the open door.* FATHER DALY, *with the light of his calling in his eyes, steps in line just ahead of* DYKE. *The*

[6] The first part of the same speech.

WARDEN, *his mouth set hard, falls in behind. When they have all gone forward a pace or two,* FATHER DALY *begins to speak, and* DYKE *to reply.* FATHER DALY'S *voice is strong and sweet; and* DYKE *speaks just after him, not mechanically, but in brave and unfaltering response.*]

FATHER DALY. "I will lift up mine eyes unto the hills—"

DYKE. "The valiant never taste of death but once."

FATHER DALY. "From whence cometh my help."

DYKE. "The valiant never taste of death but once."

FATHER DALY. [*Has almost reached the door; his voice rises a semi-tone, and gains in emotion.*] "My help cometh from the Lord which made Heaven and earth."

DYKE. "The valiant never taste of death—but once."

[*When the* WARDEN, *whose hands are tightly clenched, has passed the threshold, the* JAILER *follows and closes the door behind him. There is a very brief pause and then*

[*Curtain*]

UNDERSTANDING AND APPRECIATING THE PLAY

1. It is important for a playwright to establish the emotional tone of his play as soon as possible. How soon and in what way are we made aware of the fact that *The Valiant* is a serious, tense play?

2. Why did Dyke conceal his identity?

3. Is the struggle in this play mental, or moral, or physical? Identify clearly the opposing forces. Why is the play not a tragedy?

4. An important part of the plot is the warden's earnest effort to persuade Dyke to say what should be done with the Liberty Bonds. What was the warden's motive? Did he succeed in his attempt?

5. When we learn all the facts, it is apparent to us that Dyke really is the girl's brother. What facts in particular convince us that he is Joseph Anthony Paris?

6. Dyke admitted having killed a man. Is he sorry for it? What reason does he give for having killed the man? Do you think it possible that a man like Dyke could have been a murderer? Why do you, or do you not, think so?

7. The climax of a play has been defined as its highest point of

interest, the turning point toward which the rising action has been building. It is the moment when the suspense is at its height and when the emotional response from the audience (or reader) is greatest. In the light of this explanation, give your opinion as to when the climax of *The Valiant* is reached. Is it during Dyke's conversation with Josephine Paris, or when he is led to his execution? Justify your choice.

8. After the climax, how long is the falling action? (For an explanation of *falling action* see the discussion of *plot design* on p. 57.)

9. Dyke is a highly individualized character. He is many-sided: each of the other persons in the play sees him in a different light. Select the sentence (or two) from the dialogue which most aptly describes the reaction of each of the following persons to Dyke's character and personality:

(*a*) the Warden; (*b*) Father Daly; (*c*) Josephine Paris.

10. Why is the play called *The Valiant?*

VOCABULARY BUILDING

1. Explain the meaning of the following phrases: rule like a *despot;* constant *oscillation;* a trifle *abstractedly;* the *fortitude* of the Christian martyrs; grant a *reprieve;* a *metropolitan* girl; *literally* old-fashioned; well-poised and *insouciant;* expression of utter *vacuity.*

2. Do you ever confuse two words because they look something alike? Distinguish between *oscillation* and *osculation; immigrant* and *emigrant; ingenious* and *ingenuous.* What other such pairs can you name?

THINGS TO DO

1. James Dyke deliberately set his own judgment of right and wrong above established law and order. "The man deserved to be killed. He wasn't fit to live. It was my duty to kill him, and I did." Do you know an instance in which one of your friends or schoolmates has defied established rules? What happened to him? Was he aware before he acted that he was breaking the rules? Was he prepared to pay the penalty? Did he think he was justified in what he did? Do

you think he was? If you take such an instance and discuss it in class, you will have the material for a good story, or, better yet, a play.

2. Sociologists believe that crime and juvenile delinquency will be greatly reduced if slums are removed and if the living conditions of the slum dwellers are improved. In a short composition discuss your reactions to this belief.

PRODUCTION NOTES

The Valiant should be played very realistically. The plot is superb in working up suspense and emotional tension, and will carry the audience along even with mediocre acting. (Of course, superior acting will make it just so much better.) The only danger lies in over-playing it, and so destroying the spectator's belief in the situation. It would be far better to under-play it than to over-play it. These are unusual people facing an unusual crisis. Their control of themselves is what makes the play so emotionally powerful.

You will not need to worry much about the staging of *The Valiant*. There is no problem of costumes or of make-up, or of lighting; and the scenery is easy. The author describes the warden's office on page 205. If the clock on the wall faces the auditorium, it should be large enough to be visible to the audience and thus add to the relentless approach of Dyke's fate.

Since this play demands so little in the way of scenery or stage furniture, it is a very good one to try out at the front of the classroom, without a prepared setting.

Sparkin' *

E. P. CONKLE

Shyness is a personality problem with some teenagers. One wonders why some young people are so terribly shy, while others are so very confident. And how can a shy person show his true worth?

The action of *Sparkin'* takes place on a Midwestern farm in the first quarter of our century. Orry Sparks, the timid young hired hand, comes to spark—that is, to court—Lessie Hanna, the almost equally bashful but pretty girl on the neighboring farm. But there's nothing backward about Lessie's grandmother. Granny Painsberry is determined to find out whether Orry is good enough for her granddaughter and if he has enough "spunk to git on in this world."

In a survey of the reading interests of thousands of high school students in the State of New York, *Sparkin'* ranked second only to *The Valiant* in the order of popularity of plays.

CHARACTERS

SUSAN HANNA

LESSIE HANNA

GRANNY PAINSBERRY

ORRY SPARKS

SCENE: *Evening at* TUDE HANNA's *farm home. The room is the kitchen. On the right wall is the kitchen range, with a tea-kettle stewing and simmering. In front of the stove, with her stocking feet stuck into the oven, sits* GRANNY PAINSBERRY. *She has a shawl over her shoulders and sits all scrootched up.*[1] *She shivers at times, and sticks her hands out to warm them.*

In the center of the room is a dining table, covered with a white oil-cloth. There are victuals in dishes and uncovered. In the middle is a lamp. LESSIE HANNA, *a shy and pretty little girl, is ironing some things. One end of her ironing board rests on the table; the other end lies on the back of a chair. Throughout the play she runs to the stove and changes her irons, the hot for the cold. She irons away busily and adroitly, looking up now and then suspiciously toward the upper door left.*

In the rear of the room, SUSAN HANNA, TUDE's *wife, is working at a kitchen-cabinet mixing out bread.*

There is a door in the rear wall right; and there are two in the left wall, both identical, and very close together. There is a straight-back chair between the two doors.

At the rise of the curtain the women are working.

GRANNY *chews and spits into the wood-box. After a spell of silence,* GRANNY *speaks.*

GRANNY. Is Tude [2] gone to bed, Susy?

SUSAN. Why, yes, ma. Didn't you hear him say he was a goin' to bed?

GRANNY. Ef I'd a heerd him I wudn't a asted you. [*Pause.*] Whut'd Tude go to bed fer s' soon a'ready?

SUSAN. He said he war kind-a tired, ma. He's been a shuckin' corn on that north forty an' et's perty rough in them hills. Et wears a person clean out.

[*Silence.*]

[1] All hunched up.
[2] Tude is Susan's husband and Lessie's father.

GRANNY. What time is et?

SUSAN. Whut time is et, Lessie? I cain't see withouten my spec's.

LESSIE. It's a quarter to eight, mom.

GRANNY. What'd she say?

SUSAN. She said et war a quarter to eight.

GRANNY. Well, why don't she speak plainer-like? No wonder Lessie ain't got no fellers. A pusson cain't hear nothin' she says. Not nothin'!

LESSIE. I don't want no fellers.

SUSAN. Lessie ain't a thinkin' about the fellers, air you, Lessie?

LESSIE. No. [*She looks toward the door again. Then she lowers her head.*]

GRANNY. What say?

SUSAN. Lessie hain't thinkin' 'bout no fellers.

GRANNY. Listen to th' wind blowin'! Hain't thinkin' 'bout no fellers, ain't she? Well . . . ef she hain't, you betterd taik her inter Doc Spellzer an' have her 'zamined. Thur must be somethin' wrong somewhurs about her.

SUSAN. Ma! What air you a talkin' about annyways?

GRANNY. You heerd me th' fust time, Susy. You know well 'nough whut I'm a talkin' about. Uhhhhhh . . . [*Pause.*]

GRANNY. You a arnin' that white calicy dress-a mine,[3] Lessie?

LESSIE. I guess I am, Granny.

GRANNY. What say?

LESSIE. I guess so, Granny.

GRANNY. You guess so? Don't you know so? Don't you ever know nothin', Lessie? A person'd think you was plumb dumb. Maybe you air. I don't know. A pusson never cain hear nothin' you say. You're jest like'n your dead gran'pap Lute Painsberry. He never did know nothin', neither. Leastwise, not more'n th' law wud allow.

LESSIE. I'm a arnin'[4] your dress, Granny. Lands-a-goodness!

GRANNY. That's right! Begin a swearin' at me! Well, see you don't scorch no hole inter et!

[3] white calico dress of mine.
[4] ironing.

SUSAN. A person'd think you war old enough to know better'n to go to dances, ma. You're too old t' be doin' such things.

GRANNY. I hain't too old to do nothin'. Nobody hain't who don't think so! I'm a goin' to Hank Wagnerses barn-dance tomorry night ef I have t' put on a pair-a gum-boots an' wade. Nobody cain't talk me outen et. So shet up. Hang that dress up in th' closet thur b'hint ye.

LESSIE. That's what I was a aimin' t' do, Granny. [*She holds the dress up before her grandmother.*]

LESSIE. See. Ain't it perty, Granny?

GRANNY. It'll do . . . cainsiderin' who arned et.[5]

LESSIE. Let's see how you're a goin' to look . . .

GRANNY. Git away with yer lollygaggin'[6] 'round me, will you. You act like you'd never'd a seen me dressed up!

LESSIE. You look like a perty old rosebud, Granny! [*She lays the dress on the old lady's huddled form.*]

GRANNY. I *am* perty old. But I hain't no rosebud. I know I hain't no rosebud. An' you know I hain't no rosebud. You jest want to git my money when I'm gone. You're jest like all th' rest-a them all!

LESSIE. Aw, Granny . . . I don't want your money. [*She stoops and kisses the old lady. The latter spits and sputters.*]

GRANNY. Git away with yer lollygaggin' 'round me, will you? I never cud tolerate no lollygaggin' 'round! Lute usta be all th' time a lollygaggin' round. He didn't care who he lollygagged with, neither.

SUSAN. Ma! You're talkin' that-away before Lessie?

LESSIE. Don't pay no attention to me. She can't hurt me none.

SUSAN. Lessie!

[LESSIE *goes to hang the dress in the closet.*]

GRANNY. I reckon Lessie'll be a settin' her cap fer that new hired-hand Cornie Youngseses got.

LESSIE. Granny!

GRANNY. He don't look t' me like he 'mounted to powder an' lead t' blow him up with. One-a them slow-pokey fellers. They

[5] considering who ironed it.
[6] fussing.

don't never get nowheres in this-a world. You got to be up-an'-comin' to amount to much around here. I'll give it to your gran'-pap. He war shore up-an'-comin'. 'Specially whenever he seed a woman. I had no complaint t' make 'bout him a bein' a live one.

LESSIE. That feller over to Young's is a nice feller.

GRANNY. Oh. You been inspectin' him, have you? Oh.

LESSIE. Well . . . he is!

GRANNY. Susy.

SUSAN. What, ma?

GRANNY. Put another stick-a cord-wood inter th' fyar.[7] My feet is a freezin' off of me. That there slippery-ellum [8] is too wet. Et don't burn good when et's wet. Tell Tude t' scair up some-a that jack-oak that's on th' bottom-a th' pile.

SUSAN. [*Fixing the fire.*] It don't seem none too cold in here for me. Does it to you, Lessie?

LESSIE. I'm about burnin' up.

GRANNY. Well, et hain't no heat out-a this-here stove's a burnin' you up. Ef you're a burnin' up, et must be with curiosity er some-thin'.

SUSAN. We're a workin', ma.

GRANNY. What you a workin' at?

SUSAN. I'm a mixin' out my bread. Th' starter hain't been right th' last two times.

GRANNY. You don't put enough taters inter your tater-water.[9]

SUSAN. Et hain't that, ma.

GRANNY. Don't you go a tellin' me what ain't, an' what is. Ef you want to know what— [*There is a heavy step on the porch. All the women turn abruptly towards the upper left door.*] Who's that a prowlin' around here this time-a th' night? [*There is a stomping and scraping of feet.*] Comin' around time a person's gittin' ready fer their bed. [*There is a heavy knock on the door like the banging of a mailed fist.*]

LESSIE. Oh! [*The women turn to her.*]

SUSAN. Who is et, Lessie?

[7] fire.
[8] slippery elm: a tree from which wood had been chopped for the fire.
[9] potatoes into your potato water.

LESSIE. It's . . . him!

GRANNY. Who's *him?*

LESSIE. Him!

SUSAN. Lessie, who is et?

LESSIE. It's Orry Sparks.

SUSAN. Lessie . . . what's Orry Sparks doin' comin' over here?

LESSIE. T' see about somethin', I reckon.

GRANNY. Who'd she say et war?

SUSAN. She said et war that new feller over to Youngses.

GRANNY. Oh. I was a wonderin' what she was a wearin' them new slippers an' sox t'night fer. So she's a shinin' around fer a man, is she? I ain't got no use for that young feller over . . .

[*The knock comes again.*]

LESSIE. Mom!

SUSAN. What?

LESSIE. He's . . . out there, mom!

SUSAN. Well?

GRANNY. Don't be so green. Go an' let him in. He won't never amount to nothin'. He . . .

LESSIE. Mom . . . I don't know what to *do!*

[SUSAN *goes to the door and opens it.*]

GRANNY. Mild*ew!*

[LESSIE *stands back of the ironing board nervous and blushing.* GRANNY *scrootches up in her shawl.* ORRY SPARKS *slides in. He is a big, husky fellow. He is bashful and stands with his cap in his hand. His eyes are on* LESSIE. *Otherwise he doesn't know what to do or say.*]

SUSAN. Howdy do, Mister Sparks. Nice evenin' out, ain't et?

ORRY. Howdy do, Missus Hanna. Why, yeh, kinda.

SUSAN. Lessie, here's Mister Sparks.

LESSIE. [*Turning and stammering.*] Oh, I didn't know you was here. Howdy do. Let me have your cap.

ORRY. Howdy, Lessie. You arnin' some clo'es?

LESSIE. I'm tryin' to.

GRANNY. What does he want, Susy? Is somebody sick over to th' Youngseses? I reckon that little Betty-Sall has throwed another-a her cat fits, an' . . .

ORRY. Th' Youngses is all right, fer as I know. I jest . . . [*He casts his eyes* LESSIE-*ward.*] . . . kinda thought I'd drop in a spell to see you folks. I never been over to see you yet.

SUSAN. I'm right glad you come over, Mister Sparks. Have you ever met up with Granny, here? She's my ma.

ORRY. Oh. She's th' nice old lady comes over visitin' Missus Young, ain't she?

GRANNY. What's he a sayin'?

SUSAN. He said as how you was a nice old lady, ma.

GRANNY. Who sayed that?

SUSAN. Him.

[GRANNY *turns and looks squarely at* ORRY.]

GRANNY. Oh. [*She turns back. Pause.*] Well . . . [*Pause.*] Maybe I hain't so nice as I look, young feller. [*She feels in her pocket.*] Have a chaw-a t'baccer? [ORRY *is wide-eyed.*]

LESSIE. Granny . . . maybe he don't . . .

GRANNY. In my day all th' real fellers chawed t'baccer an' drunk strong licker.

ORRY. Well. I don't us'ally chew t'baccer. But sometimes I do. I'm a real feller, I am. I'll . . . I'll try a chaw . . . [*He grabs off the plug. He looks to* LESSIE *to see if she is watching. He bites off the chunk and returns the plug.* GRANNY *looks over her shoulder bird-like.*] . . . ef et kills me!

SUSAN. Jest set down annywheres you cain find a chair, Mr. Sparks. Looks like Lessie's got 'em all filled up with clo'es.

ORRY. Don't mind about me. I cain set on th' floor. Here's a chair over here. [*He sits on the chair between the two doors. There are clothes on the back of it.*]

LESSIE. [*Going about her ironing.*] I'm sorry I cain't ast you into th' front-room, but we ain't got our heatin' stove up in there yet.

ORRY. Aw, that's all right. I ain't usta no parlor-rooms, noway. I don't feel at home sittin' on a sofy. Do you?

LESSIE. It's 'cordin' who I'm sittin' with.

ORRY. Aw.

GRANNY. What you ca'culate t'do around here t'night, young feller?

SUSAN. Ma . . . it's time you was in bed, ain't et?

GRANNY. What say?

SUSAN. I sayed it was time you was in bed. Your bed's ready.

GRANNY. What ef et is? Cain't I set up ef I want to? There's one night ever' year I set up to nigh onto nine o'clock. I think this year, this is et. Poke up th' fyar, Susy.

SUSAN. Ma, you'll ketch your deaf a cold [10] settin' up here.

GRANNY. Whose death is et, annyway? Why should you keer? You all got your eye on my money when I do die. They ain't nobody 'round here cain make me go t' bed ef I don't want to. [GRANNY *scrootches up.*]

SUSAN. Don't pay no 'tention to ma, Mister Sparks. She's gettin' old.

ORRY. 'Tain't th' old ladies worries me much, Missus Hanna. Et's . . . [*He blushes. He looks towards* LESSIE] . . . th' young ones.

[LESSIE *blushes.*]

LESSIE. Don't let them worry you none, Mister Sparks. They ain't worth worryin' none over.

ORRY. I reckon . . . you're a talkin' through your hat, Lessie.

[LESSIE *smiles and lowers her head. She irons.*]

GRANNY. If you air a aimin' t' git inter th' good graces-a this fambly, you want t' treat me nice, young feller. I got all th' say around this fambly. What I says, goes. What I don't say, ain't wuth sayin'.

ORRY. I . . . I brung you over a sack of candy . . . Lessie. Got et into Martinses store this afternoon. Et hain't much, but et's somethin' to chaw on. Save you chawin' th' rag.[11] [ORRY *hands* LESSIE *the candy. She opens the sack and looks into it.*]

LESSIE. Oh. It's chocolate drops, isn't it?

ORRY. He'p yourse'f, and give some to th' folks. [*He arises to spit. He looks at both the doors. He decides on the down-stage one, opens it, and spits out. He closes it and sits.* LESSIE *has taken a piece of candy out to eat.*]

LESSIE. Here, mom, Mister Sparks brung us some . . .

[10] death of a cold.
[11] save you from doing a lot of talking.

ORRY. I brung 'em fer you, Lessie, private.

LESSIE. Oh.

ORRY. But your folks cain eat on 'em if you say so. They're kinda hard an' don't amount to nothin'. I reckon they been in th' store since Noah's Ark.

[SUSAN *takes one.* LESSIE *goes to the old lady.*]

LESSIE. Here, Granny. [*She holds the sack open for* GRANNY *to take one.*]

GRANNY. What is et?

LESSIE. Chocolate drops.

GRANNY. What?

LESSIE. Chocolate drops.

GRANNY. Choclit draps?

LESSIE. Yes.

GRANNY. Oh. [*She takes the whole bag.* LESSIE *stands speechless.*] Thank ye.

[LESSIE *is about to protest.*]

ORRY. Shshshsh. Let her have 'em. Don't rile her up none.

GRANNY. Whur'd you git choclit draps at?

LESSIE. Mister Sparks brung 'em.

GRANNY. Oh. [*She turns and casts a suspicious eye towards* ORRY.] They hain't so bad. [*She samples another one.*] I tasted better. [*She chews it.*] Yit . . . they ain't so bad. [*She takes another.*] How'd you know I like choclit draps, young feller?

ORRY. I . . . didn't.

[GRANNY *scrootches up over her bag of candy and munches one after another.* SUSAN *goes about her business at the cabinet.*]

ORRY. I didn't ca'culate t' stay very long. Guess maybe I orta be goin' on back home. Me and Cornie's goin' to cut fodder [12] t'morrow on th' crick bottom. Liable to frost anny night now.

LESSIE. You don't need t' be a runnin' off home yet, Mister Sparks. You ain't only just come over.

ORRY. I know I ain't been here very long. But I just thought I'd just drop in a bit to . . . to see you. An' say . . . you

---

[12] coarse food for cattle and horses; for example, hay or stalks and leaves of field corn.

wouldn't mind a-callin' me jest Orry, would you? Nobody never called me Mister Sparks much, an' ha'f th' time when a person calls me that, I don't know who they're talkin' to. Orry ain't much of a name, but I reckon *I* hain't so much, neither.

LESSIE. I got an uncle by the name of Orry, too. He's kind-of-silly-like.

ORRY. Ah . . . yeh. [*He drops his head.* LESSIE *irons.* SUSAN *putters around.* GRANNY *nibbles.* ORRY *lifts his head.*] What you doin'? arnin'?

LESSIE. I'm arnin' out some things fer Sunday.

ORRY. Oh. [*He gets up and spits out the door again.* LESSIE *looks at* SUSAN. SUSAN *looks at* LESSIE.] Shore dark out t'night. Must-a clouded up since I come in.

GRANNY. Hain't a cloud in th' sky as I cain see. [*They all look towards* GRANNY. *She munches.* ORRY *closes the door and sits down.*] You arnin' that new calicy dress-a mine, Lessie?

LESSIE. It's all arned and hung up, Granny.

GRANNY. What?

LESSIE. Yes.

GRANNY. Well, don't git sassy. I heerd you th' fust time. [*Pause.*] Susy.

SUSAN. Yes, ma. [*Going to* GRANNY.]

GRANNY. These choclit draps shore hits th' spot. You folks don't never git me no choclit draps. That young feller ain't so bad. What's he a doin' now?

SUSAN. Shshsh. He's a talkin' to Lessie.

GRANNY. What's he a talkin' 'bout?

SUSAN. About cuttin' fodder, last I heard.

GRANNY. Fodder? Oh, shucks! [*She scrootches and nibbles.* SUSAN *casts a glance at* ORRY *and* LESSIE, *smiles, and leaves by the rear door.*]

ORRY. I usta he'p my ma arn. When I had a ma.

LESSIE. Ain't you got no ma no more?

ORRY. Nope. She went an' died. I ain't got no one t' look after me no more. That's why I'm like I am. I ain't got no one to look after me.

LESSIE. Aw.

ORRY. I been kinda on th' look-out fer someone t' look after me. You . . . know.

LESSIE. Who you ca'culate you'll git, Orry?

ORRY. Gosh durn . . . I don't know. But . . . [*Lowering his head and peeking at her from the corner of his eyes.*] . . . I got my eye on someone.

[*She looks up from her work. She catches his glance. She lowers her head and blushes.*]

LESSIE. Oh.

[*There is an awkward pause. Then* ORRY *breaks it.*]

ORRY. Lessie . . . cud I he'p you arn a bit? [*He gets up.*]

LESSIE. I reckon you cud ef you was a mind to, Orry. But Granny wudn't like et.

ORRY. Why not?

LESSIE. Cause she don't like t' see men-folks doin' th' women-folks' work.

ORRY. [*Sitting down.*] Oh. Well. I guess I better not do it then. She's got a lot-a power around this house, ain't she? [*He pulls out his handkerchief and blows his nose very, very audibly.*]

LESSIE. She ain't got so much as she thinks she has. Us folks all 'umors her.

ORRY. I bet her husban' had to mind his P's and Q's, didn't he? [ORRY *puts his handkerchief into his pocket. Not noticing, he gets it mixed up with an ironed piece on the chair. The next few minutes he spends stuffing a garment,—it is a lady's garment, —into his pocket. He is talking and doesn't notice it.*]

LESSIE. Gran'pa Painsberry never went to school. He never knowed no more'n th' law'll allow.

ORRY. You're perty smart, though, ain't you, Lessie?

LESSIE. Oh, not very. But I cain read quite a bit.

ORRY. Gosh darn, I wisht I cud read more. I don't have much time to read or nothin'. I never had many books. I . . . [LESSIE *has caught sight of* ORRY *stuffing the garment into his hip pocket. She doesn't know what to say. She smiles.*] . . . I never been to school, much. But when I get a little money ahead . . . Whut you . . . grinnin' at, Lessie? [*He stops.*]

LESSIE. Oh. I was jest a grinnin' at myse'f.

ORRY. I was only a puttin' my handkerchief away, Lessie.

LESSIE. I didn't mean no harm, Orry.

ORRY. [*Looking toward* GRANNY.] Don't your folks never go to bed?

LESSIE. She's jest stayin' up 'cause you're here.

ORRY. I hain't much t' set up for.

LESSIE. No one ever comes in, much. Specially in the evenings. It gets kinda lonesome . . . for me . . . around here.

ORRY. I git kinda lonesome over to Youngses, too. They're all right. But I ain't nothin' but a hired man. They ain't no one there fer me t' talk to.

LESSIE. Us folks 'ud like t' have you come over ever' now an' then.

ORRY. [*Shyly.*] That's whut I ca'culated on doin'. [*He grins.*]

LESSIE. Aw.

ORRY. It'd be kinda cold out t' taik a walk, wouldn't et?

LESSIE. It's perty cold out.

ORRY. Yeh. Still . . . et hain't *very* cold out. Do you ca'culate you cud go a buggy-ridin' with me some time next summer, Lessie?

LESSIE. I reckon I cud ef th' weather wa'n't too bad. Of course . . . bein's you was to ast me to.

ORRY. I'm a astin' you to now, Lessie.

LESSIE. Oh. Why . . . [*Pause.*] I'd . . . kind-a like to, Orry. I never been buggy-ridin' with no boy . . . yet.

ORRY. I never neither.

LESSIE. I heard tell et's awful nice, though.

ORRY. I heard tell th' same thing. I'd like t' see fer myse'f, though. A person cain't tell nothin' from hearsay. [*He gets up and opens the door to spit out.*] Shore is dark out. Don't see a solitary star. [LESSIE *laughs to herself, but says nothing. He closes the door and sits down again.*] Well . . . [*Gets out his watch and winds it.*] . . . I reckon I orta be a moseyin' on home.

LESSIE. Don't be in no hurry.

ORRY. Don't think I have been, Lessie. When I come, I didn't ca'culate t' stay this long. I thought maybe you'd run me offn th' place.

LESSIE. Aw. You know I wouldn't run you offn th' place, Orry. You jest come on over when you git lonesome an' want to.

ORRY. Thanks, Lessie. I'll r'member that. I like t' stick around here. You folks is all so homely.

LESSIE. Homely?

ORRY. I mean . . . so kinda home-like.

LESSIE. [*Low.*] Oh. I . . . guess . . . that's 'cause we like you, Orry.

ORRY. [*Blushing.*] Aw, Lessie! Gosh durn!

GRANNY. [*Turning her head.*] You hain't very fast t' do business, air you, young feller?

ORRY. [*Perking up his head.*] Ah . . .

GRANNY. I heard ever' word you been a sayin'. I cain see you're perty sweet on Lessie. Them choclit draps you brung me is first-rate. Th' folks 'round here don't give me nothin' to chew on but t'baccer. I guess you hain't so bad. You ain't got much spunk, though. A feller's got to have spunk t' git on in this world.

ORRY. Ag'in I gits all riled up,[13] a person'd never know how much spunk I got in me! Nobody knows how much spunk I got!

GRANNY. I'm a goin' to poke off t' bed. Oh, Susy. Susy!

LESSIE. Mom's gone to bed already, Granny.

GRANNY. Well . . . why didn't she tell me she was a goin' t' bed? [GRANNY *gets up from her chair. She holds the sack of candy close to her.*]

GRANNY. Come yur, young feller.

ORRY. What you want?

GRANNY. [*Eyeing him closely.*] Lessie's a right nice little girl. But you got a good voice. You got good eyes. I reckon you ain't so bad.

ORRY. I'm perty good. Leastwise . . . I always try to be.

GRANNY. Them choclits shore filled me up right. Jest drap in anny night t' see Lessie. I likes peppamint-draps, too. Peppamint-draps is good fer th' stomick t' settle et. They're a kind of a physic, too, they say.

LESSIE. Granny!

[13] angered or irritated.

GRANNY. [*Scornfully.*] What's wrong with you? [*She passes* LESSIE *and starts for the lower door left.*]

LESSIE. What you goin' to do, Granny?

GRANNY. I'm a goin' to show this-yur young feller my bran' new white calicy dress.

ORRY. But . . . but . . . [*He doesn't understand why she goes to the door downstage. To* LESSIE.]

ORRY. But . . . her dress ain't out-doors, is et?

LESSIE. It's in the closet.

[GRANNY *opens the door and goes in.* ORRY *stands dumbfounded.* LESSIE *breaks out laughing.*]

ORRY. But . . . Lessie! What've I been a doin'?

LESSIE. You been a spittin' into th' closet, Orry!

ORRY. Aw. [*His jaw drops ten degrees.* LESSIE *has great fun.* GRANNY *comes out with the dress. She holds it before her spread out. It is spattered with tobacco juice. She hasn't seen that yet.* ORRY *is paralyzed when he discovers it.* LESSIE *stares.*]

GRANNY. They all aroun' here think I'm dead an' gone a'ready. I'm a goin' t' fool 'em a trip or two. They's a barn-dance over to Hank Wagnerses t'morry an' I'm a goin' over t' show 'em all how t' cut th' pigeon's wing.[14] This ol' chicken . . . [*She sees the two standing speechless. She views them over her spectacles. Then she looks down at the dress. Immediately she becomes alive.*]

GRANNY. Lessie . . . is them fly-specks on my bran' new white calicy dress? [*She hurries to the table and lays the dress on it to examine it.*]

ORRY. I . . . I guess I . . . better'd be goin' . . . home, Lessie.

GRANNY. T'baccer spit! [*She smells and examines.*] T'baccer spit! [*She frets and stews.*] T'baccer spit on my bran' new calicy dress! [*She turns furiously.*] Lessie! You . . . you . . . [*She spies* ORRY's *looks. He is about ready to break out crying.*]

ORRY. I . . . I . . . I . . . I . . . I . . .

GRANNY. You been a spittin' all over my dress, ain't you? You're a fine one, hain't you? Th' best thing you cain do is t' hit fer home as fast as you cain, an' never step foot onto this forty ag'in

[14] a fancy dance step.

as long's I live! Th' idea-a you a comin' into a person's house an' spittin' all over his bran' new calicy dress! You're a nice one, ain't you? Et won't come out, neither. Nothing'll take t'baccer spit out! Hain't you a nice feller to come a sparkin' a gal an' hain't got no more manners about you as to spit all over th' house this-a-way! Look at th' floor in there! Pity me! [*She stoops to examine.*]

ORRY. I . . . I . . . I guess I better'd go on . . . home, Lessie. I done enough mischief fer one night. An' I wanted to be so nice!

GRANNY. Yes. I guess you'd better'd! I'm a goin' to tell Missus Young all about this! She orta know th' kind-a feller you air. Most likely you been a spittin' in th' butter, an' spittin' down into th' cistern,[15] an' . . . spittin' . . .

ORRY. [*To* LESSIE.] I guess I . . . shore made a . . . mess-a things tonight . . . didn't I, Lessie?

LESSIE. Don't feel bad, Orry. 'Twa'nt your fault.

ORRY. My pa always sayed I was a blockhead. Now I know I am.

LESSIE. No you ain't, Orry. You ain't neither!

GRANNY. [*Raising her head from the dress which she frets over.*] Well . . . what you stickin' around fer? You done your *do*. You shore done a plenty, too. [*She holds out the dress.*] Hain't that a nice lookin' spectacle after you gone an' messed all over et?

ORRY. I'll . . . buy you another'n.

GRANNY. I'd like t' know how you'll buy me another'n? You ain't got a second paar a pants to your name, let alone buyin' me a new calicy dress!

ORRY. I . . . I know . . . et.

GRANNY. Well. [*She wads the dress up and puts it under her arm.*]

ORRY. [*To* LESSIE.] I'm awful sorry I . . . went an' done that. I guess I hadn't . . . orta come over . . . but I . . . you know . . .

LESSIE. You don't need to be sorry, Orry.

ORRY. I . . . I guess I . . . ah . . . [*He turns abruptly and takes a few steps.*] . . . good-bye, Lessie.

[15] a tank for storing water.

LESSIE. Orry . . . what you a goin' t' do?

ORRY. I'm a goin' home . . . maybe. An' . . . maybe I ain't. [*He starts out the wrong door; becomes confused; goes to the other one.*]

GRANNY. [*Mumbling.*] A pretty sight, ain't et? A perty sight t' b'hold! I'd like t' know how a person cain ever . . . [*She grumbles and starts for the rear door.*]

ORRY. [*Turning at the door.*] Good . . . good . . .

LESSIE. Orry . . . please don't go. Perty please!

ORRY. I'm goin'. An' you mayn't never see me ag'in, Lessie! [*He lunges out and slams the door after him.*]

LESSIE. Granny . . . Granny . . . looky what you've gone an' done!

GRANNY. Looky what he went an' done!

LESSIE. He's goin' out to kill hisse'f!

GRANNY. Don't be no fool, Lessie.

LESSIE. But . . . Granny? . . . [LESSIE *runs to the outside door. She throws it open, steps onto the porch, and calls.*] Orry! Orry! Orry!

> [*There is no reply. She comes back in and closes the door.* GRANNY *goes into the other room muttering to herself.* LES-SIE *goes to a chair, drops into it, and cries.*]
>
> [*Soon the outside door opens, and* ORRY *comes in, silently. He goes to* LESSIE's *chair and drops on his knees at her feet. He touches her hand with the tips of his big fingers.*]

LESSIE. Orry!

ORRY. Lessie . . . I heard you a-callin' me. I couldn't go no-wheres 'thouten astin' you . . . cud you forgive me th' way I sinned, Lessie? I guess I was . . . born silly . . . Lessie.

LESSIE. 'Course I'll forgive you, Orry. B'sides . . . you ain't silly.

ORRY. Don't cry, Lessie. Here. [*He reaches into his hip pocket for his handkerchief. He pulls out the woman's garment and dries her eyes with it.*] Don't cry, Lessie. Me and . . . you . . . we could . . . we . . . could . . . [*They both discover the "handkerchief."* LESSIE *breaks out laughing.*]

LESSIE. Oh, Orry! What you got in your hand?

ORRY. [*Arising, horrified, bashful, delighted.*] Lessie . . . gosh durn et . . . how . . . [*A gasp for breath.*] . . . how did that thing-a-ma-jigger get about me, annyways?

    [LESSIE *laughs.* ORRY *breaks out laughing. He puts the garment onto the table; but not before touching his face surreptitiously with it.*]

LESSIE. I . . . I guess you ain't yourse'f t'night, are you, Orry?

ORRY. Dog-gone, I don't know what's th' matter with me t'night. I guess . . . [*He goes to the stove to get* GRANNY's *chair to draw up to* LESSIE's.] . . . I guess . . . [*Looking shyly over his shoulder toward her.*] . . . et must be . . . *you*, Lessie.

LESSIE. I . . . guess *you're* a talkin' through *your* hat now, ain't you, Orry? [*He starts toward her with the chair.* GRANNY *pokes her head in. She has on a nightcap.* ORRY *stops short.*]

GRANNY. You cain't fool me. I knowed you was there all th' time! You ain't such a big dunce arter all. I knowed you'd come back. You don't need t' be 'fraid-a me none no more, young feller. I figured out I'll color that-thur dress coal black an' wear et t' old Granny Dill's funeral when she dies. An' ef I die fust . . . I'll wear et t' my own. [*She grins.* ORRY *grins.* LESSIE *grins.*]

[*Curtain*]

UNDERSTANDING AND APPRECIATING THE PLAY

    1. Was Lessie either expecting or hoping that Orry would call that evening? Why?

    2. Granny is not entirely satisfied with Lessie's personality. In what ways does she want Lessie to improve?

    3. Before Orry appears, what is Granny's impression of him?

    4. Point out instances of things Lessie says and does that show how shy she is? Is she as bashful as Orry? Why?

    5. Just before Granny "discovers" that Orry has been spitting tobacco juice on her white calico dress, she admits that he has some good points. What does she say she likes about him?

    6. But then Granny quickly adds, "You ain't got much spunk,

though." What does Orry say in defending himself against that accusation?

7. What is the final and most important test that Orry meets to prove to Granny's satisfaction that he does have spunk and that he is worthy of Lessie?

8. What do you think? Are Orry and Lessie worthy of and "right for" each other? Why?

9. What is the climax of the play?

10. Do you think that Granny knew all along that Orry was spitting into the closet? Why? If you think she did know, explain why she didn't stop him.

11. Do you find Granny to be a convincing character, or do you think that she is an exaggerated type? Discuss.

12. In your opinion, what are the most humorous incidents and situations in the play? Does the humor lie in what the characters do or say—or in both what they say and do?

13. Is *Sparkin'* a comedy or a farce? Why?

14. Especially in the short play form, E. P. Conkle is one of our outstanding folk playwrights. In what respect is *Sparkin'* a folk play?

15. When Orry returns, he begs Lessie to forgive him for the way he sinned. Did he actually sin? How do you explain Orry's saying that he did?

VOCABULARY BUILDING

1. In the context in which they occur, explain the meanings of the following italicized words: irons away busily and *adroitly;* touching his face *surreptitiously* with it; spitting into the *cistern;* cutting *fodder.*

2. "You folks is so homely," says Orry intending to compliment Lessie's family. What does *homely* mean? Of what work or expression was Orry thinking?

THINGS TO DO

1. Develop one of the following topics into a theme: Shy Guy; Shy Girl; How Shy I Am!; How to Overcome Shyness; How I Proved My Worth.

2. For discussion:

A. The modern teenager: Worse than his predecessors? Better? No better or worse?

B. Life on a farm nowadays. There used to be a marked difference between the speech, opportunities for education and recreation, mannerisms, degree of sophistication, etc., between city and country folk. Is that difference as great now as it was, say in the 1920's, when the action of *Sparkin'* took place? Why?

C. Do personality opposites attract? Are people of differing personalities more likely to attract each other? For example, were Lessie and Orrie too much alike? Is a quiet, reserved person more likely to be attracted to a sparkling, vivacious one? Is one possessed of an outgoing (extraverted) personality more likely to find greater appeal in an introverted person, one who is more inclined to think than to act?

D. Are adults not careful enough or too careful of what they say in front of teenagers? At one point in *Sparkin'*, for example, Susan accuses Granny of not being careful about what the elderly woman says about Grandpa Painsberry in front of Lessie. Instead of being shocked at what she had heard, the teenager protests that Granny's remark wasn't hurting her. Are adults too careless or too careful about either what they themselves say or what others may say in the presence of young people.

PRODUCTION NOTES

In casting, the first consideration is to get a strong character actress in the role of Granny. Fortunately, young people respect the opportunity and the challenge afforded by the part; and good, forceful actresses vie for it. While the role of Lessie is an attractive one, calling as it does for a pretty, appealing, and wistful girl, it does not have the meat of the Granny part. Don't feel that you must have a naturally shy boy for your Orry; it's better to get a skilled actor who can be appropriately and convincingly shy when he has to be.

In the setting, the two identical doors, placed very closely together, are essential. Note that the playwright has knowingly placed the doors in a side wall rather than upstage. By doing so he has made it easier for the audience to accept the facts that one door is to the closet in which Granny's dress is hanging and that the other door leads to the outside; moreover, placing the doors at the side makes it much easier to mask what is beyond them.

Try to get the full measure of humor out of Orry's spitting into the closet and reiterating, "Shore dark out t'night"; Orry's stuffing a

lady's garment into his hip pocket in the belief that it's his handkerchief, and, near the end of the play, pulling the garment out to dry
Lessie's eyes; and, in the third place, Granny's snatching the whole
bag of chocolate drops from Lessie, to concomitant reactions from
all four characters.

Be certain that Orry and Lessie depict their shyness and inex-
perience sincerely and credibly. An archly-exaggerated portrayal is
not only false—it can be absolutely ruinous.

Work out carefully the details of the two dramatic scenes: the
climax of the play, when Granny "finds out" that Orry has been
spitting on her dress; and Orry's return. Because of Granny's feigned
rage, Orry's despair, and Lessie's frantic pleading with Orry not to
rush out—perhaps, as she thinks, to kill himself—the climax can
be made highly-exciting theater. Then, by way of contrast, play with
skilled restraint the next scene, which begins with Orry's coming back,
dropping to his knees at Lessie's feet, and touching her hand with
the tips of his fingers.

Pauses are important in this play: pauses for the purpose of
building up to an utterance, pauses to allow meaning and humor
to be fully appreciated. Here Dr. Conkle is again very helpful; almost always he indicates pauses by a series of three dots.

Until the climax, the basic positions of the characters, from which,
of course, they vary as the situations demand, are these: Granny,
upstage right, at the stove, turned towards the audience for most of her
lines; Lessie at or near the ironing board, upstage center; Susan
also near upstage center, moving about dining table, etc. Orry seated
somewhat downstage left of Lessie, near the identical doors in the
left wall, but turned towards audience in good part so that he is
clearly audible. Avoid having any two characters on a straight line
for much of the action, however. Just before the romantic scene between Lessie and Orry, perhaps, at her line "Us folks 'ud like t'
have you come over now and then," Lessie can remove the ironing board,
and bring the chair which had been supporting the board to slightly
downstage left of Orry's chair. Naturally, if your setting differs mark-
edly from the one described by the playwright, especially in the
placement of the identical doors, you will modify the basic positions
accordingly.

Since stoves of the kind called for in this play are very hard to
come by nowadays, you can do without one. Instead, you may wish
to put Granny in a rocker; but make sure she does very little rocking, or the audience will attend to very little else about the play.
Also change the dialogue somewhat: instead of Granny's telling Susan
to put another stick of cord-wood into the fire, she can say, "I'm
cold . . . Did you put enough cord-wood into the fire?"

Back of the Yards *

KENNETH SAWYER GOODMAN

What makes some teen-agers turn to crime and other forms
of wrongdoing?

Why is juvenile delinquency more prevalent at certain times than
in other eras?

And why do young people from apparently good homes turn to
crime?

The problem of juvenile delinquency is not a new one. *Back of the
Yards,* probably the best short play on that vexing problem, was
published as far back as 1914; and it is as highly exciting and as
relevant today.

CHARACTERS

A Priest
A Police Sergeant
A Boy
The Boy's Mother
A Girl

*The Scene is the kitchen of a small flat in the district back of
the Chicago Stock Yards. It is extremely clean and neat. There
is a door at the back into a hallway, and a door at the right into
a bedroom.*

*The Time is about nine-thirty on a warm summer evening, and
the two windows at the left are open, letting in a mixture of
street-noises.*

Sergeant Bennett, *in his shirt-sleeves, sits near one of the
windows, smoking a pipe and reading the* Evening American.
Father Vincent, *in the dress of a Roman Catholic priest, sits in*

*one of the straight-backed chairs beside the table in the center
of the room. He is evidently thinking hard about something unpleasant, and from time to time mops his face with a handkerchief, which he takes from a clerical hat lying beside him on the
table.*

THE SERGEANT. [*Taking his pipe from his mouth and shaking
his head.*] It beats hell! It sure does beat—

THE PRIEST. Eh? I beg your pardon, Sergeant, I wasn't listening.

THE SERGEANT. Beg yours, your Reverence. The tongue
slipped on me.

THE PRIEST. I didn't catch what you said?

THE SERGEANT. I was saying, it beats all how they come to
do it. And them decent kids mostly, with good bringing up, too,
and fine hardworking folks back of 'em.

THE PRIEST. More about it in the evening paper?

THE SERGEANT. Column and a half. Listen here to the head-
lines, will you?

THE PRIEST. No. I don't want to. It makes me feel sick and
old.

THE SERGEANT. [*Laying down his paper.*] They're calling us
dubs. They're after McWeeney to shake things up all over the
place. As if it was his fault! Whose fault is it anyhow? I've seen
epidemics of crime before. This here ain't the same thing. It's
been happening more or less right along. It hops up where you
ain't looking for it. It ain't new and it's new all the time. It ain't
like placing the blame for regular jobs. It ain't like dealing with
regular crooks. You can't put your finger on it. How the devil—
excuse me—

THE PRIEST. Yes, how the—?

THE SERGEANT. They got one of this here last bunch anyhow,
and they got him good, too. He's at the County Hospital—a
kid not more'n nineteen with two chunks of lead in him—un-
identified—he ain't opened his head. Not a chance for him. It's
all in the—

THE PRIEST. I saw him myself this evening about an hour ago.

THE SERGEANT. Go on with you, now! You didn't know him by chance?

THE PRIEST. It was Jimmy Reegan.

THE SERGEANT. No!

THE PRIEST. Joe Reegan's boy, that I gave the holy baptism to with my own hands. Red-headed Jimmy that I danced on my own knee.

THE SERGEANT. It's proud you should be of him and you sticking up for him always. What was I telling you only last week? Wasn't I saying he'd be doing his time yet? Wasn't I now? And a long time at that.

THE PRIEST. He'll be doing longer time than this State could keep him for.

THE SERGEANT. What's that you're saying?

THE PRIEST. He's gone.

THE SERGEANT. Gone?

THE PRIEST. Without the final consolation; without a word; without a spark of hope to cheer him.

THE SERGEANT. God have mercy!

THE PRIEST. Hush! She's coming back.

THE SERGEANT. [*In a tense whisper.*] What did you get me over here for? You ain't thinking of Michael, surely?

THE PRIEST. Hush, now, and put a quiet face on you, Sergeant. It may be that I'm only an old fool after all. [*Enter* MRS. CONNORS, *a cheerful woman of thirty-nine or so.*] It's a late hour you're abroad, my dear.

[*The two men rise and* THE SERGEANT *struggles into his coat.*]

MRS. CONNORS. God save your Reverence! And you, too, Mr. Sergeant. I'd have been back earlier if I'd knowed there was two such old friends waiting for me. Think of it, the clergy and the police both to once.

THE SERGEANT. [*With labored lightness.*] Where was you all the time?

MRS. CONNORS. [*Taking off her hat.*] To the movies with a friend. [*To* THE SERGEANT.] Don't cock a jealous eye on me now, Peter. It was with Mrs. Steinbrecker I went, her and her cousin, by way of celebrating the birthday of her first twins, and them dead, poor dears, five years back. [*To* THE PRIEST.] Come now, Father, don't look at me like I'd done a black bad thing. You wouldn't grudge a poor widow her squint at the films, would you? [*She hangs up her hat and shawl.*]

THE PRIEST. God forbid, my dear. They've their educational value, doubtless.

[THE PRIEST *and* THE SERGEANT *sit down.*]

MRS. CONNORS. That they have. You should have seen 'em tonight—clear as the living image itself. The story of the taking of Jesse James. That's the bandit out Kansas way, they tell me.

THE PRIEST. [*Hastily.*] I know, I know!

[THE SERGEANT *coughs.*]

MRS. CONNORS. [*To* THE SERGEANT.] What's ailing you?

THE SERGEANT. Nothing. A dry spot in my throat.

MRS. CONNORS. You've been sitting in the draught of the window again. [*Turning to* THE PRIEST.] God save us! You've the look as if someone had laid a cold hand to the back of your neck.

THE PRIEST. I was overheated with running for a street car, a while since.

MRS. CONNORS. That black coat of yours is cruel hot this weather. You should get you an alpaca thing like Father Weaver wears. Sit still the both of you till I fetch a sup of something.

THE SERGEANT. Ahem! Thank you kindly.

MRS. CONNORS. There wasn't anything particular you come to see me about, was there? [*She goes to the cupboard and takes out a large pitcher of cold tea and three glasses.*]

THE PRIEST. No, no! We just dropped in for a friendly chat with you, Mrs. Connors.

MRS. CONNORS. [*Setting the tea and the glasses on the center table.*] Peter's no stranger to be sure. Half the nights of the week when he's off duty at the station, I have him sitting up here with me till I'm yawning my head off for sleep. [*She goes to a small ice-box and opens it.*]

THE SERGEANT. Whist, now! Do you hear that, Father? And there's many would say I was an amusing man, too.

Mrs. Connors. [*Laughing.*] There's many would say that you're trying to marry me, Peter Bennett. It's a black scandal else they'll be making about us. [*She comes back with a small piece of ice in her hand.*]

The Sergeant. The brass of her. Ain't the women the devil these days with their notions of decency? She'll be asking me to marry her next.

Mrs. Connors. [*Dropping the ice into the pitcher of tea.*] I will not.

The Sergeant. Then, I'll ask you again myself for the fifth time.

Mrs. Connors. Have you no shame—before Father Vincent? [*She goes to the cupboard and takes out a white china sugar-bowl and three spoons.*]

The Sergeant. Hear her, now!

The Priest. You might do worse, Mrs. Connors.

Mrs. Connors. [*Coming back with the sugar and spoons.*] Go on! What would I want with a husband? I can take care of myself, can't I? What with the money I got in the Savings Bank and what I can make off the shop—and Margaret earning her fifteen a week steady as clockwork—and Michael coming to be a fine man, too.

The Priest. Aye, and have you got Michael a position yet, Mrs. Connors?

Mrs. Connors. Almost! [*She pours the cold tea.*]

The Priest. I've had it on my mind that he should have more steady employment. He should be making his own way by now.

Mrs. Connors. Let the lad find his groove. It's no pinch for us to be giving him a bit of help yet a while. [*She adds a generous supply of sugar.*]

The Priest. It's the danger of idle time on a young man's hands that I'm thinking about.

The Sergeant. [*Taking his glass of tea and stirring it carefully.*] What with crap games, and such like, and the dancing they do these days in some of the halls, and the bunch of loafers hanging around the pool parlors, a saint out of heaven couldn't keep straight without he had steady work, Mrs. Connors. That's what his Reverence means to say.

MRS. CONNORS. [*Passing a glass of tea to* THE PRIEST.] Let be, I'm not worrying my head over Michael. He's a good boy, Michael is.

THE SERGEANT. Aye, he should be a good boy right enough.

THE PRIEST. You've been an indulgent mother to him.

MRS. CONNORS. Was it Michael you came to talk about after all? [*To* THE SERGEANT.] What are you both fidgeting at? I might have knowed there was something special for you to bring Father Vincent with you.

THE PRIEST. The Sergeant didn't bring me, I assure you.

THE SERGEANT. [*Stalling for time.*] Make your mind easy. It was this way. I was coming up here myself when I met his Reverence in the street below. "Come along," I says, "and have a talk with Mrs. Connors," I says. "Her flat's the coolest place I know outside of a beer-garden." It was nothing else at all.

MRS. CONNORS. [*Setting down her own tea untasted.*] Tell me it right out. Has Michael been hurt? Are you trying to break the news to me?

THE PRIEST. No, no, no! Don't alarm yourself.

THE SERGEANT. I give you my word on it.

MRS. CONNORS. He ain't got himself in any trouble? That ain't what you're trying to tell me?

THE PRIEST. My dear woman, I know no more about Michael than you do!

THE SERGEANT. You couldn't tell us when he's like to be home, could you?

MRS. CONNORS. Then it is him you want to see?

THE SERGEANT. [*Looking at* THE PRIEST *and beginning to flounder.*] Well, in a manner of speaking.

MRS. CONNORS. What about?

THE PRIEST. [*Coming to* THE SERGEANT's *aid.*] I tell you, don't alarm yourself. 'Tis only a bit of business we have with him; nothing important. It can wait.

THE SERGEANT. Sure it can. We only thought if he came in while we was here we might fix it up with him.

MRS. CONNORS. [*To* THE SERGEANT.] What was it?

THE SERGEANT. [*At a loss.*] Well, his Reverence was saying—

THE PRIEST. I was saying to Sergeant Bennett that there's to be a grand picnic of the Parish schools, Mrs. Connors. Sometime next month it's to be, and I thought if Michael would help me take charge of the boy's sports—

THE SERGEANT. He's a great hand with the kids.

MRS. CONNORS. And it was about asking Michael to take care of the boys' sports at a church picnic that you've been pulling long faces for a full half hour, was it?

THE PRIEST. 'Tis the heat, and other things beside Michael and the picnic made me pull a long face.

THE SERGEANT. Couldn't you tell me, will he be home tonight do you think, Mrs. Connors?

MRS. CONNORS. Michael's gone to Gary—where a job was offered him. He's been gone about two days now. Tuesday morning he went, and he's not sent me word. It's like enough he'll be back tonight if the job don't suit him, or to fetch him his clothes mebbe, if it's what he wants.

THE SERGEANT. Ah, well, it's early yet. One way or another he might be minded to come.

THE PRIEST. We'll sit and chat a while longer on the chance he does.

MRS. CONNORS. You can sit a while and welcome, I'm sure, though you did give me a bad turn just now. What with the accidents we're hearing of every day and the mischief some boys is forever getting into.

THE SERGEANT. Michael do have the way of taking his own advice mostly.

[*There is a knock at the door.*]

THE GIRL. [*Outside.*] Mrs. Connors, oh, Mrs. Connors! Are you there?

MRS. CONNORS. [*Rising hastily.*] There, now, what can she want? [*She goes quickly to the door and opens it.* THE GIRL, *about seventeen, cheaply but somewhat flashily dressed, enters, visibly excited.*]

THE GIRL. Thanks! [*She looks around as if somewhat dazed.*]

MRS. CONNORS. What ails the girl? Ain't you going to give Father Vincent good evening?

THE GIRL. [*Scarcely noticing* THE PRIEST.] Good evening, Father. Oh, Mrs. Connors, you got to come with me to Mrs.

Reegan's. You got to come quick—right away. They can't do nothing with her. [THE SERGEANT *and* THE PRIEST *rise.*]

THE SERGEANT. They've told her then!

THE PRIEST. Hush, man, can't you?

[*Neither* MRS. CONNORS *nor* THE GIRL *notice* THE PRIEST *and* THE SERGEANT.]

MRS. CONNORS. What's happened at the Reegan's?

THE GIRL. It's Jimmy! He's been killed. They've just broke it to her.

MRS. CONNORS. Killed? Jimmy Reegan killed? Oh, God have mercy! How was he killed?

THE PRIEST. [*Trying to stop* THE GIRL'S *story.*] Hadn't you better go with her, Mrs. Connors. They'll tell you when you—

MRS. CONNORS. How was he killed?

THE GIRL. Ain't you seen the papers? They shot him last night. There was a hold-up somewhere over on the boulevard. The guy they tried to stickup put up a fight.

MRS. CONNORS. What's this got to do with respectable people like the Reegans?

THE GIRL. I tell you it's Jimmy Reegan that's shot. He was took to the hospital. He couldn't give no name. Nobody knew who he was till Father Vincent and Father Weaver seen him there this evening. He was unconscious. He couldn't say nothing. He died at half-past eight.

MRS. CONNORS. [*Turning on* THE PRIEST.] Why didn't you tell me? Why didn't you tell me and me having knowed Molly Reegan since we was girls? What do you mean by sitting there like an image and saying nothing at all?

THE PRIEST. My heart was that heavy I had to take my own time, Mrs. Connors. I'm getting to be an old man.

MRS. CONNORS. You and your way! And your heart! And Molly Reegan crying her eyes out for her boy!

THE SERGEANT. Aye, we was getting around to tell you.

THE GIRL. Ain't you coming, Mrs. Connors? Ain't you coming along?

MRS. CONNORS. I'm coming this minute and Father Vincent with me.

THE PRIEST. No, no, Mrs. Connors! Father Weaver's there already and Joe Reegan himself. That's men enough in one house of sorrow. It's women they want now. By your leave, I'll stay here with the Sergeant for a while.

Mrs. Connors. [*Putting a shawl over her head.*] You should come with me I'm thinking.

The Sergeant. There now, my dear, his Reverence knows best.

The Priest. You can send for me if need be.

Mrs. Connors. Have it your own way.

[*She goes out and is heard clattering down the stairs.* The Girl *is about to follow her when* The Priest *stops her.*]

The Priest. Wait a minute, my lass.

The Girl. Well, what you stopping me for? I got to go back with her.

The Priest. I want to ask you if you've seen Michael this evening?

The Girl. [*With a quick look at* The Priest.] No, I ain't seen him.

The Priest. Ah, I thought you might have. Or today, perhaps?

The Girl. How would I see him and me working at the cannery?

The Priest. I only thought that you and he and Jimmy Reegan were great friends.

The Girl. I was no friend of Jimmy Reegan's. Michael wasn't thick with him either. I told him to keep clear of him—honest to God, I did.

The Priest. You showed good sense.

The Girl. Is that all you want with me?

The Priest. If you chance to see Michael, tell him I want to talk with him. That's all. Tell him I'll be here for an hour waiting to see him.

The Girl. [*Jerking her head toward* The Sergeant.] What's he doing here?

The Priest. He's Michael's friend. Take my word, we know what's best for him. He'll come to no harm through us.

The Girl. [*Sullenly.*] I ain't going to steer Michael into no pinch. I tell you he ain't done nothing. I don't know where he is at that.

THE PRIEST. Listen to me now, my girl. I've a strong notion you'll be seeing Michael for all you say. And if it's in your head to be warning him against coming home here, it's his living soul you'll put in jeopardy, as sure as you stand there hearing me. Keep your hands off God's work this night and you'll come to thank the old man that asked it.

[THE GIRL *goes out.* THE PRIEST *closes the door and comes back to his chair beside the table.*]

THE SERGEANT. He'll not come to us now with that young fly-by-night waiting at the corner to give him the tip.

THE PRIEST. No. I've faith in the girl, and in Michael, too, for the matter of that. I'd not be waiting here else.

THE SERGEANT. [*Coming over and leaning on the table.*] Can't you speak out, your Reverence? You've got in your mind that Michael was mixed up in last night's job?

THE PRIEST. I'm hardly ready to say that.

THE SERGEANT. But you heard his mother saying he's been in Gary since Tuesday morning.

THE PRIEST. I saw him last evening.

THE SERGEANT. The devil you did! And where was he?

THE PRIEST. In front of Swarz's Pool Parlor, talking with Jimmy Reegan.

THE SERGEANT. [*Eagerly.*] Couldn't he meet with Jimmy Reegan by chance and pass the time of day with him? That don't prove nothing, does it?

THE PRIEST. It may be that I am only an old fool after all, as I said to you before, but I'll not be at ease till we've seen Michael tonight.

THE SERGEANT. I'll bet my stripes on it, the boy's done nothing crooked. But if it's a scare you want thrown into him, I'm your man, and it's a grand time to do it, too.

THE PRIEST. It's a pity that it always takes an awful thing like what has just happened to show us the real need.

THE SERGEANT. The real need of what?

THE PRIEST. A change in our way of looking at things—our

educational systems, our way of dealing with the boys in the street, our police.

THE SERGEANT. What's the matter with the police?

THE PRIEST. It's not for an old man like me to say, but I've thought for a long time that there was something lacking. You don't seem to understand rightly what's best for the boys in the street.

THE SERGEANT. We don't, eh? See here, now! Ninety per cent of the force was once just what you're calling the boys in the street. Wasn't I one myself? Don't we know the poor people and their kids like none of your long-haired, down-state reformers can ever get to know them?

THE PRIEST. You know them too well. Too many of your patrolmen are stationed in their own home districts. They have too many friends. Sentiment gets into it too often. They're too easy on the small beginnings of mischief that go to make the big ends of crime.

THE SERGEANT. Are you calling me a man that would let sentiment interfere with my duty?

THE PRIEST. I remember once when they complained to you that the boys were breaking windows in Eisenthorp's vacant factory building on 46th Street, and Jimmy Reegan and Michael Connors were among the lot; I remember what the Lieutenant said when the Anti-Cruelty people got after him about the way the kids were treating the stray cats and dogs in the precinct.

THE SERGEANT. Them's little things to be raking up against the force surely, at a time like this.

THE PRIEST. You've known for a long time that half the pool parlors were running crap tables and three-quarters of the saloons selling liquor to boys under age, to say nothing of some that sell it to girls.

THE SERGEANT. You can't expect a bar-keep to spot a lad's age every time, can you? Would you have us playing nurse-girl to all the kids of the world? Would you have us pinching our friends for the little small things like you're talking about, when half the time you couldn't prove it on 'em in court if you got 'em there? Where would we get off? I know there's laws to cover what you've said, but it's up to the Department what laws are important to be pushed.

THE PRIEST. What are laws for if they're not to be enforced?

THE SERGEANT. Ask them that made them. Ask the Administration. Don't ask me. I take my orders and do the best I know how. I'm straight, too. I've never took a cent of dirty money in my life, so help me God. And that's something to say if I do say it myself.

THE PRIEST. It is a great deal to say and it's true I'm sure. Sergeant Bennett, I've great respect for you as a man. But it's not graft or politics I'm thinking of. There's something does more to send boys and girls to hell than either of them. It's the rule-of-thumb way we go at crime for the most part, making a great pother of catching and punishing the old hands at the game and letting slip the little things, slurring them over, hushing them up, passing by all the sprees and gambling and devilment that give the crook his start.

THE SERGEANT. You're a fine one to be talking; you with the name of being the softest-hearted, easiest-going man in the parish, begging your pardon.

THE PRIEST. It's come to me all at once that we're both greatly to blame, Sergeant, each in his way. I mean to make a new start —with Michael, tonight, God willing it.

THE SERGEANT. I say again, I'll bet my stripes Michael had nothing to do with it, but if he had now? Supposing he had? Have you it in your mind to help him, Father?

THE PRIEST. I have, indeed.

THE SERGEANT. 'Twould put me in a sore place.

THE PRIEST. You'll do your own duty and what's right by Michael.

THE SERGEANT. 'Twould seem a hard thing to make them both go together.

THE PRIEST. Hush! What's that?

THE SERGEANT. [*In a whisper.*] I didn't hear nothing.

[*They both listen expectantly. There is a slight shuffling out-*

side. The door opens and THE BOY *enters. He is about eighteen or nineteen, rather too well dressed. He looks very drawn and tired, and lets one arm hang limply at his side. He seems a little startled at seeing* THE PRIEST *and* THE SERGEANT.]

THE PRIEST. Well, Michael?

THE BOY. Good evening, Father Vincent. Evening, Sergeant.

THE SERGEANT. Back from Gary, eh?

THE BOY. Yes.

THE SERGEANT. Job didn't suit you or you didn't suit the job?

THE BOY. Nothing doing!

THE PRIEST. Good jobs aren't so easy to find.

THE BOY. No. Where's my mother?

THE PRIEST. She's stepped out for a little while.

THE SERGEANT. She's over at Mrs. Reegan's.

THE BOY. [*Sitting down.*] Of course, I might have known that.

THE SERGEANT. Then you know what's happened?

THE BOY. Yes. It was all in the papers. I seen one of the fellers, too, that heard all about it.

THE PRIEST. It was a terrible thing, Mickey.

THE BOY. Fierce! Can you tell me, is Jimmy as bad hurt as the papers say?

THE SERGEANT. You ain't heard, then?

THE BOY. [*Looking up.*] Heard what?

THE PRIEST. He's dead.

THE BOY. Dead? Jimmy Reegan dead?

THE SERGEANT. That's why your mother's gone over to the Reegans'. [*They are all silent for a moment.*]

THE BOY. [*Pulling himself together.*] When did she say she'd be back? I've got to see her before eleven o'clock.

THE PRIEST. Listen to me, Michael. When Sergeant Bennett and I heard about Jimmy Reegan, we just thought we'd come over and have a talk with you.

THE BOY. [*Nervously.*] I don't know nothing about Jimmy.

THE SERGEANT. It wasn't exactly about Jimmy, either. His Reverence was saying—

THE PRIEST. That it seemed like a good opportunity to point out one or two things to you, my lad.

THE BOY. [*Sullenly.*] I haven't got time to sit here and listen to preaching. I've got to see my mother before—

THE SERGEANT. What are you in such a rush to see your mother for?

THE BOY. What business is that of yours?

THE PRIEST. Easy, now.

THE BOY. I'm going away from Chicago, if you've got to know. I met a feller that was here from Denver looking for men. They're short of hands in all the building trades out there. I can get a better start and better pay, only I've got to go out with him on the eleven o'clock train tonight.

THE SERGEANT. [*Rubbing his chin with his hand.*] Oh, ho! So you're going away, are you? Out to Denver.

THE PRIEST. Denver's a long way.

THE BOY. They don't give a feller no chance here.

THE SERGEANT. Maybe you're right. I'm not saying you ain't.

THE PRIEST. Your mother'll take it hard, your going so far away where she can't tell how you're getting on all the time.

THE BOY. I can't help that. She'll have no call to worry about me.

THE SERGEANT. [*With the air of hoping to get away from an unpleasant duty.*] Mebbe you'd like a little word with Father Vincent alone, if you're going so soon? [*He gets up.*]

THE BOY. I don't know what about.

THE SERGEANT. [*Buttoning his coat.*] I'll just step around to Reegans'. If your mother ain't needed, I'll send her back to you.

THE BOY. Thanks.

THE SERGEANT. [*Taking up his cap.*] Good-bye, Mickey.

THE BOY. [*Without looking up.*] Good-bye.

THE SERGEANT. [*Holding out his hand.*] Good luck to you—in Denver.

[THE BOY *gets up, winces a little as if it hurts him to move and holds out his hand.*]

THE BOY. Thanks.

THE SERGEANT. Goodnight to you, Father Vincent. [*He goes*

out. THE PRIEST *mops his face again with his handkerchief and seems at a loss for what to say next.* THE BOY *listens as if to make sure* THE SERGEANT *has gone down the stairs, hesitates, and then seems to make up his mind.*]

THE BOY. Father Vincent, do you know anything about medicine?

THE PRIEST. Eh? What's that?

THE BOY. Do you know anything about fixing hurts; I mean fixing them temporary like, bandaging and such, so the dirt won't get into them?

THE PRIEST. A little, yes, I can do that much. But who's been hurt?

THE BOY. [*Rather desperately.*] Me. It's nothing. I mean it ain't much.

THE PRIEST. How?

THE BOY. It was this afternoon. One of the fellers out at Gary had a gun. We were fooling with it and it went off.

THE PRIEST. [*Drawing his chair toward the boy and watching his face closely.*] Where did it hit you?

THE BOY. In the arm.

THE PRIEST. Why didn't they take you to a doctor?

THE BOY. [*Sullenly.*] We was afraid we'd get pinched for having the gun. I tore a piece off my shirt. It didn't bleed hardly at all. I said I'd see a doctor when I got in town.

THE PRIEST. But you haven't.

THE BOY. I met the man from Denver that I was telling you about. I wasn't thinking much about it.

THE PRIEST. Your mother will be back shortly. She'd better have a look at it, too.

THE BOY. [*Taking off his coat with evident pain.*] I'd sooner she didn't know. She'd be keeping me from doing what I want.

[*The* PRIEST *helps* THE BOY *with the coat, swiftly unwinds the clumsy bandage from his arm and glances at the wound.*]

THE BOY. Well?

THE PRIEST. It's worse than you told me, Michael.

THE BOY. [*Almost fiercely.*] No it ain't!

THE PRIEST. [*Putting his hand on* THE BOY's *head.*] I'm afraid it is beginning to fester already and you've got a fever, my lad.

THE BOY. I tell you it don't hurt much and I ain't got a fever.

THE PRIEST. Hadn't you better go with me to a doctor?

THE BOY. There ain't time. I've got to catch the eleven o'clock train. It's after ten now. Can't you help me wash it and put on a new bandage before Mother gets back?

THE PRIEST. [*Standing squarely in front of* THE BOY *and folding his hands behind his back.*] You were never in Gary at all, Michael Connors.

THE BOY. [*Drawing back.*] Who's told you that lie?

THE PRIEST. Nobody. I saw you myself last night.

THE BOY. [*Frightened.*] When did you see me?

THE PRIEST. Some time early in the evening. I don't rightly know just what the hour was, about eight o'clock, I think, and you were with Jimmy Reegan. [*He takes a bowl from the shelf and fills it with warm water from the kettle on the stove.*]

THE BOY. What if I was? I don't have to account to you for where I was all the time, do I? Or who I talked to, either?

THE PRIEST. No, I suppose not. But it would be better if you could. [*He takes two clean dish-towels from the rack and places the bowl on the table.*]

THE BOY. I tell you I only seen Jimmy for a minute. I don't know where he went afterwards or what he done. I only know what I read in the papers and what's been told me.

THE PRIEST. Aye, but I'm afraid you do know more, Michael. I'm sorely afraid you do. [*He bathes* THE BOY's *arm with warm water from the bowl and binds it up with one of the dish-towels.*]

THE BOY. What's the good of my talking if you ain't going to believe me?

THE PRIEST. Tell me the truth, lad, and I'll believe you fast enough.

THE BOY. What makes you think I ain't telling you the truth?

THE PRIEST. You gave yourself away, Michael, the minute you came in at that door.

THE BOY. How?

THE PRIEST. By knowing it was Jimmy Reegan had been shot

and not knowing he was dead. His name wasn't in the papers at all. No one knew it was Jimmy till Father Weaver broke the news to his family. There, now, can't you see it's no use lying to me? How could you have known it was Jimmy?

THE BOY. [*Lying desperately and sullenly.*] I wasn't with him. I had it from one of the fellers, I swear I did. I ain't done nothing. Can't you take my word for it?

THE PRIEST. I'd be a happy man this night if I could.

THE BOY. What do you want me to say?

THE PRIEST. [*Taking a little cross from his own neck and holding it out to* THE BOY.] Can you swear to me on this, Michael?

[THE BOY *takes the cross and holds it in his hand with his head bowed over it, staring at it as if fascinated.*]

THE BOY. [*Without looking up.*] You'd ought to take my word.

THE PRIEST. If you've done nothing, 'twill do you no hurt to swear by the cross, lad, and you'll ease a poor heart that wishes you well, Mickey.

THE BOY. I— I— [*He looks up suddenly, his face twitching, and reaches for* THE PRIEST's *hand.*] Oh, Father Vincent, you'll not split on me.[1] You've had it out of me like I don't know what. You've dragged it out of me like you had hot pincers in your hand. I'm sick or you wouldn't have got it from me so easy.

THE PRIEST. [*Soothingly.*] There, there! Go on, go on. Tell it all to me and we'll see what's to be done.

THE BOY. [*Stumbling along incoherently.*] I never did nothing like this before. I've run with a bad bunch, I know that, but they knew I was straight—leastways straighter than they was. They never tried to pull me in on any crooked stuff, honest to God they didn't. Jimmy was white to me, too. There was five of us together yesterday. We got too many drinks. I don't know how many. Then somebody said, "Let's go to a show," but we didn't have no more money. Then somebody else said, "Let's go out and get some easy coin on the boulevards." It was all sort of foggy from that on. We went somewheres and got four guns they had hidden in a barn. Then one of them that wasn't very

_____
[1] Tell on me.

drunk went and sneaked a car out of a garage and picked us up around the corner. I don't remember where we drove to, till we came along side of a guy on the sidewalk. I didn't think what they was going to do, honest to God I didn't. Me and Jimmy and the other feller in the tonneau jumped out. Jimmy runs up to the guy on the sidewalk and shoves a gun in his face. It wasn't even loaded. None of them was except the one I had and I never took that out of my pocket. Before we could say nothing, the guy pulls a gun himself and lets Jimmy have it twice. Somebody yells "Cops" and we runs for the machine. I knew they was plugging at us but we didn't plug back. Just as I got my foot on the step something hit me in the arm. I didn't think of Jimmy till we'd got clear away. We couldn't go back for him. The feller that was driving the car had nerve all right. He took us out to a place in Englewood and ran the car back to the garage. It wasn't out more'n an hour. Nobody spotted that he had it out. That's all that happened.

THE PRIEST. I won't ask you who the other boys were.

THE BOY. [*Miserably.*] I wouldn't tell you that. Nobody'll get 'em. They're safe by now. I wouldn't have said nothing to you either, only walking made my arm come on to pain something fierce. I wish to God I hadn't opened my head.

THE PRIEST. You shouldn't wish that.

[THE PRIEST *has finished with the bandage and* THE BOY *has managed to get back into his coat.*]

THE BOY. I do.

THE PRIEST. Why did you come here?

THE BOY. To see my mother. I sort of had to see her and say good-bye before I went. I had to get a little money from her.

THE PRIEST. Then you are thinking of going away?

THE BOY. [*Pointing to his shoulder.*] I got to go somewhere. I can't hide this thing around here.

THE PRIEST. You'll go with me now to a doctor and then around to the station and give yourself up.

THE BOY. [*Startled.*] What are you talking about? What kind of a boob do you take me for?

THE PRIEST. It's the only way you can make things square.

THE BOY. [*Defiantly.*] I ain't asking to make things square. I didn't do nothing. They ain't got nothing on me, if you let me alone. [*He gets up and makes a move toward the door.*]

THE PRIEST. [*Stepping between him and the door.*] You'll stop to see your mother. You'll have a word with her.

THE BOY. No, I've changed my mind about seeing her. I'll trouble you to let me by, Father.

THE PRIEST. [*Holding his place.*] It's only a short way you'd go, Michael.

THE BOY. What do you mean by that? You wouldn't put them on to me? You daren't do it. You wouldn't play me a low trick like that. You had it from me like it was in Confession.

THE PRIEST. Oh, God, why do you tie my hands? [*He steps away from the door.*]

THE BOY. [*With an attempt to smile.*] I'd wish you good-bye, Father Vincent, and thank you kindly for the bandage. [*He holds out his hand to* THE PRIEST.]

THE PRIEST. [*Taking* THE BOY's *hand.*] God go with you, Michael.

[THE BOY *turns to the door, opens it and comes face to face with* THE SERGEANT *who stands on the threshold, his hands on his hips.*]

THE SERGEANT. Well?

THE BOY. [*Drawing back startled, but still trying to face it out, not quite sure that* THE SERGEANT *has overheard.*] Oh, it's you, is it? Did you fetch mother back with you?

THE SERGEANT. I did not. I ain't been off the landing. I ain't had my ear away from this door.

THE BOY. [*Turning on* THE PRIEST.] Then it was a dirty trap you set for me after all—you with your fine snivelling talk about being my friend. You're a fine priest! You got it out of me like it was in holy confessional and him listening at the door all the time, with you knowing it. It was a game, a dirty low game you put on to me!

THE SERGEANT. Shut your mouth, you young ruffian!

THE PRIEST. Easy, now, Sergeant! He doesn't know what he's saying.

THE BOY. You're a pair of spying Judases, the both of you.

THE PRIEST. Listen to me now, Michael.

THE BOY. I will not.

THE SERGEANT. You'd do well to keep a civil tongue and listen to Father Vincent.

THE BOY. [*Sneering.*] What more has he got to say to me?

THE PRIEST. You'll go with Sergeant Bennett and me to the station, Mickey, and give yourself up. We'll stand by you. It's the only thing to be done.

THE BOY. A fine lot of standing by me you'll do.

THE SERGEANT. Come with me now.

THE BOY. [*Desperately.*] Get out of that door, you big boob. [*He reaches to his pocket and draws a gun.*]

THE SERGEANT. [*Making a lunge for him.*] You would, would you?

THE PRIEST. [*Springing between them.*] For the love of heaven, have a care, both of you!

THE BOY. [*Covering* THE SERGEANT *with the gun and almost shrieking.*] Don't you come near me! Don't you put your hands on me!

THE SERGEANT. [*Losing his temper.*] You young devil, you'd not have got the drop on me like that if I'd of had my gun with me.

THE PRIEST. Steady, Sergeant! 'Twill do you no good to talk to him like that. [*To* THE BOY.] Give me the gun.

THE BOY. I will like heck!

THE SERGEANT. [*Regaining his coolness.*] Give the gun to Father Vincent, you fool! Would you only make things worse for yourself?

THE BOY. Get out of my road. What call have you got to pinch me? They'd have nothing on me only for you two. I'll get out of town and stay out. Let me off, can't you? Who's to know that I done it? Let me off!

THE SERGEANT. [*In doubt.*] Isn't he mebbe beginning to talk sense now, your Reverence?

THE BOY. [*Seeing a ray of hope.*] Let me off I say, and you'll never regret it! Honest to God you won't!

THE SERGEANT. [*Beginning to weaken.*] It would be a hard thing for me to know I'd had a hand in sending the lad up to the pen, your Reverence. And it's only a small thing he's done after all, and little harm intended.

THE PRIEST. Shame on you, Sergeant Bennett, for saying that.

THE SERGEANT. Mebbe we can look at things different and both of us be right. I wouldn't be hard on him. 'Tis the first time by his own account.

THE PRIEST. 'Tis not what he's done already, but what he'll do yet if we let him go his own road with one crime hanging around his neck, that I'm thinking about. There's no two ways of looking at it.

THE BOY. [*To* THE SERGEANT.] Don't you listen to what he's saying. You always was more a friend to me than he was.

THE SERGEANT. [*Shaking his head.*] If he only hadn't pulled a gun on me!

THE BOY. Where would you get off with my mother? You couldn't pinch me! Not on her account, you couldn't! You'd have a swell chance with her after that.

THE SERGEANT. [*His pride hit.*] Let be! You'll put down that gun now and come along to the station. [*He makes a move toward* THE BOY.]

THE BOY. [*Drawing back.*] Stand off, you big stiff, or you'll get yours. I give you fair warning.

THE PRIEST. Would you only make things ten times worse than they are for us?

THE BOY. [*Half sobbing.*] I don't give a damn. He'll get out of my road. He'll leave me go or I'll give him a dose of what they gave Jimmy. He ain't going to stop me, nor you either.

THE PRIEST. We'd not be your friends if we didn't try.

THE SERGEANT. [*Folding his arms.*] By God! Father Vincent's right. How far would you get before I put in a call? Not far, I'm thinking, with that arm. They'd get you in an hour at most. Like as not you'd be fool enough to put up a fight, too, and get plugged. They'd be none too careful with you, not them.

THE BOY. Damn you, you've no call to put them on to me.

THE SERGEANT. Supposing I didn't, what good would that do you? You ain't the one to take a lesson from what's happened. I'd only be turning you loose to make a real crook of yourself.

THE BOY. There's worse things in the world than crooks. There's lying priests and dirty scum like you, and—

THE SERGEANT. I tell you once more, put down that gun.

THE BOY. I'll blow your head off if you touch me.

[THE SERGEANT *and* THE BOY *stand facing each other, each waiting for the other to make a move.*]

THE PRIEST. Murder's a far worse thing than being only an accomplice in a poor attempt at highway robbery, Mickey. Have you thought of that? No, I don't think you've had the time. You're seeing things wrong tonight. Put away the fear of disgrace now, and the thought of prison. The one will pass when you put your hands to clean work, and the other will be short. It'll go by like a bad dream and you'll come out of it whole, with God's help. It's where you're standing now that I'd have you see clearly before you put out your feet onto the black road of death. There's a pit at your toes, lad, a thirsty pit that sucks men down under the red bowels of the world. You'll not come back out of it with murder on your soul, nor look at the stars again nor hear your mother's voice speaking to you; not when the seas have gone dry even, or the heavens shrivelled up like a bit of dry parchment.

THE BOY. There ain't no hell. You can't frighten me like that.

THE PRIEST. [*Patiently.*] Have it your own way. But did you ever think what sort of a life a murderer has to drag on with even if he's let to live? Not weeks and months of wishing he was out in free streets like other men with his friends to give him good-morning and good-evening, but years, and tens of years of wishing and wishing.

THE BOY. What are you giving me? I ain't going to murder anybody. I ain't going to hurt him if he lets me be. Leave off clacking at me.

THE PRIEST. Go with Sergeant Bennett, Michael. They'll not be hard on you for the first offense. 'Tis only just penance you'll be doing and, when you're through, I give you my solemn oath I'll see that you get an honest start in the world.

THE SERGEANT. [*To the boy.*] You've heard his Reverence talking sense to you. Come along with me quiet-like and it will only be a year you'll get at most, with us to give you a good character, or six months in the Bridewell mebbe, with parole for part of it.

THE BOY. I'm not taking any chances of what they'll give me.

THE SERGEANT. [*Starting for* THE BOY *in earnest.*] Come on, you fool, before I break every bone in your body.

THE BOY. [*Kicking a chair between them.*] Get away from me! Get away, I tell you!

THE SERGEANT. Would you now?

[THE BOY *dodges around the table,* THE SERGEANT *follows and grapples with him.* THE BOY *wrenches his right arm free and presses the revolver to* THE SERGEANT'S *body.*]

THE BOY. [*Screaming with hysteria.*] Leave go! Leave go, damn you! Leave go!

THE SERGEANT. [*Grunting with his exertions.*] Cut it out! Drop it!

THE BOY. [*Screaming still louder.*] Let go! Let go or I'll kill you! So help me, I will!

[THE PRIEST *is trying to drag* THE SERGEANT *away. He only succeeds in hampering him and adding to his danger.*]

THE SERGEANT. [*Now thoroughly angry and shaking off* THE PRIEST.] Ah, ha! my beauty! I'll get you now!

THE BOY. I give you three. I give you three to stand away from me.

THE PRIEST. [*Wringing his hands.*] Oh, Mary, have mercy!

THE BOY. [*Struggling, with his revolver still pressed to* THE SERGEANT'S *side.*] Don't make me do it! One!

[*They stand almost still, gasping for breath.*]

THE SERGEANT. [*Snarling.*] Drop it!

THE BOY. Damn you, then, two!

THE SERGEANT. [*Their faces are not more than a couple of inches apart.*] Drop it, I say.

THE BOY. Three!

[*They are absolutely motionless for a moment. Then the gun falls to the floor with a clatter.* THE BOY *relaxes in* THE SERGEANT's *arms, sobbing.*]

THE BOY. I couldn't! I couldn't! My nerve's gone!

THE PRIEST. No, Michael, my dear, it's only just come back to you.

[*He takes* THE BOY *by the shoulder and helps him to the chair by the table.* THE BOY *buries his face in his arms.*]

THE BOY. [*Sobbing.*] I'm a coward! I'm a coward! I couldn't do it! I couldn't! I'm a coward! [THE PRIEST *pats* THE BOY's *shoulder.* THE SERGEANT *stands beside them, panting like a bull.*]

THE PRIEST. No, no, my lad, my little Mickey, be easy now!

[*There is a clatter on the stairs.*]

THE BOY. I couldn't! I couldn't! I couldn't!

[MRS. CONNORS *enters and looks around, frightened.*]

MRS. CONNORS. For the love of God, what's happened now? Tell me, what are you doing to the boy? Can't you speak, none of you, and tell me what's happened?

THE PRIEST. Nothing that will do you any hurt in the end, Mrs. Connors. The worst is over now, God be praised. 'Twill all come right in a short while. You've no great call to worry yourself. Take my word.

[*Curtain*]

UNDERSTANDING AND APPRECIATING THE PLAY

1. What do you think of *Back of the Yards* as a play? Why do you like or dislike it?

2. "What's this got to do with respectable people like the Reegans?" Mrs. Connors asks when the girl tells her that Jimmy Reegan was killed. How do you explain the fact that young people from apparently respectable homes sometimes turn to wrongdoing?

3. As the plot approaches the climax, what are two important or exciting incidents in the rising action?

4. What is the climax of the play—the point of strongest suspense and interest toward which the rising action was constantly building?

5. "It's a pity that it always takes an awful thing like what has just happened to show us the real need," Father Vincent says. Discuss some regrettable incident that made you or others aware of the need of a more intelligent course of action or of a new way of looking at things.

6. The priest accuses the police of that time and that neighborhood of being "too easy on the small beginnings of mischief that go to make the big ends of crime." How tough or lenient should the police and courts be with youthful first offenders?

7. Michael admits that he had fallen in with a bad bunch. According to the law, was he guilty of participating in the attempted holdup? Explain.

8. What do you think of the chances of a boy or girl's staying out of trouble once he or she associates steadily with bad companions? Discuss.

9. When Michael has the sergeant and the priest covered with a gun, which of the two men begins to weaken in his determination to turn Michael over to the police? What reasons does he give for letting Michael go? What arguments does the other man adduce against permitting the boy to escape? Who is right, the priest or the sergeant?

VOCABULARY BUILDING

Explain in your own words the meanings of the following phrases: You've been an *indulgent* mother to him; It's his living soul you'll put in *jeopardy;* would not let *sentiment* interfere with my duty; speaking *incoherently;* looking at the priest and beginning to *flounder.*

THINGS TO DO

1. Write a composition on one of these topics: A Teacher Who Understands Me, A Friend in Need, Who Guides (or Guide) Me?, Are My Friends Right for Me?, How to Lead a Desirable Life, When Not to Follow the Gang, People to Whom I'm Grateful, How to Keep out of Trouble, Do My Parents Understand Me?, Having the Courage of My Convictions, Making Friends.

2. Topics for research, discussion, written composition, or individual talks.

It is interesting to have each of these topics developed by a different group and then discussed by each group in turn in front of the class. After each group has presented its ideas on the topic it has selected, the discussion is thrown open to the class.

A. *Juvenile Delinquency.* What are some of the important causes of juvenile delinquency? To what extent are adults responsible for the delinquency of young people? What can be done to reduce juvenile delinquency?

B. *Schools and Teen-Age Problems.* What school subjects are especially useful in helping students meet their problems of everyday life? What school services and school activities are helpful? Are there any problems with which the school could help but with which it doesn't? How could the school help with these problems?

C. *Places in the Community for Recreation and Self-Improvement.* Where do young people in your community go for recreation? For cultural and self-improvement activities? Do the places for recreation promote wholesome social or athletic activities? What new facilities are needed for recreation and for cultural activities? How may these facilities be obtained?

D. *Better Understanding Between Adults and Teen-Agers.* Do parents, teachers, and other adults really understand teen-agers? Do young people really understand adults? How can teen-agers and adults understand each other better?

E. *Effect of Movies, TV, Comic Books, Etc.* Are movies, television and radio programs, comic books, and magazines which deal with violence, crime, and other objectionable matters at least partly to blame for juvenile delinquency? If so, how bad an influence are they? What can be done to improve these objectionable aspects of our mass media of communication?

F. *Related Problem.* Why is juvenile delinquency more prevalent at certain times than in other eras?

PRODUCTION NOTES

The successful staging of *Back of the Yards* calls for sound character portrayal—which must, of course, begin with sound casting—and for careful attention not only to the over-all suspensefully exciting tempo of the play but also to the variations of pace and emotional intensity. Play the quiet scenes, the opening expository one and the plateau scenes between the more exciting action, more slowly and with less intensity. Then pick up in tempo and emotional drive in the important rising-action incidents and in the climax. Although the latter scenes are so apparent that a director can quite easily remember them, he may be able to evoke even more effective variety of mood from his actors by working out a plot-suspense chart.

Except for the role of the girl, the play is challenging in the opportunity it affords for character analysis and portrayal. Young people undertaking the parts of the priest, the police sergeant, and the mother must really understand these middle-aged people. The young people must have intelligent insights into what motivates these characters to think and act as they do and into their reactions to each other and to Michael. The young actors must also be able to portray the posture and bearing, the movement and the essential "rhythm" of the three characters.

The one who plays the role of Michael must show the tough and nasty facets of that boy's personality. But the actor must also convey the facts that Michael has such virtues as to make the audience believe that he is worthy of his mother's and friends' anxiety and that he is capable of being saved from a life of crime.

Pawns *

PERCIVAL WILDE

Although one of the basic principles of democracy is peace among all men, the lovers of democracy are sometimes forced onto the battlefield in defense of the ideals they cherish. But even though democratic people may be involved in war, they do not glorify it as do the dictators. On the contrary, they deplore it even as they fight. The truest lovers of the democratic way of life will dedicate themselves to achieving a world order which will bring about a just and lasting peace, in which men will no longer be the pawns of power-seeking war lords or aggressor nations, but will live together in the spirit of brotherliness.

In *Pawns*, Percival Wilde has written a stirring plea against wars instigated or dictated by rulers far removed from the common people, the pawns who must fight those wars, sometimes even against their neighbors and friends. *Pawns* was written in 1917, just before Percival Wilde became an officer in the United States Navy; its setting is Old Russia, the Russia of the Czars. It has been acted on the stage and broadcast by radio countless times, and has won many tournaments.

The characters are simple, illiterate peasants. But when you read the play, do not allow your imagination to make comic characters of them. They are rough, ignorant folk, it is true, but the sympathetic treatment by the author has endowed them with a dignity and a common sense that raise their story to the level of true tragedy.

Pawns is a tragedy in which the protagonist is not a single hero, as in a tragedy by Shakespeare, but is a group of men, who move blindly to their doom. Each of these "pawns," however, is highly individualized, and you lose something in the reading if you do not see each one's individual traits.

CHARACTERS

ILIA

GRIGOR

STEPAN

MICHAEL

PETER

THE SERGEANT

The Curtain rises in darkness.

Night: near the end of night, before morning. A forest of swampy nature. Here and there, little irregular hummocks of ground. Frogs croaking. Near the center, a little to the right, a small fire, with a thin, straight flame, casting but little light, so that ten feet away from it there is darkness.

Three men are grouped about the fire: GRIGOR, *a Russian peasant in his fifties, bearded, grave, with something of the peculiar dignity which his class acquires as it ages;* STEPAN, *his older son, enormous, powerful, bearded, stretched out full length on the ground; and the younger son* ILIA, *hardly more than a boy.*

A pause.

ILIA. An hour more, and it will be light. I can tell by the croaking of the frogs. It is as if they were afraid of the light. Their croaking is different. Listen!

[*A pause.*]

GRIGOR. Thirty versts [1] more to Zawichost.

ILIA. Is it so far? That is farther than I have ever been.

GRIGOR. What of that? By nightfall we will be there.

STEPAN. [*Moving his huge frame lazily.*] And then, God willing, one more day, and we return home!

GRIGOR. God willing!

ILIA. Is it a large city? Will there be many people?

STEPAN. [*With an indulgent smile.*] More than you have ever seen before.

[1] A *verst,* a Russian measure of distance, is about two-thirds of a mile.

ILIA. That will be wonderful!

STEPAN. [*Sitting up.*] There are streets, more streets than you can count, and shops, where they sell beautiful things, and great houses all built of stone.

ILIA. I shall love to see them!

GRIGOR. Not I! [*He shakes his head.*] I am afraid of the cities! Oh, I am afraid of the cities! [*He addresses* STEPAN.] Had you not gone to the city, they would have left us alone.

STEPAN. No.

GRIGOR. They have always left us alone. Here are the marshes and the quicksands. Who knows his way through them? Not the city people. They are too comfortable in their stone houses.

STEPAN. Nevertheless they would have sent for us. So the police said.

GRIGOR. The police? Since when do we talk with the police? Have I not said that when an honest *moujik* [2] sees a policeman on one side of the street he crosses to the other?

STEPAN. It was no use. There were too many of them. There were police at every corner. There were signs in the street, and crowds reading the signs.

GRIGOR. Signs! Ah, yes! Signs telling you what to do! Signs telling you what not to do! But read? How should a *moujik* read? How to plough a straight furrow in the earth, when to sow, when to reap, how to feed his hen, his cow, that he knows, and that is far better than reading signs! Pah! Because you could not read, they told you what they pleased!

STEPAN. So I thought at first.

GRIGOR. Well?

STEPAN. Then I asked others. They all said the same.

GRIGOR. Hm! We must go to Zawichost.

STEPAN. Yes; to Zawichost.

GRIGOR. And lose three days in harvest time.

STEPAN. So they said; all of us.

GRIGOR. While Michael and lame Peter work in their field undisturbed, on the other side of the marsh! When we return, when we ask them to help us, they will refuse; we have not helped

[2] *Moujik* (pronounced mōō·zhĭk′) is a Russian peasant.

them. [*He pauses in disgust.*] If there were only a reason it would be otherwise, but for mobilization? [*With crowning contempt.*] What *is* mobilization?

STEPAN. [*He rises.*] When I asked they pointed me out to each other; said I was a fine hulk of a man to be asking what was mobilization. They laughed at me. They threw stones at me. [*He is getting angry at the recollection.*] Then I took the biggest of them by the arm—so—and I pressed a little, so that his face went white beneath the dirt, and the sweat stood out in drops on his forehead, and he begged for mercy, and the others, they stopped laughing!

ILIA. [*Who is listening with breathless interest.*] And then?

STEPAN. Then I came away.

[*There is a pause. Then the younger brother, who has been much impressed, takes up the conversation.*]

ILIA. You took him by the arm?

STEPAN. [*Smiling.*] Yes, little brother.

ILIA. With one hand only?

STEPAN. This self-same hand. [*The boy crosses to him at left center and feels the horny palm with interest.*] Shall I show you?

ILIA. [*Darting out of his reach.*] No, no! I do not doubt you!

STEPAN. [*Laughing.*] For that, thanks!

ILIA. Still, if you *must* show me—

STEPAN. [*With the growl of a good-natured bear.*] What?

ILIA. Wait until we come to the city today.

STEPAN. And then?

ILIA. Perhaps they will laugh at us—

STEPAN. [*With understanding.*] Yes, little brother!

ILIA. Oh, I hope I shall see that!

[*There is a pause.*]

GRIGOR. [*Rising.*] For fifty years I have been a good Christian. I know every holiday of the Orthodox Church.[3] But mobilization? That I have never heard of.

STEPAN. Perhaps the Metropolitan [4] has decreed a new festival.

GRIGOR. In harvest time? Pah!

[3] The Russian Church.
[4] A high-ranking bishop.

STEPAN. Harvest time is nothing to the people who live in cities. They know nothing of harvests.

ILIA. [*Suddenly.*] I hear steps.

GRIGOR. What?

ILIA. Listen!

[*They listen. There is no sound.*]

GRIGOR. I hear nothing.

STEPAN. The boy has quicker ears than you or I. Listen.

[*Still there is no sound.*]

[*Addressing* ILIA.] What do you hear?

ILIA. Two men.

STEPAN. Which way?

ILIA. From there. [*He points towards the right.*]

GRIGOR. But who should come that way? That is the way we have come. The city is in the other direction.

[*A crackling of branches becomes audible.*]

STEPAN. Now I hear them! Hullo! Hullo!

VOICES. Hullo! Hullo!

ILIA. Michael and lame Peter. I know their voices.

STEPAN. Hullo! This way!

GRIGOR. They will not know where we are. Guide them.

[STEPAN *starts off.* GRIGOR *sits at the fire.*]

ILIA. Here! A burning faggot!

STEPAN. Since when do I need a light, little brother? [*He disappears.*]

GRIGOR. Michael and lame Peter? Are you sure?

ILIA. [*Listening.*] I hear them speaking. . . . Now he has found them. . . . They are coming this way.

GRIGOR. Why should they follow us?

[STEPAN *reappears, followed by two more peasants who carry packs,* PETER, *a farmhand of twenty-two, who walks with a pronounced limp, and* MICHAEL, *his employer, a robust man near* GRIGOR's *age.*]

[*Rising ceremoniously.*] Christ be with you!

MICHAEL. Grigor Ignátievitch, Christ be with you!

GRIGOR. [*As the others drop their packs and draw near to the fire.*] What brings you to the swamp at this time of night?

MICHAEL. We asked at the farm. They said you had gone this way.

PETER. We, too, we go to the mobilization.

GRIGOR. You also?

ILIA. You go to Zawichost?

PETER. No; to Sandomierz.

GRIGOR. Oh! So there is mobilization in more than one place at once?

ILIA. It must be a great festival indeed.

PETER. [*Eagerly.*] A festival, is it then?

GRIGOR. Who knows?

MICHAEL. But that is why we followed you. We do not know what mobilization may be. But Anna Petrovna said you had gone there. We thought you would know.

GRIGOR. [*Shrugging his shoulders.*] Whatever it is, we will know today.

PETER. But now, you cannot tell us?

GRIGOR. No. [*He pauses.*] Why do you go to the mobilization in Sandomierz while we go to that in Zawichost?

MICHAEL. A soldier said we were to go to Sandomierz.

STEPAN. A soldier here? In these swamps?

MICHAEL. All the way to the farm he came. We must go, he said. We were afraid to disobey.

GRIGOR. He did not tell you why you must go?

MICHAEL. He had no time. He had to tell many others.

STEPAN. And you asked him nothing?

MICHAEL. We asked. He swore, and said that if we were not gone when he passed again on his way back, we should be beaten.

[*There is a pause.*]

ILIA. And lame Peter, must he go too?

MICHAEL. I and all my men, he said. I have only the one.

ILIA. But he is lame.

PETER. [*Good-naturedly.*] Lame Peter will travel as far and as fast as any of them! And if there is to be a festival, why should not lame Peter be there with the others?

GRIGOR. But the harvest?

MICHAEL. Yes, the harvest!

STEPAN. When we return we will reap our fields together, and then lame Peter will have a chance to show what a worker he is!

ILIA. [*Abruptly.*] A sound!

[*They stop talking.*]

STEPAN. What is it?

ILIA. [*Listening.*] A horse.

STEPAN. [*Incredulously.*] A horse? This time you are wrong!

GRIGOR. What fool would try to ride a horse through the swamp?

ILIA. Now I hear it more plainly.

PETER. Perhaps it is a riderless horse.

ILIA. No. A rider is using the whip. [*He is looking off left.*]

GRIGOR. [*Following his glance.*] A rider from the city?

[*The peasants look at each other. The crackling of branches becomes audible.* STEPAN *rises silently, and goes out at the left.*]

MICHAEL. As if there were no better use for a good animal than that! To ride through the swamp, where the ground is hardly firm enough to carry a man!

PETER. And quicksands, quicksands to right and left of him! The horse knows better than his master.

[*There is the sound of a drunken voice raised in anger.*]

ILIA. Listen to him!

PETER. Swearing at his horse, as if the poor beast could do any more!

ILIA. He's afraid! I know he's afraid! He feels the earth crumbling under his hoofs! How he must tremble! [*The sound of a whip being used unmercifully.*] Now he's beating him! I hope he throws him! Oh, I hope he throws him!

[*There is a loud crash.*]

GRIGOR. He *has* thrown him!

ILIA. I knew he would!

PETER. It serves him right! To treat a good horse like that!

ILIA. And into the mud! The rider from the city in the mud! I should love to see that!

[*There is the report of a revolver. The peasants rise, look at each other in terrified inquiry. They all rise.*]

GRIGOR. What was that?

MICHAEL. A shot!

ILIA. And Stepan!

PETER. Perhaps Stepan said something!

ILIA. Something the rider didn't like!

MICHAEL. He was always quick tempered, your Stepan. He was not the man to stand there and see the horse beaten for no fault of its own.

GRIGOR. [*In horror.*] Christ!

[STEPAN *re-enters.*]

ILIA. [*With a shout of relief.*] Here he comes!

GRIGOR. Stepan!

MICHAEL. What happened?

STEPAN. [*Briefly.*] His horse fell. It wouldn't rise again. He shot it.

ILIA. Oh!

PETER. Shot his horse!

[*At the left there enters a Russian* SERGEANT, *booted, spurred, carrying a whip. He is very muddy and very drunk. The others are clustered together at the right.*]

[*Repeats in horror.*] He shot his horse!

THE SERGEANT. Well, what of it? It was *my* horse, wasn't it? I could do what I wanted with it.

MICHAEL. [*More mildly.*] It must have been worth many roubles.[5]

THE SERGEANT. The rich government will pay for it. [*He stumbles nearer the fire.*] Give me something to drink.

MICHAEL. What would we be doing with drink? [*He moves to the fire, and sits.*]

GRIGOR. [*Sitting at the fire.*] We are only honest *moujiks*.

THE SERGEANT. You have nothing? Well, then—[*He pulls a flask from a pocket, and applies it to his lips.*]

STEPAN. [*To* GRIGOR, *as the* SERGEANT *drinks.*] He has had too much to drink already.

[5] *Rouble* (pronounced roo'b'l) is the Russian dollar.

GRIGOR. [*Shrugging his shoulders.*] A Christian is a Christian.

THE SERGEANT. [*Wiping his lips on his sleeve, and replacing his bottle without offering it elsewhere.*] Ah! That puts the heart in you! Make place for me at your fire, you! [*He elbows his way to a seat. The peasants edge away, so that he is alone at one side, and they together at the other.*] There! That's something like. [*There is a pause.*]

GRIGOR. [*Courteously.*] May I ask your name?

THE SERGEANT. [*Warming his hands at the fire.*] What?

GRIGOR. Your name and surnames?

THE SERGEANT. Alexei Ivanovitch Liboff, Sergeant.

GRIGOR. [*Inclining his head.*] I am Grigor Ignátievitch Arshin. This is my son Stepan. This is my son Ilia. This is my good neighbor—

THE SERGEANT. [*Interrupts rudely with a drinking song.*]

> It isn't sleep that bows my head,
> But the drink, the drink that's in it!

GRIGOR. [*In amazement.*] What?

STEPAN. [*Starting to rise angrily.*] The boor!

GRIGOR. [*Laying a hand on his arm.*] A Christian is a Christian.

THE SERGEANT.

> I'll up and away to a distant glade!
> Where the wild red raspberries grow,
> And I'll meet a little Cossack girl,
> A little Cossack girl from the Don!

[*He stops suddenly.*] Well, why don't you say something?

GRIGOR. It is not for us to speak in the presence of your excellency.

THE SERGEANT. Then my excellency graciously grants you permission. [*He rises, bows grotesquely, stumbles, falls.*]

> I'll meet a little Cossack girl,
> A little Cossack girl from the Don!

[*He stops; points at* ILIA.] You, speak! [ILIA *remains silent. He points at* STEPAN.] You! [STEPAN *folds his arms and glares. He points at* Grigor.] You, old man! Are you all a pack of fools?

Grigor. Your excellency has traveled far?

The Sergeant. My excellency has traveled far. Through these cursed swamps on a stumbling horse all the way from Zawichost.

Stepan. [*Involuntarily.*] From Zawichost?

The Sergeant. Have I not said so? All the way from Zawichost, since eleven o'clock this morning.

Stepan. [*Starting to put the question which is uppermost in all their minds.*] Perhaps, then— [*He breaks off.*]

The Sergeant. Perhaps what?

Grigor. Perhaps your excellency can tell us something of the mobilization?

The Sergeant. [*Yawning.*] The mobilization, oh, yes.

Ilia. It is a festival, is it not?

The Sergeant. [*Shutting his mouth with a surprised snap.*] What?

Grigor. A festival of the Holy Church?

The Sergeant. Who told you that? [*He laughs loudly.*] A festival of the Church!

Michael. [*Somewhat nettled.*] What, then, is the mobilization?

The Sergeant. You don't know?

Peter. How should we? We live far from the cities.

The Sergeant. Then why do you go there?

Michael. We do as we are told.

The Sergeant. [*Very drunkenly.*] Quite right! Do as you are told! Obey orders! That's the way for a *moujik!*

Grigor. But what is mobilization?

The Sergeant. [*Turning on him.*] Mobilization is this: they stand you up in rows, the big men in back, and the little men in front. Then they put guns in your hands, and you shoot.

Ilia. I should love to shoot.

Michael. But we don't know how.

The Sergeant. That doesn't matter. They teach you.

Stepan. We shoot. Very well, what then? When we have shot, do we go home?

The Sergeant. Oh, no! It only begins so. When you have shot, you march. Then they stand you up in rows again, and you shoot some more.

MICHAEL. What do you shoot at?

ILIA. Targets?

THE SERGEANT. Better than that!

PETER. Animals?

THE SERGEANT. Still better than that! [*He pauses for his effect.*] How would you like to shoot at men?

ILIA. Shoot at men?

MICHAEL. What have they done that they should be shot at?

GRIGOR. What have we done that we should shoot at them?

THE SERGEANT. [*Amused.*] You don't believe me? [*He laughs; produces his bottle, drinks again.*]

STEPAN. [*To* GRIGOR.] He is very drunk. He doesn't know what he is saying.

PETER. [*With a sudden laugh.*] I have found it!

THE SERGEANT. What have you found?

PETER. I have found the trick! You shoot at men, yes, but not with real bullets!

THE SERGEANT. [*Laughing, as the others laugh, but for a different reason.*] Not with real bullets? Wait a minute. [*He fumbles in his bandolier.⁶*] Here's one of them! [*He tosses them a loaded cartridge.*]

MICHAEL. [*While they all examine it with curiosity.*] What is it?

THE SERGEANT. Give it to me. [*He demonstrates.*] This is full of powder. The hammer strikes here, and the powder explodes. And this—this—[*He bites it out.*]—is the bullet.

[*He passes it to them.*]

ILIA. What a cruel thing!

PETER. How heavy it is!

GRIGOR. And is this what we shoot at men?

THE SERGEANT. Bullets like this—and bigger.

GRIGOR. But if we hit them?

THE SERGEANT. What?

---

⁶ A *bandolier* is a band—usually made of leather, with loops for holding cartridges—worn over the shoulder.

GRIGOR. [*Repeating his question.*] If we hit them?

THE SERGEANT. You want to hit them.

GRIGOR. And hurt them?

THE SERGEANT. You want to hurt them.

GRIGOR. Or even—kill them?

THE SERGEANT. [*Reaching his climax.*] You want to kill them! [*The peasants look at one another blankly.* THE SERGEANT *is immensely pleased with the impression he has produced.*]

STEPAN. [*Rising.*] We are peaceable *moujiks.*

MICHAEL. [*Rising.*] We want to kill nobody.

PETER. [*Rising.*] They must have sent for the wrong men. They could not have wanted us.

GRIGOR. [*Voicing the general opinion. He rises.*] We—we want to kill no man. For sixty years I have been a good Christian. I have killed nothing except that which I was to eat; I and my children. We do not eat men; we do not kill men.

THE SERGEANT. [*Also rising.*] All right, then. You will learn how.

GRIGOR. I do not wish to learn how.

THE SERGEANT. So they say in the beginning. So was I in the beginning. The first time you pull your trigger, the first time you see a strong man fall, you are afraid, oh, you are afraid! But then the lust of killing sweeps over you and you shoot, and shoot, while the metal of your gun burns the flesh of your hands, and you scream with joy, and are glad, and you kill! You kill! [*He has moved down right.*]

GRIGOR. Far rather would I be killed myself!

THE SERGEANT. That may happen also! [*He drinks.*]

STEPAN. [*To* GRIGOR.] He lies.

MICHAEL. He is a soldier. Soldiers always lie.

ILIA. And he is drunk! Pah!

GRIGOR. [*To the* SERGEANT, *as he corks his bottle.*] These men, whom we shoot at— [*He stops.*]

THE SERGEANT. Yes?

GRIGOR. They have stolen? They have murdered?

[*The* SERGEANT *laughs.*]

[*Patiently.*] They must be great criminals. What crimes have they done?

THE SERGEANT. No crimes.

GRIGOR. Then why do they let us shoot at them?

THE SERGEANT. They do not *let* you.

GRIGOR. No?

THE SERGEANT. You shoot.

GRIGOR. And what do they do?

THE SERGEANT. They shoot also.

GRIGOR. At us?

THE SERGEANT. Where else, then? They are the enemy.

GRIGOR. But we—we have no enemies.

THE SERGEANT. You will learn otherwise. These men, these men whom you shoot at and who shoot at you, they are your enemies.

[*There is a pause. The peasants exchange signs of incredulity.*]

ILIA. [*Reflectively.*] To shoot, that is not so bad. But to be shot at, that I should not like at all!

GRIGOR. [*Silencing him.*] And who are these men?

PETER. [*Sarcastically.*] Yes, our enemies, who are they?

THE SERGEANT. [*Waving his hand.*] Prussians. Germans. Austrians.

GRIGOR. And what are Prussians?—Germans?—Austrians?

THE SERGEANT. Men who live on the other side of the border. Men who live on the other side of the swamps.

GRIGOR. On the other side of the swamps? [*He glances meaningly at* MICHAEL *and* PETER.] What do you mean?

THE SERGEANT. [*At center, growing drunkenly expansive.*] Well, you see, here is Russia [*A gesture to the left.*]; here are the swamps [*A gesture in front.*]; that is the border; and there is Austria. [*A gesture to the right.*] Here we are. There is the enemy.

[*Rather unaccountably the peasants begin to laugh, a hearty laugh of relief, as if the* SERGEANT *has finally exposed the falsehood of everything that he has said by venturing upon a glaringly untrue statement.*]

[*Irritated.*] Well, what are you laughing at?

MICHAEL. [*Moving forward left.*] A good joke!

PETER. [*With him.*] Yes, a fine joke!

MICHAEL. A liar! Such a liar as there never was!

STEPAN. [*At left center.*] When a man has had too much to drink he should stay home!

GRIGOR. [*Relaxing his dignity—at center.*] And for a time we believed him! We believed him!

THE SERGEANT. [*Right center.*] What?

STEPAN. Instead of telling lies to honest *moujiks*—

THE SERGEANT. [*Interrupting.*] What do you mean?

PETER. [*At left.*] We, [*Indicating* MICHAEL.] we live on the other side of the swamps!

THE SERGEANT. Well, what of it?

[GRIGOR *sits.*]

MICHAEL. We are going to the mobilization also!

THE SERGEANT. [*With superiority.*] Here is the borderline. But the line bends.

PETER. You said they shoot at us! Because we lived on the other side of the swamps! Old Grigor, and Stepan, and Ilia! They shoot at us!

STEPAN. [*Laughing.*] Rather would we shoot at you, Alexei Ivanovitch!

THE SERGEANT. [*Growing angry.*] Laugh, if you like! Laugh, but tomorrow, when you reach Zawichost, when you find that I am your superior officer, then *I* laugh!

PETER. To Zawichost? But we do not go there!

MICHAEL. We go to Sandomierz!

THE SERGEANT. [*Thunderstruck.*] To Sandomierz!

PETER. [*Snapping his fingers at him.*] Where you are *not* my superior officer!

THE SERGEANT. [*With sudden awakening.*] No, that I am not! But you—you are the enemy!

PETER. [*At left.*] What?

ILIA. Did you hear what he said?

STEPAN. [*Laughing scornfully.*] The enemy?

MICHAEL. [*Crossing to him.*] When we have tilled our fields together?

THE SERGEANT. [*Balancing himself with difficulty.*] Sandomierz, that is in Austria!

GRIGOR. [*Disregarding him.*] Enemies! When we live a single verst apart from each other!

MICHAEL. When we have helped each other with the harvest, aye, since we were children!

THE SERGEANT. [*Shouting.*] We are Russians! You are Austrians! There is war between us! [*He draws his revolver.*] I command you to surrender.

PETER. [*Mimicking him, dancing up and down in front of him at the left.*] I command you to surrender!

THE SERGEANT. [*At center.*] Surrender!

PETER. Listen to the drunken fool! Surrender!

[*The* SERGEANT *shoots.* PETER *falls. There is a sudden and dreadful pause.*]

STEPAN. [*Going left, and laying his hand over* PETER's *heart.*] Dead! Dead as the horse!

GRIGOR. [*Rising to his feet like a prophet of old.*] Are we men or are we beasts of the field?

THE SERGEANT. [*Turning triumphantly on* MICHAEL, *who is at right center.*] Now, you Austrian swine, will you surrender?

[*But* STEPAN *is already advancing upon him, breathing deep, slowly, massively, like some awful engine of destruction. At first the* SERGEANT *does not see him, but something in the expression of the others warns him. He wheels.*]

[*At right center.*] Back! Stop where you are!

[STEPAN *continues grimly, his great hands rising slowly from his sides.*]

[*In an ecstasy of fear.*] Back, I say!

[*He fires.* STEPAN *shakes himself, as if stung by a hornet, and throws his towering bulk upon the* SERGEANT. *There is a sigh of satisfaction from the moujik as his fingers lock about his adversary's throat. And there is a scream from the* SERGEANT, *a scream ending in a choke. . . . The strug-*

gling figures fall at the right, outside of the circle of light. For a moment there is a threshing, as when some small animal is caught in a trap. Then quiet.]

GRIGOR. [*Almost sobbing.*] And not so long ago I thought it was easier to be killed than to kill!

MICHAEL. [*With staring eyes.*] Murder! That I have lived to see a murder!

ILIA. Lame Peter! Poor lame Peter!

[*There is a pause. Then* STEPAN *rises, holding the* SERGEANT'S *revolver between two fingers.*]

STEPAN. What shall I do with this?

GRIGOR. [*Raising his head.*] What?

[STEPAN *hands him the revolver.*]

Pah! [*He flings it away.*]

[*A pause.*]

ILIA. [*In a trembling voice.*] I so wanted to see you use your strength, and now that I have seen it—how horrible it is, how horrible!

[STEPAN *does not reply. Instead, he turns to* GRIGOR.]

STEPAN. The bodies?

GRIGOR. The swamp will swallow them up. [*He rises, bows his head, folds his hands. The others follow his example.*] May we all be happy. May the dead reach God's kingdom. May we all be preserved in good health. Amen.

[*The others repeat the Amen. He makes the sign of the Cross. The others follow his example. A little light begins to filter through the trees.*]

[*Turning to* MICHAEL.] And now, you on your way, we on ours.

MICHAEL. Farewell, brother.

GRIGOR. Brother, farewell!

[MICHAEL *takes up two packs, his own and* PETER'S; *goes out at the back.* GRIGOR, STEPAN, ILIA *take up their own packs, go out at the left.*]

[*The Curtain Falls*]

UNDERSTANDING AND APPRECIATING THE PLAY

1. The peasants are kinder and gentler men than the sergeant. Tell some of the things he does that prove him to be coarse and cruel.

2. When the peasants say that they do not want to learn how to kill men, the sergeant confesses that he, too, once felt the same unwillingness. Quote what he says about his feelings in his first battle.

3. The sergeant explains that the Austrians are the enemies of the Russians. Why do the peasants laugh scornfully when they hear that statement?

4. The peasant characters are clearly individualized. Point out specific traits of each of them. Grigor is a particularly admirable character. What makes him so?

5. What parts of the action take place off stage? Why are they not represented on the stage?

6. In what ways does the setting contribute to the atmosphere of terror and pity?

7. Show that *Pawns* is a tragedy.

VOCABULARY BUILDING

1. Explain the following phrases in your own words. An *indulgent* smile; becomes *audible;* a *robust* man; give your name and *surname;* the *boor;* somewhat *nettled;* a glaringly untrue statement; to a distant *glade;* bows *grotesquely.*

2. What does *aud-* mean? Look it up in the dictionary if you do not know. Explain the meaning of each word listed below according to the meaning of *aud-: auditorium, audio-visual* aids, *audition, audience, audiphone, auditor.*

THINGS TO DO

1. Discuss your ideas on one of the following: (*a*) How wars can be avoided; (*b*) The causes of modern wars; (*c*) When it becomes necessary for Americans to fight; (*d*) The attitude we should adopt toward a beaten foe.

2. Dramatize an exciting or important moment of American history, such as: Custer's last fight; the capture of Nathan Hale; the fall of Fort Sumter; the Boston Tea Party; the discovery of gold in California.

3. Describe the setting for a war play that you may want to write.

PRODUCTION NOTES

In some respects *Pawns* is easy to produce, in some respects hard. There is plenty of action to maintain audience interest and suspense; the stage is in comparative darkness throughout; and there are only six persons in the cast. In these respects it is easy.

But to represent "a forest of swampy nature" with "here and there, little irregular hummocks of ground" is not easy, even in half-light. Perhaps you can contrive a campfire at the center, downstage, which will seem to be the only source of illumination. Some of the sound effects, also, may present difficulties. The croaking of frogs, the sounds of Michael and Peter approaching, the sounds of the sergeant's horse stumbling, the shot that kills the horse, the choking death gasps of the sergeant—these are enough to justify the appointment of a sound-effects man.

Finally, there is one danger in the reading of the lines. The actors must remember that while the peasants may be ignorant and exhibit incredulity and amazement over words they do not understand, they are by no means stupid, and should not be interpreted as such. If this caution is heeded, the play should go well. It is superbly written, and, like *The Valiant*, will succeed with even mediocre acting. The emotional force is there, in the play. Just give it a chance.

Trifles *

SUSAN GLASPELL

Since 1917, when it was first performed, *Trifles* has been regarded by some critics as the best one-act play ever written in America. Whether or not it deserves quite that acclaim, it is certainly written with rare competence, and it deals with significant ideas.

The importance of trifles is the principal theme. When thoughtful men and women reflect upon what the really big things in life are, they sometimes come to the paradoxical conclusion that the truly significant experiences are the seemingly unimportant details of life—those things that unimaginative people, often to their later regret, dismiss as mere trifles. This thought is strikingly developed, for example, in *Our Town*, one of the great plays of our century. The playwright, Thornton Wilder, reminds us to treasure the ordinary things in life such as a mother's calling children to breakfast and getting them off to school, a friendly chat among neighbors, and the celebration of a child's birthday. Too late, one of the principal characters, Emily, realizes all this, and she exclaims, "Good-by, good-by, world . . . Mama and Papa. Good-by to clocks ticking . . . and Mama's sunflowers. And food and coffee. And new-ironed dresses and hot baths . . . and sleeping and waking up. Oh, earth, you're too wonderful for anybody to realize you." And she asks, "Do any human beings ever realize life while they live it,—every, every minute?"

Our play *Trifles* touches upon other ideas, too: what makes for happiness or unhappiness in marriage; the importance of friendly neighborliness; the yearning for a second chance—"to have it to do over again"; how to explain strange quirks in human behavior; the masculine sense of superiority, sometimes called male supremacy—the feeling that some men have that they are intellectually superior to and more perceptive than women; and loyalty to one's sex.

These ideas are embodied in a suspenseful murder mystery. But quite apart from its being also a play of ideas, *Trifles* is no ordinary "who-dunit." For one thing, who the murderess is seems evident. The suspense is over why the murder was committed, whether the motive will be found—for unless a convincing reason for the com-

* *Trifles* from *Plays* by Susan Glaspell. Reprinted by permission of Dodd, Mead & Company. Copyright 1920 by Dodd, Mead & Company, Inc. Renewal copyright 1948 by Susan Glaspell.

mission of the crime is established, no jury will convict the accused woman—and if the motive is found, whether the discoverer or discoverers will reveal it to the authorities. Furthermore, *Trifles* is no commonplace mystery because it is written with the quiet excellence, the sympathy, and the sensitive perception that characterizes much of Susan Glaspell's writing.

CHARACTERS

GEORGE HENDERSON, *County Attorney*
HENRY PETERS, *Sheriff*
LEWIS HALE, *a neighboring farmer*
MRS. PETERS
MRS. HALE

SCENE: *The kitchen in the now abandoned farmhouse of* JOHN WRIGHT, *a gloomy kitchen, and left without having been put in order—unwashed pans under the sink, a loaf of bread outside the breadbox, a dish towel on the table—other signs of incompleted work. At the rear the outer door opens and the* SHERIFF *comes in followed by the* COUNTY ATTORNEY *and* HALE. *The* SHERIFF *and* HALE *are men in middle life, the* COUNTY ATTORNEY *is a young man; all are much bundled up and go at once to the stove. They are followed by the two women—the* SHERIFF'S WIFE *first; she is a slight wiry woman, with a thin nervous face.* MRS. HALE *is larger and would ordinarily be called more comfortable-looking, but she is disturbed now and looks fearfully about as she enters. The women have come in slowly, and stand close together near the door.*

COUNTY ATTORNEY. [*Rubbing his hands.*] This feels good. Come up to the fire, ladies.

MRS. PETERS. [*After taking a step forward.*] I'm not—cold.

SHERIFF. [*Unbuttoning his overcoat and stepping away from the stove as if to mark the beginning of official business.*] Now, Mr. Hale, before we move things about, you explain to Mr. Henderson just what you saw when you came here yesterday morning.

COUNTY ATTORNEY. By the way, has anything been moved? Are things just as you left them yesterday?

SHERIFF. [*Looking about.*] It's just the same. When it dropped below zero last night I thought I'd better send Frank out this morning to make a fire for us—no use getting pneumonia with a big case on, but I told him not to touch anything except the stove—and you know Frank.

COUNTY ATTORNEY. Somebody should have been left here yesterday.

SHERIFF. Oh—yesterday. When I had to send Frank to Morris Center for that man who went crazy—I want you to know I had my hands full yesterday. I knew you could get back from Omaha by today and as long as I went over everything here myself—

COUNTY ATTORNEY. Well, Mr. Hale, tell us just what happened when you came here yesterday morning.

HALE. Harry and I had started to town with a load of potatoes. We came along the road from my place and as I got here I said, "I'm going to see if I can't get John Wright to go in with me on a party telephone." I spoke to Wright about it once before and he put me off, saying folks talked too much anyway, and all he asked was peace and quiet—I guess you know about how much he talked himself; but I thought maybe if I went to the house and talked about it before his wife, though I said to Harry that I didn't know as what his wife wanted made much difference to John—

COUNTY ATTORNEY. Let's talk about that later, Mr. Hale. I do want to talk about that, but tell now just what happened when you got to the house.

HALE. I didn't hear or see anything; I knocked at the door, and still it was all quiet inside. I knew they must be up; it was past eight o'clock. So I knocked again, and I thought I heard somebody say, "Come in." I wasn't sure, I'm not sure yet, but I opened the door—this door [*Indicating the door by which the two women are still standing.*] and there in that rocker—[*Pointing to it.*] sat Mrs. Wright.

[*They all look at the rocker.*]

COUNTY ATTORNEY. What—was she doing?

HALE. She was rockin' back and forth. She had her apron in her hand and was kind of—pleating it.

COUNTY ATTORNEY. And how did she—look?

HALE. Well, she looked queer.

COUNTY ATTORNEY. How do you mean—queer?

HALE. Well, as if she didn't know what she was going to do next. And kind of done up.

COUNTY ATTORNEY. How did she seem to feel about your coming?

HALE. Why, I don't think she minded—one way or other. She didn't pay much attention. I said, "How do, Mrs. Wright, it's cold, ain't it?" And she said, "Is it?"—and went on kind of pleating at her apron. Well, I was surprised; she didn't ask me to come up to the stove, or to set down, but just sat there, not even looking at me, so I said, "I want to see John." And then she—laughed. I guess you would call it a laugh. I thought of Harry and the team outside, so I said a little sharp: "Can't I see John?" "No," she says, kind o' dull-like. "Ain't he home?" says I. "Yes," says she, "he's home." "Then why can't I see him?" I asked her, out of patience. " 'Cause he's dead," says she. "*Dead?*" says I. She just nodded her head, not getting a bit excited, but rockin' back and forth. "Why—where is he?" says I, not knowing what to say. She just pointed upstairs—like that [*Himself pointing to the room above.*]. I got up, with the idea of going up there. I walked from there to here—then I says, "Why, what did he died of?" "He died of a rope round his neck," says she, and just went on pleatin' at her apron. Well, I went out and called Harry. I thought I might —need help. We went upstairs and there he was lyin'—

COUNTY ATTORNEY. I think I'd rather have you go into that upstairs, where you can point it all out. Just go on now with the rest of the story.

HALE. Well, my first thought was to get that rope off. It looked . . . [*Stops, his face twitches.*] . . . but Harry, he went up to him, and he said, "No, he's dead all right, and we'd better not touch anything." So we went back downstairs. She was still sitting that same way. "Has anybody been notified?" I asked. "No," says she, unconcerned. "Who did this, Mrs. Wright?" said Harry. He said it businesslike—and she stopped pleatin' of her apron. "I don't know," she says. "You don't *know?*" says Harry.

"No," says she. "Weren't you sleepin' in the bed with him?" says
Harry. "Yes," says she, "but I was on the inside." "Somebody
slipped a rope round his neck and strangled him and you didn't
wake up?" says Harry. "I didn't wake up," she said after him.
We must 'a' looked as if we didn't see how that could be, for
after a minute she said, "I sleep sound." Harry was going to ask
her more questions but I said maybe we ought to let her tell her
story first to the coroner, or the sheriff, so Harry went fast as he
could to Rivers' place, where there's a telephone.

COUNTY ATTORNEY. And what did Mrs. Wright do when she
knew that you had gone for the coroner?

HALE. She moved from that chair to this one over here [*Pointing to a small chair in the corner.*] and just sat there with her
hands held together and looking down. I got a feeling that I
ought to make some conversation, so I said I had come in to see
if John wanted to put in a telephone, and at that she started to
laugh, and then she stopped and looked at me—scared. [*The*
COUNTY ATTORNEY, *who has had his notebook out, makes a
note.*] I dunno, maybe it wasn't scared. I wouldn't like to say it
was. Soon Harry got back, and then Dr. Lloyd came, and you,
Mr. Peters, and so I guess that's all I know that you don't.

COUNTY ATTORNEY. [*Looking around.*] I guess we'll go upstairs
first—and then out to the barn and around there. [*To the*
SHERIFF.] You're convinced that there was nothing important
here—nothing that would point to any motive.

SHERIFF. Nothing here but kitchen things.

[*The* COUNTY ATTORNEY, *after again looking around the
kitchen, opens the door of a cupboard closet. He gets up on
a chair and looks on the shelf. Pulls his hand away, sticky.*]

COUNTY ATTORNEY. Here's a nice mess.

[*The women draw nearer.*]

MRS. PETERS. [*To the other woman.*] Oh, her fruit; it did
freeze. [*To the* LAWYER.] She worried about that when it
turned so cold. She said the fire'd go out and her jars would
break.

SHERIFF. Well, can you beat the women! Held for murder
and worryin' about her preserves.

COUNTY ATTORNEY. I guess before we're through she may have something more serious than preserves to worry about.

HALE. Well, women are used to worrying over trifles.

[*The two women move a little closer together.*]

COUNTY ATTORNEY. [*With the gallantry of a young politician.*] And yet, for all their worries, what would we do without the ladies? [*The women do not unbend. He goes to the sink, takes a dipperful of water from the pail and, pouring it into a basin, washes his hands. Starts to wipe them on the roller towel, turns it for a cleaner place.*] Dirty towels! [*Kicks his foot against the pans under the sink.*] Not much of a housekeeper, would you say, ladies?

MRS. HALE. [*Stiffly.*] There's a great deal of work to be done on a farm.

COUNTY ATTORNEY. To be sure. And yet [*With a little bow to her.*] I know there are some Dickson county farmhouses which do not have such roller towels. [*He gives it a pull to expose its full length again.*]

MRS. HALE. Those towels get dirty awful quick. Men's hands aren't always as clean as they might be.

COUNTY ATTORNEY. Ah, loyal to your sex, I see. But you and Mrs. Wright were neighbors. I suppose you were friends, too.

MRS. HALE. [*Shaking her head.*] I've not seen much of her of late years. I've not been in this house—it's more than a year.

COUNTY ATTORNEY. And why was that? You didn't like her?

MRS. HALE. I liked her all well enough. Farmers' wives have their hands full, Mr. Henderson. And then—

COUNTY ATTORNEY. Yes—?

MRS. HALE. [*Looking about.*] It never seemed a very cheerful place.

COUNTY ATTORNEY. No—it's not cheerful. I shouldn't say she had the homemaking instinct.

MRS. HALE. Well, I don't know as Wright had, either.

COUNTY ATTORNEY. You mean that they didn't get on very well?

MRS. HALE. No, I don't mean anything. But I don't think a place'd be any cheerfuller for John Wright's being in it.

COUNTY ATTORNEY. I'd like to talk more of that a little later. I want to get the lay of things upstairs now. [*He goes to the left, where three steps lead to a stair door.*]

SHERIFF. I suppose anything Mrs. Peters does'll be all right. She was to take in some clothes for her, you know, and a few little things. We left in such a hurry yesterday.

COUNTY ATTORNEY. Yes, but I would like to see what you take, Mrs. Peters, and keep an eye out for anything that might be of use to us.

MRS. PETERS. Yes, Mr. Henderson.

[*The women listen to the men's steps on the stairs, then look about the kitchen.*]

MRS. HALE. I'd hate to have men coming into my kitchen, snooping around and criticizing. [*She arranges the pans under sink which the* LAWYER *had shoved out of place.*]

MRS. PETERS. Of course it's no more than their duty.

MRS. HALE. Duty's all right, but I guess that deputy sheriff that came out to make the fire might have got a little of this on. [*Gives the roller towel a pull.*] Wish I'd thought of that sooner. Seems mean to talk about her not having things slicked up when she had to come away in such a hurry.

MRS. PETERS. [*Who has gone to a small table in the left rear corner of the room, and lifted one end of a towel that covers a pan.*] She had bread set. [*Stands still.*]

MRS. HALE. [*Eyes fixed on a loaf of bread beside the breadbox, which is on a low shelf at the other side of the room. Moves slowly toward it.*] She was going to put this in there. [*Picks up loaf, then abruptly drops it. In a manner of returning to familiar things.*] It's a shame about her fruit. I wonder if it's all gone. [*Gets up on the chair and looks.*] I think there's some here that's all right, Mrs. Peters. Yes—here; [*Holding it toward the window.*] this is cherries, too. [*Looking again.*] I declare I believe that's the only one. [*Gets down, bottle in her hand. Goes to the sink and wipes it off on the outside.*] She'll feel awful bad after all her hard work in the hot weather. I remember the afternoon I put up my cherries last summer. [*She puts the bottle on the big kitchen table, center of the room. With a sigh, is about to sit down in the rocking chair. Before she is seated realizes what chair it is; with a slow look at it, steps back. The chair which she has touched rocks back and forth.*]

MRS. PETERS. Well, I must get those things from the front room closet. [*She goes to the door at the right, but after looking into the other room, steps back.*] You coming with me, Mrs. Hale? You could help me carry them.

[*They go in the other room; reappear,* MRS. PETERS *carrying a dress and skirt,* MRS. HALE *following with a pair of shoes.*]

MRS. PETERS. My, it's cold in there. [*She puts the clothes on the big table, and hurries to the stove.*]

MRS. HALE. [*Examining the skirt.*] Wright was close. I think maybe that's why she kept so much to herself. She didn't even belong to the Ladies' Aid. I suppose she felt she couldn't do her part, and then you don't enjoy things when you feel shabby. She used to wear pretty clothes and be lively, when she was Minnie Foster, one of the town girls singing in the choir. But that— oh, that was thirty years ago. This all you was to take in?

MRS. PETERS. She said she wanted an apron. Funny thing to want, for there isn't much to get you dirty in jail, goodness knows. But I suppose just to make her feel more natural. She said that it was in the top drawer in this cupboard. Yes, here. And then her little shawl that always hung behind the door. [*Opens stair door and looks.*] Yes, here it is. [*Quickly shuts door leading upstairs.*]

MRS. HALE. [*Abruptly moving toward her.*] Mrs. Peters?

MRS. PETERS. Yes, Mrs. Hale?

MRS. HALE. Do you think she did it?

MRS. PETERS. [*In a frightened voice.*] Oh, I don't know.

MRS. HALE. Well, I don't think she did. Asking for an apron and her little shawl. Worrying about her fruit.

MRS. PETERS. [*Starts to speak, glances up, where footsteps are heard in the room above. In a low voice.*] Mr. Peters says it looks bad for her. Mr. Henderson is awful sarcastic in a speech and he'll make fun of her sayin' she didn't wake up.

MRS. HALE. Well, I guess John Wright didn't wake when they was slipping that rope under his neck.

MRS. PETERS. No, it's strange. It must have been done awful crafty and still. They say it was such a—funny way to kill a man, rigging it all up like that.

MRS. HALE. That's just what Mr. Hale said. There was a gun in the house. He says that's what he can't understand.

MRS. PETERS. Mr. Henderson said coming out that what was needed for the case was a motive; something to show anger, or —sudden feeling.

MRS. HALE. [*Who is standing by the table.*] Well, I don't see any signs of anger around here. [*She puts her hand on the dish towel which lies on the table, stands looking down at table, one half of which is clean, the other half messy.*] It's wiped to here. [*Makes a move as if to finish work, then turns and looks at loaf of bread outside the breadbox. Drops towel. In that voice of coming back to familiar things.*] Wonder how they are finding things upstairs. I hope she had it a little more redd-up [1] up there. You know, it seems kind of *sneaking.* Locking her up in town and then coming out here and trying to get her own house to turn against her!

MRS. PETERS. But Mrs. Hale, the law is the law.

MRS. HALE. I s'pose 'tis. [*Unbuttoning her coat.*] Better loosen up your things, Mrs. Peters. You won't feel them when you go out.

[MRS. PETERS *takes off her fur tippet, goes to hang it on hook at back of room, stands looking at the under part of the small corner table.*]

MRS. PETERS. She was piecing a quilt. [*She brings the large sewing basket and they look at the bright pieces.*]

MRS. HALE. It's a log-cabin pattern. Pretty, isn't it? I wonder if she was goin' to quilt it or just knot it?

[*Footsteps have been heard coming down the stairs. The* SHERIFF *enters followed by* HALE *and the* COUNTY ATTOR- NEY.]

SHERIFF. They wonder if she was going to quilt it or just knot it!

[*The men laugh, the women look abashed.*]

COUNTY ATTORNEY. [*Rubbing his hands over the stove.*]

_____
[1] redd-up: cleared up, straightened.

Frank's fire didn't do much up there, did it? Well, let's go out to the barn and get that cleared up.

[*The men go outside.*]

MRS. HALE. [*Resentfully.*] I don't know as there's anything so strange, our takin' up our time with little things while we're waiting for them to get the evidence. [*She sits down at the big table smoothing out a block with decision.*] I don't see as it's anything to laugh about.

MRS. PETERS. [*Apologetically.*] Of course they've got awful important things on their minds. [*Pulls up a chair and joins MRS. HALE at the table.*]

MRS. HALE. [*Examining another block.*] Mrs. Peters, look at this one. Here, this is the one she was working on, and look at the sewing! All the rest of it has been so nice and even. And look at this! It's all over the place! Why, it looks as if she didn't know what she was about!

[*After she has said this they look at each other, then start to glance back at the door. After an instant MRS. HALE has pulled at a knot and ripped the sewing.*]

MRS. PETERS. Oh, what are you doing, Mrs. Hale?

MRS. HALE. [*Mildly.*] Just pulling out a stitch or two that's not sewed very good. [*Threading a needle.*] Bad sewing always made me fidgety.

MRS. PETERS. [*Nervously.*] I don't think we ought to touch things.

MRS. HALE. I'll just finish up this end. [*Suddenly stopping and leaning forward.*] Mrs. Peters?

MRS. PETERS. Yes, Mrs. Hale?

MRS. HALE. What do you suppose she was so nervous about?

MRS. PETERS. Oh—I don't know. I don't know as she was nervous. I sometimes sew awful queer when I'm just tired. [*MRS. HALE starts to say something, looks at MRS. PETERS, then goes on sewing.*] Well, I must get these things wrapped up. They may be through sooner than we think. [*Putting apron and other things together.*] I wonder where I can find a piece of paper and string.

MRS. HALE. In that cupboard, maybe.

MRS. PETERS. [*Looking in cupboard.*] Why, here's a bird cage. [*Holds it up.*] Did she have a bird, Mrs. Hale?

MRS. HALE. Why, I don't know whether she did or not—I've not been here for so long. There was a man around last year selling canaries cheap, but I don't know as she took one; maybe she did. She used to sing real pretty herself.

MRS. PETERS. [*Glancing around.*] Seems funny to think of a bird here. But she must have had one, or why would she have a cage? I wonder what happened to it?

MRS. HALE. I s'pose maybe the cat got it.

MRS. PETERS. No, she didn't have a cat. She's got that feeling some people have about cats—being afraid of them. My cat got in her room and she was real upset and asked me to take it out.

MRS. HALE. My sister Bessie was like that. Queer, ain't it?

MRS. PETERS. [*Examining the cage.*] Why, look at this door. It's broke. One hinge is pulled apart.

MRS. HALE. [*Looking too.*] Looks as if someone must have been rough with it.

MRS. PETERS. Why, yes. [*She brings the cage forward and puts it on the table.*]

MRS. HALE. I wish if they're going to find any evidence they'd be about it. I don't like this place.

MRS. PETERS. But I'm awful glad you came with me, Mrs. Hale. It would be lonesome for me sitting here alone.

MRS. HALE. It would, wouldn't it? [*Dropping her sewing.*] But I tell you what I do wish, Mrs. Peters. I wish I had come over sometimes when *she* was here. I—[*Looking around the room.*]—wish I had.

MRS. PETERS. But of course you were awful busy, Mrs. Hale —your house and your children.

MRS. HALE. I could've come. I stayed away because it weren't cheerful—and that's why I ought to have come. I—I've never liked this place. Maybe because it's down in a hollow and you don't see the road. I dunno what it is, but it's a lonesome place and always was. I wish I had come over to see Minnie Foster sometimes. I can see now—[*Shakes her head.*]

MRS. PETERS. Well, you mustn't reproach yourself, Mrs. Hale. Somehow we just don't see how it is with other folks until— something turns up.

MRS. HALE. Not having children makes less work—but it makes a quiet house, and Wright out to work all day, and no company when he did come in. Did you know John Wright, Mrs. Peters?

MRS. PETERS. Not to know him; I've seen him in town. They say he was a good man.

MRS. HALE. Yes—good; he didn't drink, and kept his word as well as most, I guess, and paid his debts. But he was a hard man, Mrs. Peters. Just to pass the time of day with him— [*Shivers.*] Like a raw wind that gets to the bone. [*Pauses, her eye falling on the cage.*] I should think she would 'a' wanted a bird. But what do you suppose went with it?

MRS. PETERS. I don't know, unless it got sick and died.

[*She reaches over and swings the broken door, swings it again, both women watch it.*]

MRS. HALE. You weren't raised round here, were you? [MRS. PETERS *shakes her head.*] You didn't know—her?

MRS. PETERS. Not till they brought her yesterday.

MRS. HALE. She—come to think of it, she was kind of like a bird herself—real sweet and pretty, but kind of timid and —fluttery. How—she—did—change. [*Silence; then as if struck by a happy thought and relieved to get back to everyday things.*] Tell you what, Mrs. Peters, why don't you take the quilt in with you? It might take up her mind.

MRS. PETERS. Why, I think that's a real nice idea, Mrs. Hale. There couldn't possibly be any objection to it, could there? Now, just what would I take? I wonder if her patches are in here—and her things.

[*They look in the sewing basket.*]

MRS. HALE. Here's some red. I expect this has got sewing things in it. [*Brings out a fancy box.*] What a pretty box. Looks like something somebody would give you. Maybe her scissors are in here. [*Opens box. Suddenly puts her hand to her nose.*] Why— [Mrs. Peters *bends nearer, then turns her face away.*] There's something wrapped up in this piece of silk.

Mrs. Peters. Why, this isn't her scissors.

Mrs. Hale. [*Lifting the silk.*] Oh, Mrs. Peters—it's—

[Mrs. Peters *bends closer.*]

Mrs. Peters. It's the bird.

Mrs. Hale. [*Jumping up.*] But, Mrs. Peters—look at it! Its neck! Look at its neck! It's all—other side *to.*

Mrs. Peters. Somebody—wrung—its—neck.

[*Their eyes meet. A look of growing comprehension, of horror. Steps are heard outside.* Mrs. Hale *slips box under quilt pieces, and sinks into her chair. Enter* Sheriff *and* County Attorney. Mrs. Peters *rises.*]

County Attorney. [*As one turning from serious things to little pleasantries.*] Well, ladies, have you decided whether she was going to quilt it or knot it?

Mrs. Peters. We think she was going to—knot it.

County Attorney. Well, that's interesting, I'm sure. [*Seeing the bird cage.*] Has the bird flown?

Mrs. Hale. [*Putting more quilt pieces over the box.*] We think the—cat got it.

County Attorney. [*Preoccupied.*] Is there a cat?

[Mrs. Hale *glances in a quick covert way at* Mrs. Peters.]

Mrs. Peters. Well, not *now.* They're superstitious, you know. They leave.

County Attorney. [*To* Sheriff Peters, *continuing an interrupted conversation.*] No sign at all of anyone having come from the outside. Their own rope. Now let's go up again and go over it piece by piece. [*They start upstairs.*] It would have to have been someone who knew just the—

[Mrs. Peters *sits down. The two women sit there not looking at one another, but as if peering into something and at the same time holding back. When they talk now it is in the manner of feeling their way over strange ground, as if afraid of what they are saying, but as if they cannot help saying it.*]

MRS. HALE. She liked the bird. She was going to bury it in that pretty box.

MRS. PETERS. [*In a whisper.*] When I was a girl—my kitten—there was a boy took a hatchet, and before my eyes—and before I could get there— [*Covers her face an instant.*] If they hadn't held me back I would have—[*Catches herself, looks upstairs where steps are heard, falters weakly.*]—hurt him.

MRS. HALE. [*With a slow look around her.*] I wonder how it would seem never to have had any children around. [*Pause.*] No, Wright wouldn't like the bird—a thing that sang. She used to sing. He killed that, too.

MRS. PETERS. [*Moving uneasily.*] We don't know who killed the bird.

MRS. HALE. I knew John Wright.

MRS. PETERS. It was an awful thing was done in this house that night, Mrs. Hale. Killing a man while he slept, slipping a rope around his neck that choked the life out of him.

MRS. HALE. His neck. Choked the life out of him. [*Her hand goes out and rests on the bird cage.*]

MRS. PETERS. [*With rising voice.*] We don't know who killed him. We don't *know.*

MRS. HALE. [*Her own feeling not interrupted.*] If there'd been years and years of nothing, then a bird to sing to you, it would be awful—still, after the bird was still.

MRS. PETERS. [*Something within her speaking.*] I know what stillness is. When we homesteaded [2] in Dakota, and my first baby died—after he was two years old, and me with no other then—

MRS. HALE. [*Moving.*] How soon do you suppose they'll be through looking for the evidence?

MRS. PETERS. I know what stillness is. [*Pulling herself back.*] The law has got to punish crime, Mrs. Hale.

MRS. HALE. [*Not as if answering that.*] I wish you'd seen Minnie Foster when she wore a white dress with blue ribbons

[2] homesteaded: lived on a farm on free land made available by the government to settlers by the Homestead Act of 1862.

and stood up there in the choir and sang. [*A look around the room.*] Oh, I *wish* I'd come over here once in a while! That was a crime! That was a crime! Who's going to punish that?

MRS. PETERS. [*Looking upstairs.*] We mustn't—take on.

MRS. HALE. I might have known she needed help! I know how things can be—for women. I tell you, it's queer, Mrs. Peters. We live close together and we live far apart. We all go through the same things—it's all just a different kind of the same thing. [*Brushes her eyes, noticing the bottle of fruit, reaches out for it.*] If I was you I wouldn't tell her her fruit was gone. Tell her it *ain't*. Tell her it's all right. Take this in to prove it to her. She— she may never know whether it was broke or not.

MRS. PETERS. [*Takes the bottle, looks about for something to wrap it in; takes petticoat from the clothes brought from the other room, very nervously begins winding this around the bottle. In a false voice.*] My, it's a good thing the men couldn't hear us. Wouldn't they just laugh! Getting all stirred up over a little thing like a—dead canary. As if that could have anything to do with—with—wouldn't they *laugh!*

[*The men are heard coming downstairs.*]

MRS. HALE. [*Under her breath.*] Maybe they would—maybe they wouldn't.

COUNTY ATTORNEY. No, Peters, it's all perfectly clear except a reason for doing it. But you know juries when it comes to women. If there was some definite thing. Something to show—something to make a story about—a thing that would connect up with this strange way of doing it—

[*The women's eyes meet for an instant. Enter* HALE *from outer door.*]

HALE. Well, I've got the team around. Pretty cold out there.

COUNTY ATTORNEY. I'm going to stay here awhile by myself. [*To the* SHERIFF.] You can send Frank out for me, can't you? I want to go over everything. I'm not satisfied that we can't do better.

SHERIFF. Do you want to see what Mrs. Peters is going to take in?

[*The* LAWYER *goes to the table, picks up the apron, laughs.*]

County Attorney. Oh, I guess they're not very dangerous things the ladies have picked out. [*Moves a few things about, disturbing the quilt pieces which cover the box. Steps back.*] No, Mrs. Peters doesn't need supervising. For that matter, a sheriff's wife is married to the law. Ever think of it that way, Mrs. Peters?

Mrs. Peters. Not—just that way.

Sheriff. [*Chuckling.*] Married to the law. [*Moves toward the other room.*] I just want you to come in here a minute, George. We ought to take a look at these windows.

County Attorney. [*Scoffingly.*] Oh, windows!

Sheriff. We'll be right out, Mr. Hale.

[*Hale goes outside. The* Sheriff *follows the* County Attorney *into the other room. Then* Mrs. Hale *rises, hands tight together, looking intensely at* Mrs. Peters, *whose eyes make a slow turn, finally meeting* Mrs. Hale's. *A moment* Mrs. Hale *holds her, then her own eyes point the way to where the box is concealed. Suddenly* Mrs. Peters *throws back quilt pieces and tries to put the box in the bag she is wearing. It is too big. She opens box, starts to take bird out, cannot touch it, goes to pieces, stands there helpless. Sound of a knob turning in the other room.* Mrs. Hale *snatches the box and puts it in the pocket of her big coat. Enter* County Attorney *and* Sheriff.]

County Attorney. [*Facetiously.*] Well, Henry, at least we found out that she was not going to quilt it. She was going to —what is it you call it, ladies?

Mrs. Hale. [*Her hand against her pocket.*] We call it—knot it, Mr. Henderson.

[*The Curtain Falls*]

UNDERSTANDING AND APPRECIATING THE PLAY

1. It is by means of the little things which they notice, by what most people would dismiss as trifles, that Mrs. Hale and Mrs. Peters discover the motive for the commission of the crime.

A. By what trifle did the women realize that Mrs. Wright had been very nervous and agitated recently?

B. What significant trifle do the women discover about the bird cage?

C. What discovery do they make about the manner in which the canary had died? According to Mrs. Hale, why did the death of the bird mean so much to Mrs. Wright?

D. What is significant about the fact that the Wrights did not have a cat?

2. Little by little, we get a definite impression of John Wright's personality. What kind of man was he? Did he have any virtues?

3. The character with whom we are most concerned, Mrs. Wright, never appears. What kind of woman was she? Why was her marriage an unhappy one?

4. The women come to the conclusion that Mrs. Wright had murdered her husband. What do they infer was her motive?

5. Do you agree with Mrs. Hale and Mrs. Peters? Do you think that Mrs. Wright was guilty? Why? Do you find the motive for the crime convincing? Explain.

6. Mrs. Peters says, "The law has got to punish crime, Mrs. Hale." Yet neither she nor Mrs. Hale reveal to the authorities the details they have pieced together which would probably convince a jury that Mrs. Wright had a motive for killing her husband. Why do the women decide not to reveal what they had discovered? Should they have kept what they knew to themselves?

7. "That was a crime! That was a crime! Who's going to punish that?" Mrs. Hale rebukes herself. For what wrongdoing was she blaming herself? What excuse did she have for not doing as her heart had told her to do?

8. Mrs. Hale also speaks these meaningful lines: "We live close together and we live far apart. We all go through the same things—it's all just a different kind of the same thing." As applied to the relationship between her and Mrs. Wright, what did Mrs. Hale mean? Can you apply the meaning of those words to life in general? How? What does the play say about the need for friendly neighborliness?

9. In what ways do the men show their feeling of condescending superiority to the women? What is the significance of the women's

replies to the men's patronizing questions: first, Mrs. Peters' "We think she was going to knot it" and, in the final line of the play, Mrs. Hales's "We call it—knot it, Mr. Henderson"?

10. "Ah, loyal to your sex, I see," remarks the young county attorney to the women. Besides not revealing what they knew about what could have motivated Mrs. Wright to commit the crime, in what other ways do the women show their loyalty to their sex?

11. In recalling an incident from her childhood, Mrs. Peters suggest that even a mild-mannered person may be capable of an act of violence. What was that incident?

12. *Trifles* is a dramatization of one of Susan Glaspell's short stories called *A Jury of Her Peers.* If you don't know the meaning of the word *peers,* look it up; then discuss the appropriateness of both titles. Which title do you prefer? Why?

13. What kind of serious play is *Trifles?* Is it a tragedy? A melodrama? Or because you think it is neither a tragedy nor a melodrama, should it simply be called a drama? Explain.

VOCABULARY BUILDING

In the context in which they occur, explain the meanings of the italicized words: speaking in a *preoccupied* manner; glances in a quick, *covert* way; taking off her fur *tippet;* looking *intensely* at Mrs. Peters; speaking *facetiously;* looking *abashed.*

THINGS TO DO

1. Topics for themes: Good Neighbors; The Important Things in My Life; Lending a Helping Hand; If I Had It to Do Over Again; The Importance of Trifles; People Are Funny; Controlling My Emotions; A Regret; When I Was Angry; I Can't Understand It; A Resentment; I Did Not Realize It; Mistreated; What Makes for a Successful Marriage; Why Did He (or She) Do It?

2. Since it is apparent that Mrs. Wright will be freed, *Trifles* tells only part of her story. In either story or play form, develop what happens after she is released from jail. Consider the part that Mrs. Peters and Mrs. Hale will play in her life.

3. For discussion:
A. Intellectually, who is superior: boys or girls? (Or if you wish, men or women?) Or are the sexes equally intelligent? Is it only individuals that vary? How about achievement in school? Do boys

or girls get better marks and achieve higher ranking in class? Or
does it depend upon the individual? Do girls achieve better in
certain subjects and boys in others? In which subjects?

B. Should a girl friend or a wife be as educated as her boy friend
or husband? Is a college education as important for a girl as for a
boy?

C. Do you believe in capital punishment—that is, in the death
penalty—for those convicted of murder?

PRODUCTION NOTES

The effectiveness of a production of *Trifles* depends upon the degree of success which your two character actresses have in portraying the roles of Mrs. Hale and Mrs. Peters with poised restraint, perceptive insight, and sympathetic understanding. As the evidence they
have pieced together leads them relentlessly to the conclusion that
Mrs. Wright had in fact murdered her husband and that, according
to their way of thinking, she had sufficient reason for doing so, they
should indeed talk as if they were "feeling their way over strange
ground, as if afraid of what they are saying, but as if they cannot
help saying it." Later they are called upon to portray the sense of
indecision, the feeling of guilt each has—and the feeling is stronger
with Mrs. Peters—about suppressing evidence from the county attorney and the sheriff. And, finally, they show that they are at peace
with themselves for what they did out of sympathy for Mrs. Wright.

One of the emotional highlights of the play, Mrs. Hale's yearning
for a second chance for neighborly helpfulness to Mrs. Wright, requires building—especially her crying out "That was a crime! Who's
going to punish that?" as she rebukes herself.

The principal characteristics to emphasize in the men are (1) their
vigorous but non-too-perceptive pursuit of evidence that would convict Mrs. Wright and (2) their condescending and patronizing sense
of superiority to the women.

MORE GOOD ONE-ACT PLAYS ABOUT PERSONAL AND SOCIAL PROBLEMS AND ABOUT DEMOCRACY

America in Action. [Thomas Y. Crowell] Twelve easily understood and well-written one-act plays for young people, dealing with

freedom and democracy. Paul Green, E. P. Conkle, and Dan Totheroh are among the authors represented.

The Bishop's Candlesticks. Norman McKinnel. [French]   Popular adaptation of an incident from Victor Hugo's *Les Miserables*. A bishop's kindness makes a convict determine to start life over again.

Confessional. Percival Wilde. [Baker]   An arresting, serious play in which an honest banker is faced with a great temptation.

The Curtain. Hallie Flanagan. [French]   Tense little drama in which a fugitive from justice tells his daughter how he has ruined his life through a series of falsehoods. Her integrity is tested when the police arrive to look for him.

Haven of the Spirit. Merrill Denison. [Dramatists Play Service] With Roger Williams as the protagonist, this simply written play dramatizes a situation in the Providence Plantation in which the ideal of religious tolerance was challenged and defended.

In the Zone. Eugene O'Neill. [Dramatists Play Service]   This one-act play of the sea is a good one with which to introduce young people to America's foremost dramatist. It combines suspenseful action with the themes of the need for fair play and of a man's having ruined his life through drink.

Man of Destiny. Bernard Shaw. [Penguin Books]   Witty, interesting, thought-provoking one-acter, in which the principal characters are Napoleon and a lady spy.

Plays of Patriotism for Young Americans. Edited by S. Emerson Golden. [Dodd, Mead]   Seventeen easily staged plays. Dodd, Mead and Company also publishes Samuel S. Ullman's *Plays of America's Achievement* and *Plays of America's Growth.*

Shirt-Tail Boy. W. P. Covington III. [Chilton]   Effectively written play about Abe Lincoln as a boy of twelve and of the beneficent influence exerted upon him by Sarah Bush Johnson, who was about to become his stepmother.

The Teacher. Fred Eastman. [French]   A fairly good play defending a teacher's freedom to instruct as she sees fit.

We'd Never Be Happy Otherwise. E. P. Conkle. [Dramatists Play Service]   Simply written and easily staged, the play depicts vividly Elijah Lovejoy's struggle on behalf of the democratic principle of freedom of the press.

FULL-LENGTH PLAYS

Unless otherwise indicated, the following plays may be purchased—generally in paper-bound form—from Dramatists Play Service, 14 East 38th Street, New York 16, New York: *Abe Lincoln in Illinois,* Robert Sherwood; *The Admirable Crichton,* J. M. Barrie [French]; *All My Sons,* Arthur Miller; *Barefoot in Athens,* Maxwell Anderson; *The Barretts of Wimpole Street,* Rudolf Bessier; *Billy Budd,* Louis O. Coxe and Robert Chapman; *The Caine Mutiny Court-Martial,* Herman Wouk [French]; *Candida,* Bernard Shaw [Dodd, Mead]; *The Corn Is Green,* Emlyn Williams; *The Crucible,* Arthur Miller; *Dark at the Top of the Stairs,* William Inge; *An Enemy of the People,* Henrik Ibsen [Random House]; *The Glass Menagerie,* Tennessee Williams; *The Hasty Heart,* John Patrick; *The Heiress,* Ruth and Augustus Goetz; *Home of the Brave,* Arthur Laurents; *Inherit the Wind,* Jerome Lawrence and Robert E. Lee; *The Inspector General,* Nikolai Gogol [French]; *Journey's End,* R. C. Sherriff [French]; *The Member of the Wedding,* Carson McCullers; *The Plough and the Stars,* Sean O'Casey [French]; *A Raisin in the Sun,* Lorraine Hansberry [Random House]; *The Silver Cord,* Sidney Howard [French]; *Stage Door,* Edna Ferber and George S. Kaufman; *Strife,* John Galsworthy [French]; *Sunrise at Campobello,* Dore Schary; *The Teahouse of the August Moon,* John Patrick; *Valley Forge,* Maxwell Anderson [French]; *The Winslow Boy,* Terrence Rattigan; *Winterset,* Maxwell Anderson.

Staging the Plays

AT SOME TIME in your experience with the plays in this book you will surely find yourself wishing to produce some of them, perhaps informally before the class, perhaps more formally in an assembly period, or even as a program before an audience who have bought tickets to your performance. Such an adventure in play production will be a valuable and memorable experience for you. This chapter is to give you, briefly, some help in this new experience.

CHOOSING THE PLAY

If, as a class or a club, you want to produce one of the plays in this volume, there is no serious problem of choice involved. But if you wish to organize a club to go on producing other plays, you need to consider how you are to secure the most satisfactory plays for your group to put on.

Perhaps a reading committee can be created. When this group has found some plays it considers suitable, the whole class or club can then make its decision. The plays can be read to the whole group, or summaries made and bits read.

When the group is trying to decide on a play, it should consider the plays from the following four points of view:

First, the play must be considered on the basis of the cast. Do you have enough actors in the group to present this play? Does the cast of the play seem to call for the types of actors you have in the group? Will the parts be too difficult for beginners to attempt? Begin by choosing a play with a small cast and with characters you thoroughly understand.

In the second place, can your group handle the production problems involved in this play? How many sets are there? Does the set present problems you cannot solve with your stage and equipment? Your best choice will be a play with a single scene, a plain set, and few properties. Don't be too ambitious at first.

When you have found several plays which you consider suited to your abilities as a group, you are ready for the third consideration; namely, is the play suited to the audience for whom it will be presented? You will be unwise to ignore the tastes and capacities of any audience you hope to entertain.

The final consideration in choosing a play is its own merit as drama. For a good production choose a good play. Read each suggested play carefully to see whether it has suspense, clear-cut characterization, and convincing situations, and is also good enough in dramatic quality to keep you interested all through the hard work of rehearsals. Even if you wish to give a farce or a melodrama, choose a good one. It is true that a play may be inferior and still be entertaining; but why expend time and energy on mediocre plays when there are so many plays available that combine true literary merit with audience appeal?

Where do you find such plays? There are many guides and many collections. At the end of each unit in this book you will find recommendations for more good plays. Perhaps you would like to try writing some yourselves. If so, turn to page 342 in this book, where you will find a chapter on how to write your own play. It goes without saying that your plays will not be judged by professional standards.

ORGANIZING THE GROUP

Producing a play cannot be a haphazard affair. You must have an adequate organization to carry the project through successfully.

Your first concern should be to secure a director. The director is the master-mind of the whole production and bears the final responsibility for the performance. He is boss. The other members of the group will have their responsibilities, and they should feel free to make suggestions at all times, but the director must be in control. He interprets the play, coaches the actors during rehearsals, and has the final say on all decisions as to properties, costumes, scenery, and lighting. He can make or spoil the play. He must, therefore, be someone capable of leadership, and experienced enough to know what he is doing. Your teacher or your club sponsor will probably direct most of your plays, but it will be wonderful training for members of the group to assume the responsibilities of the director for some of the plays. The experience will be fun, and the young directors will gain greatly from it.

To take charge of various details, the director should have the following assistants: a stage manager, a technical director, and several committees.

With his crew, the stage manager has the responsibility of keeping everything moving smoothly during the actual performance. He and his helpers see to it that the curtain is opened and closed at just the right moment, that the actors are ready for their cues, that someone is ready to prompt the actors whenever necessary, and that all the properties are on hand at the time they are needed.

The technical director is in charge of those who provide the setting and lighting: those with construction, carpentry, artistic skills and with lighting and electrical "know-how." They also see to it that scenes are set up correctly and changed quickly. Instead of being led by a technical director, the people involved in these activities are sometimes headed by a leadership team of stage carpenter, scene designer or artist, and lighting specialist or electrician.

Usually, three committees round out this organization: a properties committee, a costume committee, and a make-up committee. The properties committee assists the director in finding or making the furniture and all other properties (guns, lamps, pictures, mirrors, letters, etc.) that are needed in the performance. When things are borrowed, this committee is responsible for seeing that they are returned to the people who lent them. The costume committee borrows, rents, purchases, or makes whatever clothing is needed. If the costumes are rented or borrowed, it is this committee's responsibility to care for them and return them in good condition.

If the play is to be given for profit, you will need a publicity committee and a finance committee. The former is to handle newspaper stories, posters, room announcements; the latter is to manage the sale of tickets and to pay the bills. The chairman of the finance committee should be practical and hardheaded. He should allow no one to run up bills without due authorization and should keep all expenditures well within the sum received from the sale of tickets, unless the organization is able and willing to take care of a possible deficit. If the chairman of the finance committee does not keep close enough check on the organization, the project may end in financial disaster.

Properties, make-up, lights, publicity, ticket-sales are all major considerations in the success of a play. The committees who work for weeks on these details are the unsung heroes of every successful theatrical production. The actors will get most of the glory, but the committee workers will take satisfaction in a job well done—and perhaps the reward of a place in the cast of one of the later productions.

CASTING THE PLAY

The method of choosing a cast for the plays you want to produce will depend on the purpose of the production. If the aim of the group is to give acting experience to as many as possible, the director puts that objective ahead of his natural desire to give a finished performance. He casts each play as well as he can under the circumstances, but he sees to it that every member of the group gets a fair chance at some good part. The boy or girl who happens to get the best role in the first play and makes a great hit in it must not automatically be cast in the good parts for the rest of the season. Of course, with this sort of procedure the final performances will in many cases be far from perfect, and the director must not be criticized if he fails to achieve a finished production.

But if the aim of the group is to present the best performances of which it is capable, the method of choosing the casts will be quite different. In this case the director should try to select the best possible casts from the people available.

There are several ways in which a director can select his cast. If the group has never given a play before, the usual method of getting a cast is by tryouts. Each applicant for a part is given an opportunity to show his aptitude in the important phases of acting.

First, each person is judged according to the quality and suitability of his voice. Some directors prefer to hear an applicant recite a passage from memory—any prose or poetry selection that he may know by heart, perhaps, or a bit from another play in which he may have had a part. Other directors prefer to hear readings selected from the play which the group is preparing to do. Still others like a combination of both methods. The speaker or reader is rated for the clearness, distinctness, and expressiveness of his voice. Next, the applicant may be asked to present a dramatic episode in pantomime. This gives him a fine opportunity to demonstrate his skill in movement, gesture, and facial expression, and to display his carriage and appearance—his "stage presence." If the play being cast calls for singing roles, then those who aspire to the roles are also tested for their singing voices.

The director, who has in mind what he wants the characters to be like, then matches his ideas to the people as they speak, read, act, or sing. Often the director may ask a committee to help him judge the tryouts; but even then, he himself should have the final say.

Another effective method of choosing a cast is for the director, especially if he is the teacher or sponsor or someone with considerable experience, to hold interviews with the applicants. An experienced director can tell from talking to people and by observing them just what types of parts those people would best portray.

For a class or a club the safest procedure may well be a combination of the tryout and the interview. And the efficient director or casting committee is careful to file away the data resulting from the tryouts and interviews for future castings.

After the group has given several plays, the director knows the capacities and temperaments of the actors. When the group wishes to cast a new play, it is well to let him select the actors on the basis of his previous experience. He knows which actors will develop into the parts and which will not, with which he can work pleasantly and with which he cannot. However, some provision should be made for giving newcomers a fair chance to make their way in the group. Perhaps they should take small parts until the director has had a chance to gauge their work.

REHEARSING THE PLAY

The rehearsals of your play must be serious business. They should be carefully scheduled, fully attended, and well managed. Usually, rehearsing for a performance follows four distinct steps.

The first of these steps is the reading of the play. Depending upon the nature and the length of the play, this step takes from one to several sessions. First, the director wants the cast to get an over-all view of the play. Sometimes jointly with the group, he then clarifies such matters as type of play and "style" and tempo of acting, the theme and other important meanings, and basic interpretation of dialogue. He also straightens out any defects in pronunciation and articulation.

Before the actors take to the stage, the director has hours of very painstaking and highly creative "homework" to do. He cannot rely upon the inspiration of the moment while the actors are on stage to determine such essentials as where furniture is to be placed; where entrances and exits are to be made; how actors are to be placed, grouped, and told to move; and what business and properties are to be used. All of this has to be planned, blocked out, and noted into the prompt book, or, as it is sometimes called, the production book.

The prompt book is the record of and the source book for everything related to the production, from the time the play is selected through the manner in which the actors take their curtain call at the end of the final performance. It has several purposes. It provides the director with a record of his prestaging research, thinking, and planning. In it he records all the steps he has taken in interpreting the play, in blocking out action—in fact, in noting all the details and directions essential to an effective production of the play. During rehearsals, he uses it as a conductor does a musical score: to guide him in directing others. The prompt book, moreover, provides the various crews and committees with the data and directions they need. And, naturally, as its name implies, the prompt book may also be used to prompt.

Since most published plays do not have sufficient space in the margins to include notations, the prompt book may be prepared in one of two ways. If a printed script is used, the director staples or pastes the pages of the script on to the right-hand pages of a large loose leaf notebook; he then uses the left-hand pages of the notebook for his notations, drawings, and diagrams. He needs two copies of the play for this purpose, of course. If the director is going to work from a typewritten or mimeographed script, he should instruct the typist to provide large margins at the top, bottom, and to one side of the pages.[1]

Although the director has prepared himself thoroughly, by means of the prompt book, before rehearsal time, the cast nevertheless should feel free to work with him in the process of getting the best staging of the play of which the group is capable. They may suggest pieces of business and preferences as to oral interpretation, position, grouping, and movement. The director decides which of the suggestions fit in with his own conception of the whole play and, of course, has the final say on every detail. During this cooperative process, which should also include the various crews and committees, the stage manager or director should record all changes in the prompt book.

[1] On pages 209 to 213 of *Play Direction*, by John E. Dietrich (Prentice-Hall, Inc.), you will find a detailed discussion of the prompt book.

1. Door (not essential) leading to other part of house
2. Door leading to outside
3. Closet door
4. Stove (not essential)
5. Chair or rocker for Granny
6. Table
7. Chair for table
8. Ironing board supported on backs of two chairs
9. Chair upon which Orry later sits

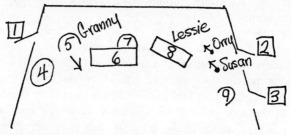

① Lessie back of ironing board, blushing, showing her nervousness
② Granny scrootches up in her shawl
③ Orry slides in u.s. and slightly forward of Susan. Stands bashfully, twisting his cap— eyes on Lessie
④ Lessie turns towards Orry
⑤ Lessie x's to Orry, takes his cap

FIGURE 1. Sample Pages from Prompt Script for *Sparkin'*

GRANNY. Mil*dew!*

①[LESSIE *stands back of the ironing board nervous and blushing.* ②GRANNY *scrootches up in her shawl.* ③ORRY SPARKS *slides in. He is a big, husky fellow. He is bashful and stands with his cap in his hand. His eyes are on* LESSIE. *Otherwise he doesn't know what to do or say.*]

SUSAN. Howdy do, Mister Sparks. Nice evenin' out, ain't et?

ORRY. Howdy do, Missus Hanna. Why, yeh, kinda.

SUSAN. Lessie, here's Mister Sparks.

LESSIE. ④[*Turning and stammering.*] Oh. I didn't know you was here. Howdy do. Let me have your cap.⑤

ORRY. Howdy, Lessie. You arnin' some clo'es?

LESSIE. I'm tryin' to.⑥

GRANNY. What does he want, Susy? ⑦Is somebody sick over to th' Youngseses? I reckon that little Betty-Sall has throwed another-a her cat fits, an' . . .

ORRY. Th' Youngses is all right, fer as I know. I jest . . . ⑧[*He casts his eyes* LESSIE-*ward.*] . . . kinda thought I'd drop in a spell to see you folks. I never been over to see you yet.

SUSAN. I'm right glad you come over, Mister Sparks.

⑥ Lessie turns away shyly, x's to chair at table, puts cap back of it. Then returns to iron, u.s. of board

⑦ Susan x's to Granny

⑧ Orry casts his eyes Lessie-ward

FIGURE 1. Sample Pages from Prompt Script for *Sparkin'*

After the action has been blocked out by the director and mastered by the cast, the third step, the most important and difficult of all, is undertaken. The director now concentrates on the individual actors and works to develop them into the characters the play is trying to present. By this time the members of the cast are strictly required to know their lines by heart. No one is to be permitted to use his script, no matter how uncomfortable or embarrassed the laggards may be. Now comes the crucial point in preparing any play, where Johnnie Medwick and Ellen Wright cease to be themselves and take on, for example, the characters of James Dyke and Josephine Paris in *The Valiant*. Here the attention is on details—gestures, facial expressions, tricks of voice, mannerisms—all the little things that make the audience forget they are in a theater and think they are watching actual events take place before their eyes.

In order to train his actors to speak loudly enough and clearly enough, the director may, during rehearsals, place people in the back rows of the auditorium and in the balconies. If they can't hear clearly what the actors are saying, they may sing out, "I can't hear you!"; or they may ring a bell. Devices of this kind are good for your play and they are good for your players. Those boys and girls who are careless in their speech may be annoyed, it is true, but they will never again speak as though they were encumbered with a mouthful of hot potato.

The last step in rehearsing is to run through the play as a whole. In fact, the cast should have the advantage of at least two or three uninterrupted rehearsals during which the players may learn how to pace themselves and to acquire confidence in their ability to "go it alone." At this stage, attention is centered on the tempo, the continuity, the general effect of the play as a whole. Here the director does not make corrections as he sees mistakes or new possibilities for improvement; instead, he jots down his criticisms and suggestions in a notebook, and he discusses them with the cast at the conclusion of the rehearsals. It is preferable to do the last rehearsal or two in complete costume and make-up, and it is certainly imperative to hold at least one rehearsal with the stage setting and all the stage furniture and properties in use. Sometimes it is a good idea to have a small friendly audience at the dress rehearsal. It helps the actors time their speeches to bridge the excitement and the laughter in the audience.

STAGE MOVEMENT

Of prime consideration in the matter of stage movement is the underlying, fundamental rhythm—or tempo, or pace—of the play. This is determined chiefly by the type of play it is. Comedies and tragedies, being true to life, move more slowly than do farces and melodramas, which are not nearly so true to life and in which the action should be so swift that the audience has no time to reflect upon the incredibility of the events going on before their eyes.

While some plays should move quickly and others deliberately, there should be, within the over-all tempo of any play, variations of pace and emotional intensity. It does not do to keep an audience—or actors, either, for that matter—on edge constantly. If every scene is played at a fast tempo or with an extreme emotional intensity, there is no provision for the important crises and for the grand climax. So the group and their director must decide which scenes to speed up and intensify and which scenes to ease up on.

There are some useful devices which may help the director and his cast to sense the proper tempo for each of the various parts of the play they are working on. Perhaps the best of these is for the director and the group to study the play carefully and work out a plot-suspense chart similar to the one in Figure 2 on page 335. The plot-suspense chart shows clearly the places where the action is to pick up in intensity and speed, and the places where it should slow down or maintain a plateau-like evenness.

A device similar to the plot-suspense chart is to head the left-hand side of a page Build Up To and the right-hand side Come Down On, and then to list those incidents in the play that fall appropriately under one heading or the other. Or, the director may wish to gather the group together and beat out with a pencil the rhythm and tempo of the play. He can begin softly, slowly, and steadily for the expository conversation, step up the tapping for a crisis, come down softly and steadily for an emotional lull, come up sharply at the next crisis, and so on, until at the climax he is tapping away rapidly and sharply, ending with a loud thump and a rapid dying away for the brief falling action.

Another simple scheme is to assign to each incident in the play an emotional intensity value ranging in number from one to ten. And certain directors play for their casts music that interprets for the actors the rhythm of the play.

By the use of such simple devices as those described here, your cast will soon learn where to intensify and where to retard the emotional stress of the play.

How do you intensify the emotional stress of a play? How do you increase the tempo? You may achieve the effect you desire by picking your cues up more quickly. You may, moreover, achieve a greater intensity by the gradual raising of voices, with one voice building on another progressively with each line. You may, in addition, telescope lines, so that by the time one character is finishing his speech, a third or fourth is starting. You ought to know, also, that shorter lines make for a greater intensity. So, if your author does not provide you with short lines when you are "building," you must split some of his lines by injecting an occasional "Yes" or "No" or anything else that is short and appropriate. Sound effects are also very useful in "building" scenes. Repeated noises—such as increasing gun fire or increased tramping of feet off stage or a growing crowd onstage—are especially useful.

"Shall I move before I speak this line, or on it, or after I have spoken it?" is the anguished inquiry of many an amateur actor. The following principle will guide you: If you wish to emphasize the line, then move before you speak the line; if you wish to remove emphasis from the line, then move as you speak it; and if you wish to point up a movement or an action that is to follow, then move after you have spoken.

Remember, too, that a movement toward the audience is a strong one, whereas a movement away from the audience is a weak one.

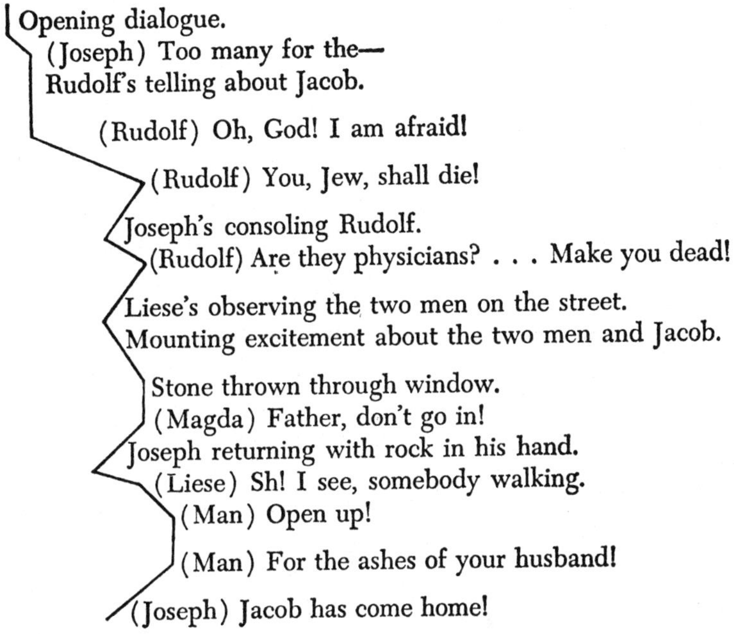

Opening dialogue.
(Joseph) Too many for the—
Rudolf's telling about Jacob.

(Rudolf) Oh, God! I am afraid!

(Rudolf) You, Jew, shall die!

Joseph's consoling Rudolf.
(Rudolf) Are they physicians? . . . Make you dead!

Liese's observing the two men on the street.
Mounting excitement about the two men and Jacob.

Stone thrown through window.
(Magda) Father, don't go in!
Joseph returning with rock in his hand.
(Liese) Sh! I see, somebody walking.

(Man) Open up!

(Man) For the ashes of your husband!

(Joseph) Jacob has come home!

FIGURE 2. Plot-Suspense Chart for *Jacob Comes Home*

STAGE GROUPING

Another feature the director must constantly give his attention to is the stage picture which the actors are making at one time.

The director must see to it that the actors do not crowd together in one corner of the stage, leaving sparse areas elsewhere and smothering the action in the corner of the stage which they do occupy. It is important to keep the stage in balance, to arrange the players so that neither side of the stage seems overweighted. (See Figure 3.) The actors should not, of course, be placed in one straight line parallel to the footlights. They should be dis-

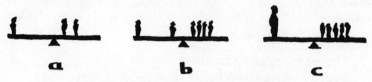

FIGURE 3. Balancing the Stage

tributed about the stage, some standing, some sitting, some mounted on stairs, one seated near a table over here, another standing by a chair over there—in short, with as much variety and pleasing composition as possible.

The actors must also be trained to assume such positions that the attention of the audience is always directed at the player who should dominate the scene. For instance, if, in Figure 4, A is

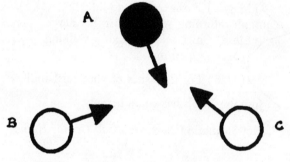

FIGURE 4. Directing Attention of the Audience

the important speaker, B and C should be so placed that A forms the apex of a triangle, and B and C are both half turned from the audience and are looking directly at A, whose face the audience must be able to see clearly.

In directing attention to a figure upstage at the side or downstage at the side, the same principle applies. Though the audience no longer gets a full view of the face of the person who is the center of interest, he still forms the apex of the triangle, and the other characters both look at him. It is natural for the eyes of the audience to follow the direction in which *most* of the eyes on the stage are turned.[1] This method applies to large groups as well as to small ones. In fact, much of stage grouping is done by means of triangular arrangements.

WORKING OUT THE MECHANICS OF PRODUCTION

While the cast is busy at rehearsals, there is much work of a different kind to be done. Some of this work should be planned and perhaps started even before the rehearsals begin.

The Stage. If you present your play in the classroom, where there is no stage at all, or only a raised platform, and certainly no curtain, you may have to modify your play slightly. This is particularly true of three-act plays, where the ends of scenes are marked by the closing of the curtain, and where the changing of the stage set and the removal of "dead" bodies and stage properties is concealed by a drawn curtain. In the one-act plays perhaps the only change you will have to make is to arrange the action in such a way that everyone leaves the stage at the end, to mark the end of the scene. Possibly even some re-writing of lines will be necessary to adapt your play.

You might enjoy an attempt at central staging, or the so-called arena style of actor-audience arrangement. In this type of production the audience is seated on chairs on all four sides of the room, facing the center, where the play is presented. The actors enter and exit at any of the four corners.

The Stage Setting. If your performance calls for careful design of the stage setting, your stage carpenter and his crew of artists will have to prepare the stage design. The design should of course provide for all the doors, windows, fireplaces, etc., called for in the action of the play. It should also provide an eye-effect that will contribute to the desired tone, or atmosphere. For instance, your artist will know that blue and green and violet are soothing colors,

[1] Samuel Selden, *First Principles of Play Direction.* University of North Carolina Press. Figures 3 and 4 on page 336 are reproduced with the permission of Mr. Selden.

while red and yellow and orange are exciting. He will know also which colors harmonize, and which ones fight one another. He knows that long, even lines tend to have a stately, serious effect; that jagged lines and sharp curves are disturbing. Thus his stage design will combine color and line in such a way as to enhance the emotional effect aimed at in the play.

If you are planning a production with scenery, you will use either draperies or painted panels called flats. Perhaps you will have no choice in the matter; the auditorium you are going to use may have only one kind of equipment, which you must adapt to your purpose as best you can. If you do have a choice, and are planning to give a number of plays, you had better choose the painted scenery. Draperies are easy to handle, but after two or three performances they become monotonous to the audience. Painting panels to give the effect you want is not too difficult, and there is an inexpensive scene paint which can be washed off the canvas flats after four or five applications; the flats are then as good as new. The stage carpenter knows, or can easily learn, how to provide the necessary doors, windows, gables, beams, mantels.

Costumes. Long before the day of production, costumes must be planned by the costume committee. If you are giving a classroom performance, the matter of costumes can be handled very simply: a shawl, a raincoat, an heirloom hat, a Sam Browne belt may do the trick. Remember that you are aiming at suggesting the type of character that is being portrayed, rather than giving a reproduction accurate enough to stand inspection in a detective story. Of course, if you are giving an auditorium performance, you will want to be a good deal more attentive to detail.

If your stage design provides a definite color scheme, you should see to it that the costumes harmonize with it. The stage manager or art director should know how to make this adjustment.

THE AUDIENCE

Like a personal letter, or a short story, or a fireside talk, a play is a communication; that is, there is both a giver and a receiver. In a play the playwright, the director, and the cast are the giver; the audience is the receiver. And the audience can have a real part in the success or failure of a play. Often a carefully trained cast has seen its efforts ruined by the bad manners of a few inconsiderate spectators who have felt free to express their personal reactions to the play loudly and emphatically, with no thought of the effect upon the performance. On the other hand, many a production succeeds through a sympathetic response on the part of a co-operative audience.

If your play is to be given in school and your audience is to consist only of your schoolmates, you can make the success of the performance more certain by giving the prospective audience some advance information to put them into the proper mood and attitude. It may be advisable to make announcements in home rooms, explaining the purpose and atmosphere of your play, and indicating the kind of attention you hope to have.

In school or out, you yourself will probably oftener be a part of the audience than a member of the cast. This does not mean that you will be indifferent to the success of the play. Your own experience as an actor—or as a member of the company in another capacity—should make you eager to share responsibility by being a helpful and sympathetic spectator.

FURTHER STUDY OF PLAY PRODUCTION

In this book it is possible to present only a few of the salient points in play production. There are a number of excellent books on the subject, three of the most helpful of which are the following:

Alexander Dean, *Fundamentals of Play Directing*, Holt, Rinehart & Winston, Inc., New York.

This is a sound book which formed the basis of the late Professor Dean's course during the many years in which he trained some of our outstanding directors at the Yale University School of Dramatic Art.

John E. Dieterich, *Play Direction*, Prentice-Hall, Inc.

A very thorough, yet concise, treatment of the principles of play direction by the Associate Theater Director at the University of Wisconsin.

John Gassner, *Producing the Play*, Holt, Rinehart & Winston, Inc., New York.

Several eminent and articulate directors, technical directors, producers, and teachers of acting have contributed admirable chapters to this comprehensive treatment. *The New Scene Technician's Handbook*, by Philip Barber, former Technical Director of the Yale University Theater, is part of the volume.

FOR DISCUSSION

1. What are the four considerations that should guide you in selecting a play for a public performance? Discuss each consideration briefly.

2. In this chapter it is said of the director, "He is the boss." Does that mean that he is to consider the actors as so many marionettes for him to manipulate? What is your idea of the kind of "boss" the director should be?

3. Before the actors take to the stage, there is a reading of the play. What are some of the things the director hopes to accomplish in the reading?

4. In planning the production of the play and in getting ready for rehearsals, the director should prepare a prompt book. What is a prompt book? How is it prepared? What is put into it? How is it used?

5. Actors should be trained to arrange themselves so that the attention of the audience is always directed at the player who should dominate the scene. How should actors be arranged to direct atten-

tion to (a) a figure upstage center? (b) a figure upstage and to the side? (c) a figure downstage and to the side? With Figure 4 on page 336 serving as a model, draw a diagram for each of the three explanations.

6. How is the plot-suspense chart used?

7. What can be done to prepare an audience for an intelligent and appreciative reception of a play? As a member of the audience, in what responsibility to the company presenting the play should you share?

Writing Your Own Play

IT HAS BEEN SAID in jest that almost everybody these days has a play up his sleeve. Like many another jest, this exaggeration has an element of truth in it, for in almost every group there are some who like to write plays—or who would like to write them, if only they knew how. Perhaps you are one of these —perhaps you have been inspired by your work with this book to attempt to create a play of your own, no matter on how modest a scale. The effort should yield both profit and pleasure.

Much of the profit will come from a better understanding of plays. It is with a play as with a baseball game. If you learn at least a few of the rules and fundamentals of baseball, you can enjoy watching a game. If, moreover, you have played the game yourself, you can watch a game with still greater enjoyment; for now you see just about all that's going on, including many of the clever moves and strategic inside plays that other people miss completely. Just so, a knowledge of a few of the principles of playwriting enables you to experience satisfaction in reading, or seeing, or staging plays; but the greatest understanding and appreciation will come to you only when you have tried your own hand at playwriting.

Much of the pleasure will come from fulfilling the urge to create. There is a deep satisfaction in doing any original piece of work—the knitting of a sweater, the building of a model airplane, or the writing of a story or play. It is true that it may mean hard work—sometimes harder work than you've ever done before. But when you become engrossed in your creative effort, you do not begrudge the time or the work which goes into it. There is something about it that is comforting and absorbing and even ennobling. The late Frederick H. Koch, Director of the Carolina Playmakers, believed that the Biblical saying that God created man in his own image means that God gave us some of His own creativeness, and thus in a way made us co-creators with Him. If this is true, we ought surely to cherish and to cultivate the creative spark within us.

In writing a play there is much creative joy—in making the people of your imagination come to life, in breathing movement and thought into them, in shaping their personalities, and in determining their earthly fortunes. Naturally you do not expect to set the dramatic world on fire with your very first effort; but if you write something that is as good as you can make it and that satisfies your friends and yourself, you have reward enough.

GETTING IDEAS

"Where do I get ideas for my play? How do I go about starting it?" you ask.

Writing out of Personal Experience. The first step is to decide upon a subject. In general it is safe to say that your best work will come out of a subject in which you are vitally interested. You are likely to be most interested in *people and things you know and understand best.* Sing your own song: write out of your personal knowledge and experience.

Very likely you will be tempted to write a murder mystery, with seven corpses falling out of seven closets, and with the romantic detective saving the beautiful heroine from the foul clutches of the fiendish murderer. Your mystery may thrill your audience, and you may get a lot of laughs (many of them, unfortunately, at your expense). But before you succumb to this temptation, see what you can do with material that is drawn from your everyday life. Your first impulse may be to set your play in faraway China or India. Restrain that impulse, too; almost certainly you can write a better play about people and places that you really know.

Paul Green, who says that so far as he knows "the only requirement for a writer is to write about what he knows and has made his own," concerns himself for the most part with what he has seen and experienced in his native state of North Carolina. Eugene O'Neill based a number of his plays on his experiences as a sailor. And the authors of *Three's a Crowd* drew their inspiration from the boys and girls with whom they worked at school and in their little backyard theater. You cannot do better than follow their example. "Every day, in homes and offices, on street corners, and in hospitals, stores, and schools . . . wherever a human soul reveals itself at a crucial moment, there is drama ready to be born. You yourself, in your home and among your friends and associates, are constantly taking part in embryonic dramas or watching them in the lives of others." [1] Your own experience is your best material; use it.

Adapting Stories. "But what if my personal experience does not yield the material I need?" you ask. You are then obliged, unfortunately, to turn to other sources, the simplest of which, perhaps, is the dramatization of a story which you know well and love. In the vast field of narrative literature are many plays not yet written—in short stories, incidents from novels, narrative poems, Bible stories, ballads, myths, legends, tales of all kinds.

Stephen Vincent Benét's dramatization of his own short story *The Devil and Daniel Webster* is an outstanding one-act adaptation. *Short Plays from Great Stories,*[2] by Hartley and Power, is a collection of such adaptations. Among plays made from longer works of fiction are such fine dramas as Zona Gale's Pulitzer Prize play, *Miss Lulu Bett,* converted by the author from her novel of the same title and *Pride and Prejudice,* dramatized by Helen Jerome from Jane Austen's early nineteenth-century classic.

Before making your own dramatization of a story, you would do well to study the methods employed in some particularly successful adaptation. First read the story in its original form; then study the dramatic version in order to see how the dramatist met the technical problems of transferring the story to the stage. Some of these problems are suggested in the following questions: Of the many scenes in the story, which did the playwright choose for the setting of his one-act play? What parts of the action did he de-

---

[1] Katherine Anne Ommanney, *The Stage and the School.* Harper Brothers.
[2] Published by the Macmillan Company, New York.

cide to portray on the stage, and what parts omit? How did he expand the conversational passages of the story into the dialogue of his play? Did he succeed in retaining the spirit and the style of the original work? Observing how a master playwright solves these problems may help you to solve them for yourself.

Remember, however, that unless you are thoroughly acquainted with the characters and the places you are using you can never make them seem convincing to others. Many stories suitable for dramatization deal with matters beyond the range of your experience. When you undertake to write about people and places that are unfamiliar to you, reading and research must take the place of first-hand knowledge. If you are really in earnest, you will make yourself an authority on what you are writing about.

Looking for Other Sources. If your desire to write plays is strong, you will keep a constant lookout for ideas in every direction. Your study and reading of history and biography will reveal many interesting characters and incidents which may be converted into plays. Frequently your newspaper contains accounts of happenings more dramatic than fiction could ever be. In your study of such subjects as science, social studies, health, safety, and current events you will find material for many a play. Special occasions—Lincoln's Birthday, Veteran's Day, Christmas—may provide both inspiration and subject matter for simple dramatization.

THE SCENARIO

In starting your play, it is best to begin with a scenario—that is, a plan or outline. You wouldn't think of trying to build a house without a blueprint. Why, then, try to write a play in the spirit of "I'm on my way, but I don't know where I'm going"?

The scenario is a fairly complete synopsis of the play, in which everything that is to happen is outlined, and the causes and the effects of the happenings are made clear. It contains very little or no dialogue, but is expressed almost entirely in terms of action.

Before developing the scenario of your own play, you must make a number of decisions. You must decide what your play is to be about, and whether it is to be primarily a story play, a character study, or a play of ideas. If it is a character study, you must know exactly what traits of your principal character you wish to emphasize; if your play is designed to present a theme, you must know exactly what that theme is.

Above all, you must have a clear idea of the action. Unlike the long play, in which the action is frequently complicated, the one-act play should have a story plan which is simple and direct. The plays in this volume take from about fifteen to forty minutes to perform or to read, yet the story of each play may be told briefly in a few sentences. Indeed, it is generally true that when the action and the theme of a one-act play cannot be stated briefly and clearly the play is confused in the writer's own mind.

The action of most plays involves a conflict between two opposing persons or forces. The hero has some object or goal, and the action consists of his struggle against obstacles to achieve this goal, a struggle ending in failure or success. Such a conflict constitutes a plot. Although a few successful plays have been written without plot, our advice to you is to follow the example set by most playwrights, and build your story plan about some kind of struggle. If you are writing a comedy, the struggle should end in the success of the protagonist; if you plan a tragedy, the end will be defeat.

To begin your scenario write out a description of the setting in which the story is to develop.

Next, list and describe your characters. As you write your characterizations, you must decide whether the persons of your play remain the same sort of people throughout the action, or whether they will be changed by the influence of events.[1] If they change, you have the very difficult task of revealing the change; and it is not enough merely to have the character assert that he is changed. Unless your plot demands it, you had better not try to portray developing characters. You must also decide whether your characters are types or individualized.[2] To show individual-

---

[1] For a definition of *static* and *developing* characters see page 31.
[2] See page 77.

ized characters distinctly demands a mature writing skill; even experienced writers find it hard to do in the short space of a one-act play. Type characters may be identified by some characteristic gesture or movement, or some oft-repeated remark.

Finally, write a summary of the action, scene by scene. If in the scenario you lay out the action of the play scene by scene, you you can later write your play one scene at a time. Playwriting no longer seems so difficult, once you realize this simple but important truth.

In a scenario the word *scene* has a special meaning: a scene is thought of as beginning or ending with the entrance or exit of a character or of a group of characters, and not with the rise or fall of the curtain. Thus, *Three's a Crowd* may be analyzed into four scenes: (1) the exposition, involving Eddie, Madeline, and Ellen; (2) the rising action, beginning with the appearance of Elmer, and climbing steadily to the climax; (3) the falling action—starting when Madeline and Elmer ride away together, leaving Ellen and Eddie alone, free to reminisce and to console each other; (4) the final scene, which gets under way with the appearance of Eddie's father, and brings the play to a satisfactory conclusion.

In planning the action of your play in your scenario, you will find the following hints helpful: Limit yourself to a one-act play. Develop the exposition in the beginning; otherwise you will clutter up your play with explanations which should have been made earlier. (You can't afford to appear to be saying throughout the play, "Oh, I forgot to tell you this or that about so and so.") Keep the actors, director, and scene designer constantly in mind; don't ask them to do the impossible. Avoid going off on false leads; make every detail count. Don't have important scenes take place off stage. Do not leave out a scene you have led the audience to expect; your audience will feel cheated if you do. For instance, one of your principal characters, a Mr. Smith, says of the hero, "When I find that Mr. Jones, I'll make him pay!" Your audience is now looking forward to seeing the meeting of Jones and Smith; don't disappoint them.

Once the scenario is clearly established, you are ready to begin the actual writing of the dialogue of your play. As you proceed, you may depart from your outline and change details if it seems advisable, but you will at least be aware of the general direction in which you are headed.

DIALOGUE AND CHARACTERIZATION

George Pierce Baker, who was very successful as a teacher of playwrights, once said that the chief purpose of dialogue "is to convey necessary information clearly." Every speech, and indeed every word you write, should contribute toward the portrayal of character or toward the development of the plot or the theme.

In writing your dialogue, nothing will offer so great a challenge to you as the problem of characterization. It is certainly true that a play lives in its characters. Your problem is to present these characters clearly and convincingly and with economy of time. And you cannot step forward and describe them yourself; you must reveal your characters by what they say or do, or by what the other people on the stage say about them. Skillful characterization is the most difficult task in playwriting.

As you write your play, you must develop an intimate knowledge of the people you are creating. They cannot be strangers to you. If you are to portray them truthfully, you must, as it were, live with them, think with them, and experience with them. When they start acting independently, without your guidance, you may be sure they have come alive in your imagination.

Try to make the dialogue natural. Listen carefully to the speech and the idiom of as many different kinds of people as you can. Look for effective snatches of dialogue. Pick up everyday expressions, slang, and colloquialisms. Practice constantly the writing of effective dramatic speech. Try to become so good at characterization through dialogue that the speech of one of your characters could not possibly come from the lips of another.

Don't try to write too much of the dialogue at one time. Refer to your scenario, pick out a scene, or even a portion of a scene, that seems to come to life for you, and write that. Then later, you may decide to write another scene, or a portion of a scene. Build your play in this manner, bit by bit. Then put it all together and smooth it out, checking for contradictions and inconsistencies in the action, and seeing to it that all parts hang together to emphasize the main idea of the play.

CO-OPERATIVE PLAYMAKING

Playwriting is best fostered in a communal spirit. From that moment when you get the first idea for your play, through the planning of the outline, and all through the writing of the play, you will do well to consult with your teacher and your classmates. You will profit greatly at all stages of your playwriting from their suggestions and criticism. And if in the course of your discussions with the other members of your group it becomes apparent that your play needs to be revised, do not hesitate to revise it. Plays are not written; they are re-written.

With some groups playwriting is entirely a co-operative undertaking and everyone contributes to the writing of each play. Sometimes the stage action and the dialogue are developed by the whole group working as a single unit. In other instances the work is divided among committees, the best points being finally combined into one script.

Some groups even evolve their plays spontaneously—on the stage. Together they first work out a story plan, and discuss its broad outlines; then they analyze, describe, and select the characters. The actors take their places and act out the scene in accordance with the preceding discussion, making up their dialogue as they go along, and doing things which they think natural for the characters to do under the circumstances. When plays are created in this fashion every actor is a playwright.

And if your play is good enough to merit production, your class or club ought to see to it that it is staged. A play doesn't live until it gets some kind of performance; the very lifeblood of a play is its production. The staging of your own plays will provide an exciting climax to the group's work in the drama, and will constitute a pleasurable event not only for the playmakers but for the entire school. It is even more fun when the event is conducted in the form of a tournament.

FOR DISCUSSION

1. How will the knowledge of a few of the principles of playwriting help the play-reader and the playgoer? What satisfactions are there for those who try their own hand at playwriting?

2. List the various sources from which one may get ideas for plays. Check those which you think are best. Why do you prefer those sources?

3. How would you go about studying the methods of playwrights who have been successful in dramatizing other forms of literature? What technical problems would you note especially?

4. What dramatizations of stories or of other narrative forms of literature have you seen or heard recently in the movies, on the TV screen, the radio, or on the stage? What did you think of the adaptations? What were some of the technical problems met by the dramatists in making their adaptations? How well did they solve the problems?

5. Concerning the scenario, explain briefly: (*a*) What is a scenario? (*b*) Why is it advisable to use one? (*c*) What are some of the things one must decide upon in developing a scenario? (*d*) What is one way of writing a scenario?

6. Why is it best to build your play about some kind of struggle? What kinds of conflict may there be in plays? (See also p. 98, number 1.)

7. What is the purpose of dialogue? What steps should you take to make the dialogue you write seem natural?

8. What is meant by characterization? Why does it offer so great a challenge?

Those Who Wrote the Plays in This Book

SARA SLOANE AND E. CLAYTON MC CARTY

When Mr. E. Clayton McCarty was a teacher of dramatics and creative writing in the school system of Pasadena, California, he and his wife spent their free time running a backyard garden theater, where anyone from six to sixty might act. In this little theater they tried out plays which they themselves wrote and also those which their friends wrote. It was there that *Three's a Crowd* was first presented.

The daughter of a Presbyterian minister, Sara Sloane McCarty was born in Storm Lake, Iowa, in 1905. At the age of eight she had already sold her first work to a children's page. Later she gained valuable training by contributing to her high school and college publications. She was graduated from the University of California.

E. Clayton McCarty was born in Louisville, Kentucky, in 1901. He was educated at the University of Colorado, and his experience on the staff of the University's humor magazine, *The Colorado Dodo*, undoubtedly influenced his choice of a career.

The McCartys were married in 1927. They (with their three daughters) now live in California, Pennsylvania, where Mr. McCarty is a member of the English Department at the California State Teachers College.

JOSEFINA NIGGLI

The winner of numerous awards, fellowships, and other honors, Josefina Niggli is achieving increasing prominence as a writer of folk literature. Unusually versatile and creative, she has written such varied forms as plays, novels, poems, textbooks, and scripts for television, motion pictures, and radio. She is also a teacher, stage director, and photographer. Miss Niggli now teaches and directs the Little Theater at Western Carolina College, Cullowee, North Carolina.

Born in Monterrey, Nuevo León, Mexico, Josefina Niggli received part of her education in Mexico City and San Antonio, Texas. She then studied at the University of North Carolina, from which she received the degree of M.A. in Drama. There she was a member of the famous Carolina Playmakers and a student in the playwriting class of the late Professor Frederick H. Koch, who had made the University "on the hill" the center of our folk play movement. "Proff" Koch, as he was affectionately known throughout the country, encouraged her to create folk literature. Miss Niggli received her training as a director at the famous Old Vic School in England. Later she herself taught playwriting and other forms of theater arts at the University of North Carolina and elsewhere in the United States and Great Britain.

Northern Mexico is the setting of much of Miss Niggli's writing. Some of her folk plays were published in a collection called *Mexican Folk Plays*. Her novels are *Mexican Village* and *Step Down, Elder Brother;* her textbooks include *Pointers on Playwriting* and *Pointers on Radio Writing*.

ANTON CHEKHOV

Anton Chekhov (1860–1904) is regarded as Russia's foremost dramatist and as one of the world's supreme short story writers. He has greatly influenced the technique of many writers in Europe and in America.

Chekhov, a native of South Russia, was of humble origin. His grandfather and father were serfs, and it was only nineteen years before the birth of Anton that the grandfather bought his own freedom and that of the family for 3,500 rubles. Almost as soon as he learned to walk, Anton began to work in his father's grocery. By listening to the idlers in the store, Anton gathered many humorous stories, which he would later relate to his laughing schoolmates. Despite his ready wit and unusual skill at story-telling, the boy who was to become one of the acknowledged masters of modern literature received his lowest marks in composition, in which he never earned anything higher than a C (*troika* in Russian).

Nevertheless, Anton graduated from high school with high honors and enrolled at the University of Moscow as a student of medicine. During his five years as a medical student he tossed off hundreds of short stories and sketches of Russian life for newspapers and magazines, and even after he began to practice medicine, literature continued to be a great love of his. It was not long before the whole world saw in him a superb teller of whimsical and humorous tales. Although he was essentially a short-story writer, his fame was established mainly by his plays. Of his one-acters, *The Boor* and *The Marriage Proposal* are the most popular. They are simple, merry farces, readily understood and enjoyed by people of all lands, and by young and old alike. His masterpieces, however, are four full-length plays which the famous Moscow Art Theater produced: *The Cherry Orchard, The Sea Gull, The Three Sisters,* and *Uncle Vanya.*

RACHEL FIELD (MRS. ARTHUR S. PEDERSON)

Rachel Field (1894–1942) won distinction as a novelist, poet, playwright, and writer of children's books. She was born in New York City. When she was a year old, her father, who was a doctor, died, and the family moved to Stockbridge, Massachusetts. In this beautiful town Rachel received her elementary education in a little country school. Of her school days—first at Stockbridge and then at Springfield, Massachusetts—she later said that she had been an inept pupil, particularly "dumb" in mathematics and Latin. She used to picture herself as an old lady in spectacles and gray hair still going to school because she couldn't pass the tests that would permit her to graduate from high school. Graduate she did, however, the teachers passing her in sheer desperation. But the truth of the matter is that Rachel was more interested in the creative activities of writing, acting, and drawing than in her regular class work.

Later she enrolled as a special student at Radcliffe College, where she studied only the subject she liked best, English. She also studied playwriting at Harvard in George Pierce Baker's "English 47," the well-known playwriting course. Needless to say, she enjoyed her college studies immensely. While she was a student in Professor Baker's class, she wrote her famous one-act fantasy, *Three Pills in a Bottle,* which ranks with *The Fifteenth Candle* and *The Patchwork Quilt* as the most popular of her dramatic writings. Indeed, so well-liked are these three little plays that they are performed with great frequency, year in and year out, by groups all over the country.

It is not as a dramatist, however, that Rachel Field is primarily known; she is best known as a novelist and as a writer of children's books. As a novelist, she attracted an unusually wide reading public. Three of her novels—*Time out of Mind, All This, and Heaven Too,* and *And Now Tomorrow*—won unstinted praise from the literary critics and for many months appeared on the best-seller lists. Of her many excellent books of stories and verse for children, *Hitty: Her First Hundred Years,* the story of a wooden doll, is the best. For this book, which authorities on literature for young people consider the only true juvenile classic written since the First World War, she was awarded the Newberry Medal for the year 1929, thus becoming the first woman to win that honor.

ROBERT FINCH

Robert Finch is the folk-dramatist of the American Northwest. It was he who made the first earnest effort to portray that region in narrative literature. Although he was born in Iowa, he spent his boyhood and youth in Montana. In that state and in that part of our nation were centered his most vivid memories.

After graduating from the University of Montana, he came east to study and to work in the theater. While holding a Rockefeller fellowship in playwriting at the University of North Carolina, he came under the influence of Paul Green, America's outstanding folk-dramatist, and of that master inspirer of folk playwrights, Professor Frederick H. Koch. It is therefore not surprising that Robert Finch turned to memories of the country and people of his youth as subjects for his own writing. Of the fifteen plays in his first published collection, *Plays of the American West,* thirteen are set in Montana; the other two are placed in Utah and Nevada. As Samuel Selden points out in the foreword to that book, "Mr. Finch has painted a lively gallery of portraits: ranch owners, cowpunchers, prospectors, road agents, proprietors of cafes and barrooms, carnival entertainers, and their women. . . . the dramas in this book are folk plays; they deal with the lives of common men and women—mostly close-to-the-soil people—affected by strong but simple emotions."

In addition to short plays, Robert Finch wrote several full-length ones. Because he was a skilled dramatist and understood and liked the people about whom he wrote, Mr. Finch's plays make good reading and interesting staging. Several of them have achieved distinction, including television, motion picture, and Broadway production and inclusion in many anthologies. *Goodbye to the Lazy K,* for example, was one of the earliest plays to be performed on television. *The Desert Shall Rejoice,* filmed as *Star in the Night,* won the Motion Picture Academy Award for the best two-reel picture of 1945. It is interesting to note that Mr. Finch's plays have enjoyed a vogue in England, where a collection of his plays is read in secondary schools.

In 1959, while he was in the prime of life, Robert Finch died suddenly of a heart attack. Our theater and literature lost a writer of considerable talent and achievement.

STEPHEN VINCENT BENÉT

Stephen Vincent Benét, one of the leading American poets of the twentieth century, also excelled in the writing of prose fiction, plays, and critical prose. His most important work is *John Brown's Body,* a stirring 100,000 word poem that tells a swiftly moving story of the Civil War in all its aspects. For this he was awarded the Pulitzer Prize for Poetry in 1928.

Stephen Vincent Benét was born in South Bethlehem, Pennsylvania, on July 22, 1898. He was a descendant of army men—his father, grandfather, and great-grandfather all having been army officers. Since his father, Colonel James Walker Benét, went wherever duty called, the family lived during Stephen's youth in New York, California, and Georgia. Stephen thus got to know much about our country and its history. He started writing when he was only seven years old, his desire to be an author being stimulated by the fact that his older brother and sister, William and Laura, were both noted poets and critics. He was educated at Yale, graduating with the class of 1919. While still a college freshman he published his first book of verse; before he left college he had written a second book of poems. Critics saw in Stephen Vincent Benét a youth of great literary promise. Time has proved them right in their judgment, for when he died of a heart attack on March 13, 1943, at the age of forty-four, he was considered one of America's most brilliant men of letters. His death was undoubtedly hastened by his vigorous efforts to serve his country in the Second World War. Toward this end he directed all his time and energy, saying that he wished to do his share "to maintain the great shape of democracy, the great, daring and limitless dream of man's free mind."

It is in his short stories and ballads that Benét's quality of being "all embracingly American" is most evident. He deals with all the country and with all the people that make up our land. Whether they are colored or white, the descendants of our earliest families or immigrants or the children of immigrants, he has equal respect and affection for them; and he wants them to take equal pride in being Americans. As he tells a story—for example, that of an Irish immigrant subway construction worker in the early part of our century in *O'Halloran's Luck*, or of a Jewish peddler in the early history of our country in *Jacob and the Indians*, or of a Negro slave yearning for freedom in the pre-Civil War South in *Freedom's a Hard-Bought Thing*—he vividly re-creates the appropriate times, atmosphere, and characters. His contributions to our folk lore—in such stories as *The Devil and Daniel Webster*, *Johnny Pye and the Fool Killer*, and *A Tooth for Paul Revere*—are noted for their delightful mixture of fantasy, humor, and dramatic incidents. They have been judged true classics, comparable to Washington Irving's *Rip Van Winkle* and *The Legend of Sleepy Hollow*.

JAMES TRUEX

A Phi Beta Kappa and a graduate of Haverford College, James Truex acted on the New York stage from 1935 to 1942. Since his father is the noted actor Ernest Truex, it was not surprising that James should have been interested in the theater. During World War II he enlisted in the Navy, studied Japanese, and spent two years as a translator and interpreter. After the war, Mr. Truex became more interested in writing than in acting.

One of his early writing ventures was to be co-author of a television series known as *The Truex Family*, which featured eight members of the Truex acting family, including James Truex's two-year-old daughter Penelope and his father Ernest. In the early 1950's Mr. Truex was one of the leading historical dramatists for NBC's Hallmark Hall of Fame. He also wrote shows of varying length for such programs as the Lux Video Theater, the Kate Smith Show, and the Campbell Sound Stage. "These were the good years of live television drama, when there existed in the East a will to experiment and to develop new talent," he recalls. "Since that time most television writers have moved to other media or packed their six-shooters along with their scruples and settled in California's badlands."

Mr. Truex's chief interest at the present time is in public relations work. He turned to this career in 1955, when he became a publicity aide to Averell Harriman, who was then Governor of New York. In 1960 he had what is a unique opportunity for a public relations man, the chance to write and deliver his own speeches. He did so while he was a candidate for Congress in New York's 28th Congressional District. "I ran strongly—and lost," he says. Mr. Truex hopes that some day circumstances will permit him to resume his interrupted television career.

WILLIAM INGE

When William Inge's first success, *Come Back, Little Sheba,* was produced in 1950, he was acclaimed by drama critics as "Broadway's most promising new playwright." Since his next three plays—*Picnic,* for which he was awarded both the Pulitzer Prize and the New York Drama Critics' Circle Award; *Bus Stop;* and *Dark at the Top of the Stairs*—were also resounding artistic and financial successes, he established himself firmly as one of the most important American dramatists of the mid-century era.

Inge was born in Independence, Kansas, the youngest of five children, none of whom shared his strong interest in the theater. At the age of seven, he began to recite poems and monologues publicly; and early in his school career he started to act in school plays. He graduated from the University of Kansas, with the B.A. degree in speech and dramatics. For five years Inge taught English, speech, and dramatics—in a high school in Columbus, Kansas; at Stephens College in Columbia, Missouri; and at Washington University in St. Louis. Growing restless with teaching, he left that profession in 1943 to become drama, music, and movie critic for the St. Louis *Star-Times.*

In his formative years, it had never occurred to Inge to attempt to write plays. During his three years as a critic in St. Louis, however, he began to wonder whether he could write better plays than some of those he was assigned to review. His final motivation to turn to playwriting came in December 1944. It was then that he traveled to Chicago to see Tennessee Williams's *The Glass Menagerie*, which Inge found so beautiful and deeply moving that he reproached himself for having led what he felt had been an unproductive life.

William Inge is not interested in writing plays that primarily tell a story. He is much more interested in people, of whom he has a sympathetic awareness and understanding, and in observing life faithfully and honestly. In addition, Inge has a gift for writing beautifully accurate dialogue. "I have been most concerned with dramatizing something of the dynamism I myself find in human motivation and behavior," he wrote. "I strive to keep the stage bubbling with a restless kind of action that seeks first one outlet and then another before resolving itself." There is so much truth and compassionate understanding in Inge's character portrayal, moreover, that at times one has the feeling that the people he is reading about or viewing are laying bare their hearts for him.

WILLIAM KOZLENKO

William Kozlenko has been acclaimed by critics as the leading figure in the short play movement in the United States. He was the original editor of the notable *One Act Play Magazine*, and he has also been the author and editor of more than a dozen play and story anthologies. With Ernest Hemingway, he was the co-editor of the best-seller *Men at War*.

Mr. Kozlenko has written a number of short plays which have been widely produced both in America and abroad and published in several "Best One Act Play" anthologies. Among the best known of his short plays are *This Earth Is Ours, The Devil Is a Good Man,* and *One of These Days*. His full-length play *A World to Live In* was recently produced in Europe. Mr. Kozlenko has also written critical articles on music, the theater, and literature; short stories; and for motion pictures and television.

This marks the first publication of *Jacob Comes Home* in an anthology. Probably the best short play to come out of the World War Two era, it has been a consistent contest winner over the years in city, state, and regional drama tournaments.

ROBERT MIDDLEMASS

Two men are credited with the authorship of *The Valiant,* but only one of them, Robert Middlemass, wrote the play. The story of how Holworthy Hall came to be credited with collaboration in the writing of *The Valiant* is interesting. "Holworthy Hall" is the name of a dormitory at Harvard, a name which the late Harold Everett Porter took as his pen name when he became a professional writer. Porter had contracted with a magazine to produce six articles or stories within a specified time. Unable to meet the deadline on one occasion, he turned for assistance to his old Harvard classmate and chum, Robert Middlemass, who generously offered to let him use *The Valiant*. It was agreed that Porter's pen name should appear along with the name of Robert Middlemass as co-author.

Mr. Middlemass has been actively connected with the theater as actor, director, and dramatist since his graduation from Harvard in 1909. He has never composed anything else comparable to *The Valiant*. But to have written what is probably the most popular one-act play in America is achievement enough. His career as an actor includes appearances in fifteen Broadway successes.

E. P. CONKLE

Ellsworth Prouty Conkle has been growing steadily in stature as a writer and is now recognized as one of our outstanding folk-dramatists. He first attracted the attention of Broadway in 1936 with *200 Were Chosen*, an intensely gripping and human account of the pioneer families who were sent out of our dust bowl area into Alaska in the early 1930's. Another full-length play to win success was his *Prologue to Glory*, perhaps the best drama ever written about the youthful period in the life of Abraham Lincoln. For a decade before Broadway had seen his full-length plays, E. P. Conkle's name was well known to the Little Theater public for his splendid one-act folk plays of rural life in the Midwest—notably *Crick Bottom Plays* and *Loolie and Other Plays*.

Doctor Conkle was born in Peru, Nebraska, in 1899. Having descended from pioneer stock, he naturally has made frequent use in his plays of the theme of the unconquerable American pioneer spirit. He spent his boyhood on a farm—planting, plowing, harvesting; his knowledge of rural life and characters was acquired, therefore, at first hand.

Now he spends most of his time as a teacher of speech and dramatics to college students. Playwriting is a hobby with him, as it is with Paul Green; and he says, "I've earned my life insurance, my daily bread, and my wife's shoes teaching school." Professor Conkle has taught at the state universities of North Dakota, Delaware, Iowa, and Texas. He, too, was a student in the playwriting class of George Pierce Baker, and he has the further distinction of having been the first to earn a doctorate in "creative dramatic literature." This degree was granted by the University of Iowa, the writing of the play *200 Were Chosen* serving as a major requirement.

KENNETH SAWYER GOODMAN

Kenneth Sawyer Goodman died in 1918 while serving his country as a lieutenant in the United States Navy. Because he had already established himself as an outstanding writer in the one-act play form and as a leader in the civic theater, his untimely death was widely mourned.

He was born in Chicago in 1883 and educated at Princeton University. As an undergraduate, he wrote a good deal of poetry and won the Poetry Prize in 1904.

Imbued with the desire to contribute towards the development in Chicago of a theater of beauty, poetry, and integrity, Kenneth Goodman became associated, in 1910, with the Chicago Stage Society. Working with such highly competent associates as Walter Hampden, Whitford Kane, and Thomas Wood Stevens, he proved himself to be a dedicated and talented playwright, producer, director, and actor. His work with the Chicago Stage Society did much to inspire the growth of the civic theater and Little Theater movements throughout the country.

Usually written for a specific occasion or purpose and for immediate production, his short plays quickly won popularity with Little Theaters and with school and college dramatic groups both in America and England. Characterized by a variety of subject matter and mood, sound dramatic craftsmanship, and a fine command of language, his plays have been published in three volumes: *Quick Curtains, More Quick Curtains,* and *The Wonder Hat and Other Plays.* In addition to *Back of the Yards,* the religious fantasy *Dust of the Road,* and the humorous fantasy *The Wonder Hat*—written in collaboration with Ben Hecht—are among the most appealing of Kenneth Sawyer Goodman's plays.

In 1925 the Chicago Art Institute dedicated its theater, one of the most complete in the world, to his memory. To the Kenneth Sawyer Goodman Memorial Theater was added, in recent years, the School of Drama—a specialized degree-granting institution for the training of professional actors, directors, designers, and technicians. It has become one of the foremost schools of its kind in the country.

PERCIVAL WILDE

Percival Wilde is prominent as a playwright, as a critic, and as a teacher of playwrights. He early dedicated himself to the writing of one-act plays. His wisdom in so doing is demonstrated by the fact that he has had more plays produced in American Little Theaters than any other author. He has written more than one hundred plays —almost all of them short ones—which have been performed in cities and towns throughout the United States and its possessions. His popularity extends to many foreign lands as well, his dramas having been translated into many languages and acted on the stages and broadcast over the radios of every continent. His book *The Craftsmanship of the One-Act Play* is used as a text in many colleges and universities.

Percival Wilde entered Columbia University in 1903 after studying for three years at Horace Mann High School. In his college career he proved himself unusually brilliant and versatile: he took only three years to earn his B.S. degree; he was a member of the university orchestra, the chess team, and the water polo team; and he won one of the intercollegiate swimming championships. Following his graduation from Columbia he spent four years in the banking business. He then decided to devote himself to writing as a profession. Upon the publication of his first short story, in 1912, he received so many requests for dramatic rights that he decided to do his own playwriting. In the years since—with the exception of the years of the First World War, during which Mr. Wilde served with the rank of ensign in the United States Navy—he has been busy writing, producing many one-act plays and a large number of novels and short stories.

SUSAN GLASPELL

A writer of short stories, a novelist, and a Pulitzer Prize-winning dramatist, Susan Glaspell spent her early life in the Middle West. Although she later lived for twenty-five years in New England, spent many of her winters in New York City, and traveled extensively in other countries, most of her stories, novels, and plays have their roots in the Middle West. "I have never lost the feeling that this is my part of the country," she explained.

Susan Glaspell was educated in the public schools of Davenport, in her native state of Iowa, and later at Drake University in Des Moines. "I cannot remember the time when I did not want to write, and I began my creative efforts while still in grammar school," she recalled. While she was in college, she was sending stories to the magazines, and she helped pay for her college education by doing some work for the Des Moines newspapers.

The day after her graduation she joined the staff of the Des Moines *News*. Her assignment by that newspaper to the State House was responsible for her discovering good material for the short stories she was to write. The idea for the short story *A Jury of Her Peers*, which she later dramatized as *Trifles*, came out of her newspaper experience.

After less than two years of newspaper reporting, she boldly gave up her job and returned home to Davenport to devote all her time to the writing of short stories. Fortunately for her, for she had to earn her own living, she was successful in the short story form. The restrained excellence of her style, the understanding sympathy, the sensitive perception: all of these were already apparent in her early work. After a few years, she decided to write a novel, and again with some fearful doubt, turned her back on the short story form and wrote *The Glory and the Conquered,* the first of her several novels.

In 1913 she married George Cram Cook, also a writer, and when he organized the Provincetown Players in the fishing and resort town of Provincetown, Massachusetts, she turned her considerable talent to writing for the theater. The result was such one-act masterpieces as *Trifles* and *Suppressed Desires,* and the full-length play *Alison's House,* which was awarded the Pulitzer Prize in 1931.

After *Alison's House,* Susan Glaspell wrote no more plays. With mature insight and sure artistic competence, she continued to write novels and a book about her husband and herself, *The Road to the Temple.* While the writings of her later years did not win for her a wide and enthusiastic reading public, she did continue to earn the respect and admiration of discriminating readers and critics. She died in 1948, at the age of sixty-six, in Provincetown.